The Exceptional Child: Conditioned Learning and Teaching Ideas

Papers by
Sidney W. Bijou, Lois Elliot,
Virginia Armbruster, Thomas Ryan, Peter Watson,
Marcene Powell, et. al.

MSS Information Corporation
655 Madison Avenue, New York, N.Y. 10021

150410

TABLE OF CONTENTS

Child Psychiatry . . . . Freeman   8

Behavior Therapy With Children:
A Review and Evaluation of
Research Methodology . . . . Gelfand and Hartmann   23

Behavior Modification in the Mentally Retarded . . . . Bijou   36

Reinforcement Procedures and the Increase
of Functional Speech by a Brain-Injured Child . . . . Hall   55

A Behavior Modification Approach
to Head Banging . . . . Harmatz and Rasmussen   67

The Comparison of Matching-to-Sample With
Discrimination Learning in Retardates . . . . . Heal and Bransky   70

Reward Schedules and Instrumental Conditioning
in Normal and Retarded Children . . . . Johnson   74

Programed Instruction and the Exceptional Learner . . . Johnson   86

Strengthening Self-Help Behavior
in the Retardate . . . . Karen and Maxwell   91

Toilet Training . . . . Lohmann, Eyman, and Lask   96

Attention Span: An Operant
Conditioning Analysis . . . . Martin and Powers   103

Changes in Response Force During Acquisition and
Extinction in Retarded Children . . . . Morris   109

Frustrative Nonreward Theory Applied to
Children's Behavior . . . . Ryan and Watson   116

Reinstatement of an Operant Response by the
Delivery of Reinforcement
During Extinction . . . . Spradlin, Fixsen, Girarbeau   131

The Dimensions of a Science of Special Education . . . Blackman   138

An Interpretation of Effective Management and
Discipline of the Mentally Retarded Child . . . . Powell   146

Parent Education in Managing Retarded Children
With Behavior Deficits and
Inappropriate Behaviors . . . . Terdal and Buell   160

Hearing Standards—Fact or Fiction? . . . . House   168

Picture-Sound Association in Deaf Children . . . . Doehring   174

Hearing Aids and Children in
Elementary Schools . . . . Gaeth and Lounsbury   188

Some Possible Effects of the Delay of
Early Treatment of Deafness . . . . Elliott and Armbruster   195

CREDITS AND ACKNOWLEDGEMENTS

Bijou, Sidney W., "Behavior Modification in the Mentally Retarded: Application of Operant Conditioning Principles," *Pediatric Clinics of North America*, November, 1968, 15:969-987.

Blackman, Leonard S., "The Dimensions of a Science of Special Education," *Mentally Retarded*, August, 1967, 5:7-11.

Doehring, Donald G., "Picture-Sound Association in Deaf Children," *Journal of Speech and Hearing Research*, March, 1969, 11:49-62.

Elliot, Lois L., and Virginia B. Armbruster, "Some Possible Effects of the Delay of Early Treatment of Deafness," *Journal of Speech and Hearing Research*, June, 1967, 10:209-224.

Freeman, Roger D., "Child Psychiatry," *Progress in Neurology and Psychiatry*, 1968, 23: 454-468.

Gaeth, John H.; and Evan Lounsbury, "Hearing Aids and Children in Elementary Schools," *Journal of Speech and Hearing Disorders*, August, 1966, 31:283-289.

Gelfand, Donna M.; and Donald P. Hartmann, "Behavior Therapy With Children: A Review and Evaluation of Research Methodology," *Psychology Bulletin*, March, 1968, 69:204-215.

Hall, R. Vance, "Reinforcement Procedures and the Increase of Functional Speech by a Brain-Injured Child," *American Speech & Hearing Association Monographs*, January, 1970, 14: 48-60.

Harmatz, Morton G.; and Warren A. Rasmussen, "A Behavior Modification Approach to Head Banging," *Mental Health*, October, 1969, 53:590-593.

Heal, Laird W.; and Malcolm L. Bransky, "The Comparison of Matching-To-Sample With Discrimination Learning in Retardates," *American Journal of Mental Deficiency*, November, 1966, 71:481-485.

House, Howard P., "Hearing Standards—Fact or Fiction?" *Archives of Otolarynology*, August, 1969, 90: 208-213.

Johnson, Bette M., "Reward Schedules and Instrumental Conditioning in Normal and Retarded Children," *Child Development*, September, 1966, 37:633-644.

Johnson, Gordon F., "Programed Instruction and the Exceptional Learner," *Exceptional Children*, February, 1968, 34:453-457.

Karen, Robert L.; and Sandra J. Maxwell, "Strengthening Self-Help Behavior in the Retardate," *American Journal of Mental Deficiency*, January, 1967, 71:545-550.

Lohmann, Werner; Richard K. Eyman; and Emanual Lask, "Toilet Training," *American Journal of Mental Deficiency*, January, 1967, 71:551-557.

Martin, Gary L.; and Richard B. Powers, "Attention Span: An Operant Conditioning Analysis," *Exceptional Children*, April, 1967, 33:565-570.

Morris, John P., "Changes in Response Force During Acquisition and Extinction in Retarded Children," *American Journal of Mental Deficiency*, March, 1967, 71:864-868.

Powell, Marcene, "An Interpretation of Effective Management and Discipline of the Mentally Retarded Child," *Nursing Clinics of North America*, December, 1966, 1:689-702.

Ryan, Thomas J.; and Peter Watson, "Frustrative Nonreward Theory Applied to Children's Behavior," *Psychology Bulletin*, February, 1968, 69:111-125.

Spradlin, Joseph E.; Dean L. Fixsen; and Frederic L. Girarbeau, "Reinstatement of an Operant Response by the Delivery of Reinforcement during Extinction," *Journal of Experimental Child Psychology*, February, 1969, 7:96-100.

Terdal, Leif; and Joan Buell, "Parent Education in Managaing Retarded Children With Behavior Deficits and Inappropriate Behaviors," *Mental Retardation*, June, 1969, 7:10-13.

General Introduction to Behavior Therapy With Children

Child Psychiatry

By ROGER D. FREEMAN, M.D.

T HE YEAR 1967 was notable for a number of provocative challenges to accepted concepts, reports of innovative approaches, and the publication of
the results of several long-term studies. A large number of significant contributions to the field were made by non-psychiatrists. The unsettled controversy
between those advocating a behavioristic, non-motivational approach and the
more traditional psychodynamic practitioners has been highlighted by many
articles and books, in which the writers devote excessive space to condemning
those of the other persuasion. One cannot help concluding that a more fruitful
approach would be the reexamination of one's theories and assumptions in the
light of the data provided by those who do not share such assumptions. The
dispute seems to involve much more than issues of logic, scientific method, and
results. Many psychiatrists have ignored the claims of the behavior modifiers
and are poorly informed as to the methods and the difference between operant
and classical (Pavlovian) conditioning. On the other hand, the psychologists
who reject the "medical model" and enthusiastically espouse behavior therapy
as a panacea seem to have erected a straw man of psychoanalysis which bears
little, if any, resemblance to the current practice and theoretical state of flux
of analytically-oriented therapy. Fortunately, a number of publications attest
to the fact that some investigators and therapists eschew polemics and dogma
and are trying to utilize both the concepts and techniques of the two orienta-
tions, despite assertions that they are mutually exclusive.

RESEARCH METHODOLOGY

Magder and Werry[64] questioned earlier reports that defectors from a child
guidance clinic waiting list could be used to determine the rate of spontaneous
remission and as a group of untreated controls. Their group of defectors was
found to differ significantly from those accepting treatment when it was offered.

CHILD DEVELOPMENT

Tennes and Lampl[104] studied 27 infants during their first two years of life to
better delineate the predictors and correlates of separation anxiety. They report

The writing of this chapter was supported by U.S. Children's Bureau Grant No. 416,
Personnel Training Project For Handicapped Children.

8

that the level of aggression in the infants did not correlate well with intensity of the anxiety. The best predictors are the mother's inhibition of the child's aggression and maternal hostility towards the child.

An excellent review of the effects of parental influence on cognitive development in early childhood is provided by Freeberg and Payne.[37] Scott, Burton, and Yarrow[97] report on their studies of social reinforcement under natural (as opposed to the more usual experimental) conditions.

We tend to assume that if "mothering" is important, then the mother is the best person to do it, although data to demonstrate this conclusively are unavailable. Caldwell[15] discusses the evidence and questions current beliefs about the importance of the first three years in cognitive development.

Another challenge to traditional beliefs is expounded by Chodoff,[18] who examines the Freudian theory of infantile sexuality. He suggests both alternative explanations and the need for objective re-examination. Although a partisan in the internecine strife among "schools" of psychoanalysis, his reasoning is well presented and worth reading no matter what one's bias.

It is generally assumed that verbal language is of great importance in the thinking process. Vernon[106] surveys 33 independent research projects and concludes that verbal language is not the mediating symbol system for thought.

It has been suggested that the children referred to a child guidance clinic do not differ significantly from "normal" children, except by virtue of their parents' level of anxiety or intolerance of symptomatic behavior. Wolff[111] has tested this hypothesis as applied to elementary school children. The results indicate a significantly higher prevalence of antisocial behavior, soiling, enuresis, anxiety, unhappiness, and difficulties in interpersonal relationships in the clinic population. The 100 controls and 100 consecutive clinic referrals could not be differentiated, however, on the basis of physical complaints, speech disorders, overeating, or sleep disturbances.

ADOLESCENCE

An excellent summary of adolescent psychiatry has been provided by Schonfeld.[96] Corday[25] discusses the limitations of analytically-oriented therapy. He feels that a therapist of the opposite sex is often contraindicated because of the real excitement in the relationship, the perpetuation of which may become a spurious goal of treatment.

Hertzig and Birch[53] studied a group of 114 adolescent girls admitted to an in-patient unit, two-thirds of whom were diagnosed as schizophrenic. As compared with the general population of similar age, they showed a significantly higher proportion of abnormal neurological findings, motor overflow, mental defect, and inadequate intersensory integration. Despite possible sampling bias, the authors conclude that primary central nervous system disorder is strongly associated with psychiatric abnormality in adolescence, and that this is especially true of schizophrenia.

Coddington and Offord[21] found that four child psychiatrists had a very high degree of reliability in judging ego function in unstructured interviews. It is suggested that an operationally defined measure such as "ego quotient" may be more useful than diagnostic labels.

Korner and Opsvig[58] discuss the significance of the developmental point of view in the interpretation of the meaning of symptoms in an unusually clear fashion.

The limitations of office or hospital evaluation of children is stressed by Freeman.[40] Seeing the child in his most secure setting is felt to be advisable, especially with very young, handicapped, overprotected, or disturbed and non-verbal children. Results in a home visiting program are described, along with the implications for training. This point of view is also supported by Behrens[5] for lower-class patients.

PREVENTION

Bolman and Westman[10] review current approaches to prevention and conclude that many of the necessary tools are already at hand but not being employed. Biber and Franklin[7] state that any program attempting to compensate for deprivation should aim to enrich communication and relationships, expand the variety of encounters with the environment, and foster exploration, integration, and the development of symbolic expression through play.

FOLLOW-UP STUDIES

A book by Robins[89] raises serious questions about the outcome of certain childhood disorders. This is a controlled study with 30-year follow-up of 524 clinic patients, of whom 82 per cent were located and interviewed, and 100 control subjects. Many problems thought to be indicative of neurosis appeared as often in children who were well-adjusted on follow-up as in the group which was not. Children with antisocial behavior had the greatest difficulty, and it seems to be from their ranks that the majority of later problems derived. Of those with early antisocial behavior, 61 per cent persisted in this category at follow-up, without reduction in severity; 12 per cent had ceased acting out in this fashion, usually between ages 30 and 40. It is of interest that adults who gave up antisocial behavior did not substitute other observable psychopathology for it, and that many antisocial adults had a large number of "neurotic" symptoms and/or somatic complaints. Robins concludes that antisocial and neurotic symptoms do not serve a common defensive purpose. The implications for prevention and practice may be that we are treating many neurotic children who will do fairly well anyway, while children with less comfortable behavior patterns may need it more. The question of which forms of treatment might be applied most effectively is not a consideration in Robins' investigation, nor is any conclusive answer available as yet.

Pollack et al.[82] report that the earlier onset of adult schizophrenia requiring hospitalization is associated with more deviant childhood psychopathology, apparent confirmation of an expected relationship. Gardner[43] has also been interested in the relationship between childhood symptomatology and later schizophrenia. In males who later became schizophrenic there was more pronounced anxiety, and a greater number and severity of phobic and obsessive-compulsive traits, whereas hysterical traits could not differentiate the two groups; these relationships did not obtain for females. The concept of "adolescent turmoil" and the tendency to discount the ominous prognostic significance in many cases are challenged by Masterson,[66] who concluded that in most clinic cases (certainly a selected sample) the symptoms are an adolescent exaggeration of previous pathology which will continue to plague the patients in adult life.

Heston et al.[54] compared the later adjustment of children placed in foundling homes (for a mean period of 24.7 months after birth) with those never institutionalized and report no significant IQ differences. Prevalence of psychopathology was not significantly different. They conclude that the long-term effects of institutionalization in early life are not necessarily as severe as usually supposed, and that a corrective experience in family living can reverse deleterious influences, at least by adult life.

Three studies from Great Britain focus on the late effects of childhood bereavement, particularly depression. The conclusions are somewhat contradictory. Hill and Price[56] found no differences between depressed and non-depressed adults in respect to loss of mothers, but found that more depressed females had lost fathers. Gay and Tonge[45] also report that loss of the parent of the opposite sex is significant, but Wilson et al.[110] (using the MMPI) that loss of the mother is significant for both sexes. The latter also interpret their data to indicate that childhood bereavement increases the severity of a depression if it occurs.

TRAINING

Sylvester and Cooper[102] provide a witty exposition of some of the pitfalls in child psychiatric training associated with the trainee's search for relief from his anxiety through false certainty. Other aspects of interest include mental retardation (Philips[78] and Menolascino[70]) and residential treatment (Noshpitz[73]).

CLINICAL OBSERVATIONS AND PSYCHOPATHOLOGY

Depression. Within a psychoanalytic framework, Rie[86] points out the lack of adequate criteria for the diagnosis of depression and questions whether the concept (as developed in adult psychiatry) can be applied to childhood at all. On the other side of this issue, Glaser[46] suggests that depressive "elements" should be suspected more often, especially in learning disorders and mental retardation, where the child realizes his disability but can do little to compensate for its effects. Lorand[61] provides a good review of the application of psychodynamic principles to adolescent depression. He emphasizes the need for direct support in helping the patient deal with current difficulties, rather than a non-directive initial approach. By implication, he goes rather surpris-

11

ingly far in suggesting a pragmatic technique without being too closely bound to theory.

Childhood psychosis. McDermott et al.[68] report that there were no significant differences in the five social class groups as to probability of the diagnosis, but differences in expression were found. Withdrawal and autism were more frequent among the upper classes, suggesting that child-rearing style may influence the expression of psychotic manifestations. Eaton and Menolascino[33] provide an interesting five-year (average) follow-up of 32 psychotic children, 22 of whom were considered to be organic. Some of the latter progressed from minor to major neurological signs. They suggest that in the child with organic dysfunction there may be a special vulnerability to psychosis and that psychotic reactions may subside fairly readily when stress is removed. Rutter et al.[91, 92] contribute significant knowledge of this area in their reports of a 5- to 15-year follow-up of 63 children and matched nonpsychotic controls. Although initially none appeared obviously neurologically impaired, on follow-up 29 per cent showed evidence of probable brain disorder, including 16 per cent who developed seizures long after the onset of psychosis. The poorer social outcome among the psychotics was associated statistically with low or untestable IQ and lack of speech by age 5. Improvement in relating was not necessarily followed by improvement in speech.

Self-mutilation is a frequent accompaniment of psychosis. Green[48] reports on 70 school-age children and finds this manifestation more common in girls and in those with an early history of head-banging. Evidence of cerebral dysfunction did not distinguish self-mutilators within the psychotic group. This pattern of behavior is viewed as developing in the face of sensory deficits and ego impairment which have been environmentally reinforced. Symbolic psychodynamic significance seems to be secondarily acquired, and a disorder of pain perception may also be a contributory influence.

Mental retardation. A new book edited by Baumeister[3] contains especially noteworthy chapters on: definition, diagnosis, and classification (by David Brison); psychotherapy (by Irv Bialer); and parent counseling (by Wolf Wolfensberger). Clausen[20] also reviews the development of concepts and issues in the field in a particularly lucid fashion.

The old question of environmental (social) causation is raised again in a study by Davis,[29] who studied apparently non-organic cases and their families. He suggests that in many cases the family structure is inadequate in providing the developing infant with opportunities for mother-child attachment and protection from excessive stress during critical periods.

Philips[79] points out three common misconceptions in work with the retarded: that disordered behavior is the direct result of retardation; that it is caused by specific brain damage; and that the psychopathology is different in kind from that observed in the child of average intelligence.

Two studies (Gardner[44] and Berman[6]) exemplify the conflicting evidence for a greater or lesser vulnerability of the retarded to depressive illnesses. Much of the confusion seems to rest upon whether the diagnosis is based upon readily observed affective changes or inferred from "depressive equivalents" in depth studies.

Birch et al.[8] dispute the value of the WISC in the differentiation of "brain-damaged" and "garden-variety" educable retarded children. No pattern of intellectual functioning was clearly associated with the presence or absence of independent neurological evidence of brain damage. They conclude that either the WISC is insensitive to etiology or both groups may have some form of "brain damage."

In a superbly written article, Zigler[113] reviews the claims regarding the specific cognitive deficit characteristic of retardates. He feels that there is no evidence for the existence of such a deficit, and that most reported findings can be adequately explained on the basis of differing life experiences, motivational levels, and training practices.

A study by Brown[11] suggests that the usual laboratory or office testing situation may be inappropriate for assessing distractibility, since classroom research leads to different conclusions and may be more meaningful.

In phenylketonuria, Wood et al.[112] propose that some part of the intellectual deficit may be attributable to restrictions imposed upon free play and exploration, the latter being an outgrowth of parental concern over lapses in the diet. Finally, two papers describe programs of prevention and management. Dupont[31] asserts that community mental health centers can meet many of the clinical needs of the retarded. Santostefano and Stayton[94] report that a program of "training of early focal attention" by mothers seemed to generalize to higher cognitive functions and result in greater receptiveness to later school learning, though no controls were employed.

Organic brain syndromes, epilepsy, and hyperactivity. A workshop in Great Britain[47] reports on the need for psychiatric services in special clinics for children with neurological dysfunctions, and discusses the possible areas of contribution according to age ranges, as well as the problem of how the psychiatrist can relate to other staff members. This is a succinct and commendable initial effort.

Much controversy is still apparent around the issues of terminology and etiology in these areas. Gallagher[42] has suggested the broad term "children with developmental imbalances," which has the virtue of avoiding etiologic assumptions and also avoids specifying only one area, in contrast to a term such as "perceptual handicaps." Regarding the latter designation, Haywood[52] writes an iconoclastic plea against premature assumptions. He does not think the evidence warrants the usage of such a term, which he regards as an artifact of our own ignorance. He advocates a reduction in the number of areas of "exceptionality" in schools, and program modification rather than special classes.

Bee[4] hypothesized that any experience fostering impulse control should affect distractibility. She reports that the parents of less distractible children encouraged more independence, were less intrusive, and made less specific suggestions to their children.

A research study by Birch and Bortner[9] lends some experimental support to stimulus-reduction as a special educational technique. They show that children with known brain damage (cerebral palsy) lag in the normal shift from behavioral control by "stimulus attributes" to control by "concepts of function and class." Reducing "stimulus competition" permitted latent, more mature modes of functioning to emerge and dominate behavior.

What happens to children diagnosed "minimally brain damaged" as adults? There is no equivalent term in the adult nomenclature. Menkes et al.[69] make a preliminary attempt at answering this question with a 25-year retrospective follow-up of 14 patients. Only 3 were still "hyperactive," and 8 still had neurological signs. Eight were self-supporting, though 4 of these had spent some time in institutions; 4 were psychotic; 2 were retarded and dependent. A major predictive factor seemed to be initial IQ, but the small numbers and other factors only permit the conclusion that varied outcomes are possible.

The 14- and 6-per second spike and wave complex in the EEG has been reported to correlate with many types of neuropsychiatric conditions, but Lombroso et al.[60] find it in 58 per cent of healthy adolescents, casting doubts upon its significance, at least in this age group. Aird et al.[1] report that behavior disorders, developmental abnormalities, and peculiar nocturnal symptoms were much more common among those children who developed temporal lobe epilepsy in the second decade or later, than among controls. They suggest that latent cerebral dysfunction antedated the onset of the overt convulsive disorder in about half the cases studied.

The Institutes for the Achievement of Human Potential have been widely publicized because of their claims to cure a large proportion of children with brain damage, mental retardation, and learning and behavior problems. Freeman[38] critically reviews the controversy, concluding that the claims and publicity seem unwarranted by the evidence, and Robbins[88] reports that a controlled study of the rationale with retarded readers could demonstrate no benefit.

Finally, Sak et al.[93] postulate a central as well as peripheral neurological defect in children with familial dysautonomia. Some of the psychopathology may be related to sensory distortions and body-image problems.

Physical and sensory handicaps. Continuing interest in the *blind* child is evident in several publications. Burlingham[14] follows up her previous studies with an excellent practical outline of how an understanding of the developmental vicissitudes can be applied in early preventive work with the parents. Two very optimistic programs for the habilitation of severely disturbed blind children are described by Elonen et al.[34] and Ross et al.[90] They confirm the impression that many handicapped children are being committed to institutions who do not need such custodial care. Child psychiatric consultation at a residential school for the blind is reported to be helpful by Bucknam.[12] Methods of interviewing such children are described by Phillips,[80] and Guess[50] provides a thoughtful review of the issues and research needs in work with the blind retarded. Experiments with reducing stereotyped behaviors in the latter group are reported by Guess and Rutherford.[51]

14

Cytryn et al.[27] studied 27 boys with *cryptorchism* and conclude that they are unusually prone to emotional disorders. Offord and Aponte[75] investigated 19 children with *congenital heart disease*. Overprotection, as operationally defined, was related more to the mother's distortion of the disability than to realistic limitations. Applications to other handicapping conditions are suggested.

Psychosomatic and medical problems. Two significant papers by Powell et al.[83, 84] report striking reversals of growth retardation that simulated hypopituitarism when children were removed from emotionally depriving homes. No other form of treatment seemed necessary. Bullard et al.[13] also investigated children with "failure to thrive" and found that many of them had problems of mental retardation, emotional disturbance, or growth failure on follow-up.

Pinkerton,[81] studying asthma, asserts that psychodynamic factors operate throughout the physiological spectrum and that psychotherapeutic intervention may be more indicated with the more severe cases.

McDermott and Finch[67] were interested in relating the type and severity of psychiatric disorder to the status of tissue involvement in chronic ulcerative colitis. They found a poor correlation, and suggest that other factors are significant in progression of the disease, although psychiatric treatment has a place in the combined medical-surgical management.

Swift et al.[101] report the results of an extensive study of juvenile diabetics. Significant differences were found in degree of psychopathology, anxiety, body-image, adjustment, and dependence-independence balance, as compared with matched controls. Good diabetic control seemed related to adequate self-perception and normal dependence-independence behavior.

Learning disorders. Controversy continues in this heterogeneous area, both as to etiology and management. Oettinger et al.[74] suggest that subclinical reading epilepsy may account for some cases of reading disability, and describe five interesting cases. Stevens et al.[100] studied 26 "minimally brain damaged" children and 26 matched controls. They conclude that the presumption of such a diagnosis is reasonable in school-age children with average or better intelligence who present learning and/or behavior problems. Questions as to the adequacy of matching still remain, however. Stephens et al.[99] come to opposite conclusions with regard to reading disability.

Gilles de la Tourette's syndrome. This peculiar condition, characterized by multiple tics with the later development of coprolalia, is of unknown etiology. Continuing interest in the natural course and treatment are indicated by a number of papers (Clark,[19] Chapel,[16] Feild et al.,[35] Fernando,[36] and Lucas[63]). A pessimistic prognosis, assumed in the past, does not seem warranted, and at least three forms of treatment (psychotherapy, behavior therapy, and drugs) have been reported to be of value in some cases.

COMMUNITY PSYCHIATRY, CHILD WELFARE, SOCIAL PROBLEMS

A model for community child psychiatry planning is presented by Rafferty.[85] Chethik et al.[17] describe the effects of integration in a Caucasian treatment center and some of the identity problems observed in disturbed Negro children.

Three papers represent the current interest in the "disadvantaged" population. Scott[98] suggests the introduction of special toys into the home to foster cognitive development during critical learning periods. Guerney et al.[49] describe the use of an approach to the parents which might improve a child's motivation for academic pursuits, utilizing group training sessions, feedback, encouragement, and modeling. Finally, the idea that low activity level may increase an infant's vulnerability to deprivation is supported by Schaffer.[95]

A panel report of the American Psychoanalytic Association[2] on adoption has raised many pertinent questions, although final conclusions are still unavailable. There was no agreement on the prevalence or type of psychopathology associated with the adoptive state.

EDUCATION

The second edition of Cruickshank and Johnson[26] on the *Education of Exceptional Children and Youth* appeared during 1967, and is generally an excellent and detailed work which will be of great use to the psychiatrist. A possible exception is the chapter on the brain-injured child, which is rather narrow in its viewpoint.

Many specific approaches to the education of handicapped and disturbed children are premature and without demonstrated validity, according to a critique by Mann and Phillips.[65] The diagnosis of a handicap does not seem to provide adequate educational guidelines, by itself.

TREATMENT METHODS

Psychodynamic psychotherapy. It is difficult to isolate specific contributions since most studies are of a small number of cases and represent, at most, an elaboration of earlier work. Tessman and Kaufman[105] describe the phases of therapy, ways of actively dealing with primitive thinking, and the role of bizarre behavior and fantasy in maintaining the pathological tie to the mother in childhood psychosis. Easson[32] coins the apt term "continued nonpatient" for some adolescents who are prone to form a relationship they can't stand, yet can't do without. How long treating personnel can tolerate such a tangential relationship is crucial, and correlations with weak ego resources and "acting-out" are discussed. An interesting case of psychotic identical twins, in which management of the "twinning reaction" was essential, is described by Zrull.[114]

Behavior therapy. Many studies reported in this relatively new area are case reports without adequate controls. Nevertheless, every psychiatrist should be aware of the theories, limitations, and claimed accomplishments. The best single source for this material is without doubt the magnificent review by Werry and Wollersheim.[109] Applications to the treatment of psychotic children are contributed by Lovaas et al.,[62] Jensen and Womack,[57] Tate and Baroff,[103] and Risley and Wolf.[87] Weiss and Born[107] describe a case in which speech patterns were successfully taught, but failed to generalize outside of the experimental situation. They ask whether perhaps only "speech," but not language, can be acquired by such techniques. Other investigators would no doubt feel more optimistic about this. Patterson and Brodsky[77] report on the successful treatment of a child with multiple symptoms, and raise the question of how successful or enduring such changes can be without "reprogramming the social environment." Mogel and Schiff[71] discuss the reasons for the unexpectedly rapid extinction of a head-banging symptom of 8 years' duration, and conclude that "the nature of interpersonal relationships and motives . . . must be measured before an adequate theory of behavioral change can emerge." Other examples of recent applications include the reduction of aggressive and destructive sibling interactions, carried out in the home (O'Leary et al[76]); the control of hyperactive behavior in retarded children, regardless of presumed etiology (Doubros and Daniels[30]); the teaching of basic reading skills to severely handicapped children through the use of programmed instruction and learning theory (Hewett et al.[55]); and operant principles in work with rehabilitation of the handicapped (Myerson et al.[72]).

Psychopharmacology. There were only a few drug studies of any significance during the year. The newer antidepressants are being tried with children diagnosed as autistic (Kurtis[59]) and depressed (Frommer[41]), but these studies have many faults. Connell et al.[22] treated adolescent tiqueurs with both diazepam and haloperidol and found the latter much superior, which suggests a relationship to its reported superiority in Gilles de la Tourette's syndrome (Chapel,[16] Fernando,[36] and Lucas[63]). Two studies tend to support the long-held assumption that the amphetamines are useful with hyperactive and/or brain-damaged children. Conners et al.[23] employed a double-blind crossover design with random assignment and a standard dose of dextroamphetamine with 52 children with learning problems, who had a mean age of 11.6 years, over a two-month period. There was a significant improvement in teacher ratings, but not in intelligence. They conclude that the change was in a factor reflecting assertiveness and drive. Conrad and Insel[24] performed a retrospective study (without a control group) to determine the characteristics of children who responded to the same drug. In general, positive responders tended to be those with an "organic" background, but with a positive parent-child relationship and without severe psychiatric disability in the parents. They feel that improvement is probably related to increased ability to attend and concentrate; no significant changes in IQ were found.

The limitations of drug use to facilitate learning in children, as well as a critical review of the literature of the past thirty years, is provided by Freeman,[39] who concludes that there is little evidence to demonstrate the efficacy of such treatment methods at the present time.

Residential treatment. D'Amato[28] raises many pertinent questions about the emerging movement to relate state institutions to the community. Wenar et al.[108] evaluated three different residential settings for autistic children: a custodial care institution, a more therapeutically-oriented state institution, and a small, psychoanalytically oriented day care unit. None of these settings produced measurable changes in the tested areas of communication and vocalization, but the third setting was most effective in the areas of relationship, mastery, and psychosexual development. The authors conclude that progress with these children is slow, and tends to generalize poorly.

REFERENCES

1. Aird, R. B., Venturini, A. M., and Spielman, P. M.: Antecedents of temporal lobe epilepsy. Arch. Neurol. 16: 67–73, 1967.
2. American Psychoanalytic Association: Psychoanalytic theory as it relates to adoption. J. Amer. Psychoanal. Ass. 15: 695–708, 1967.
3. Baumeister, A. A. (Ed.): Mental Retardation: Appraisal, Education, and Rehabilitation. Chicago, Aldine, 1967.
4. Bee, H. L.: Parent-child interaction and distractibility in 9-year old children. Merrill-Palmer Quart. 13: 175–190, 1967.
5. Behrens, M. I.: Brief home visits by the clinic therapist in the treatment of lower-class patients. Amer. J. Psychiat. 124: 371–375, 1967.
6. Berman, M. I.: Mental retardation and depression. Ment. Retard. 5: 19–21, 1967.
7. Biber, B., and Franklin, M. B.: The relevance of developmental and psychodynamic concepts to the education of the preschool child. J. Amer. Acad. Child Psychiat. 6: 5–24, 1967.
8. Birch, H. G., Belmont, L., Belmont, I., and Taft, L. I.: Brain damage and intelligence in educable mentally subnormal children. J. Nerv. Ment. Dis. 144: 247–257, 1967.
9. Birch, H. G., and Bortner, M.: Stimulus competition and concept utilization in brain damaged children. Develop. Med. Child Neurol. 9: 402–410, 1967.
10. Bolman, W. M., and Westman, J. C.: Prevention of mental disorder: an overview of current programs. Amer. J. Psychiat. 123: 1058–1068, 1967.
11. Brown, R. I.: The effects of varied environmental stimulation on the performance of subnormal children. J. Child Psychol. Psychiat. 7: 257–261, 1966.
12. Bucknam, F. G.: Preventive child psychiatry at a residential school for the blind. New Outlook for the Blind 61: 232–237, 1967.
13. Bullard, D. M., Glaser, H. H., Heagarty, M. C., and Pivchik, E. C.: Failure to thrive in the "neglected" child. Amer. J. Orthopsychiat. 37: 680–690, 1967.
14. Burlingham, D.: Developmental considerations in the occupations of the blind. Psychoanal. Stud. Child 22: 187–198, 1967.
15. Caldwell, B. M.: What is the optimal learning environment for the young child? Amer. J. Orthopsychiat. 37: 8–21, 1967.
16. Chapel, J. L.: Gilles de la Tourette's disease: the past and the present. Canad. Psychiat. Ass. J. 11: 324–329, 1966.
17. Chethik, M., Fleming, E., Mayer, M. F., and McCoy, J. N.: A quest for identity: treatment of disturbed Negro children in a predominantly white treatment center. Amer. J. Orthopsychiat. 37: 71–77, 1967.
18. Chodoff, P.: A critique of Freud's theory of infantile sexuality. Amer. J. Psychiat. 123: 507–518, 1967.
19. Clark, D. F.: Behaviour therapy of Gilles de la Tourette's syndrome. Brit. J. Psychiat. 112: 771–778, 1966.
20. Clausen, J.: Mental deficiency—development of a concept. Amer. J. Ment. Defic. 71: 727–745, 1967.
21. Coddington, R. D., and Offord, D. R.: Psychiatrists' reliability in judging ego function. Arch. Gen. Psychiat. 16: 48–55, 1967.
22. Connell, P. H., Corbett, J. A., Horne, D. J., and Mathews, A. M.: Drug treatment of adolescent tiqueurs: a double-blind trial of diazepam and haloperidol. Brit. J. Psychiat. 113: 375–381, 1967.
23. Conners, C. K., Eisenberg, L., and Barcai, A.: Effect of dextroamphetamine on children. Arch. Gen. Psychiat. 17: 478–485, 1967.
24. Conrad, W. G., and Insel, J.: Anticipating the response to amphetamine therapy in the treatment of hyperkinetic children. Pediatrics 40: 96–98, 1967.
25. Corday, R. J.: Limitations of therapy in adolescence. J. Amer. Acad. Child Psychiat. 6: 526–538, 1967.

18

26. Cruickshank, W. M., and Johnson, G. O. (Eds.): Education of Exceptional Children and Youth (ed. 2). Englewood Cliffs, N.J., Prentice-Hall, 1967.

27. Cytryn, L., Cytryn, E., and Rieger, R. E.: Psychological implications of cryptorchism. J. Amer. Acad. Child Psychiat. 6: 131–165, 1967.

28. D'Amato, G.: Metamorphosis in a children's residential treatment center. Psychiatry 30: 317–331, 1967.

29. Davis, D. R.: Family processes in mental retardation. Amer. J. Psychiat. 124: 340–350, 1967.

30. Doubros, S. G., and Daniels, G. J.: An experimental approach to the reduction of overactive behavior. Behav. Res. Ther. 4: 251–258, 1966.

31. Dupont, H.: Community mental health centers and services for the mentally retarded. Commun. Mental Health J. 3: 33–36, 1967.

32. Easson, W. M.: The continued nonpatient. Arch. Gen. Psychiat. 16: 359–363, 1967.

33. Eaton, L., and Menolascino, F. J.: Psychotic reactions of childhood: a follow-up study. Amer. J. Orthopsychiat. 37: 521–529, 1967.

34. Elonen, A. S., Polzien, M., and Zwarensteyn, S. B.: The "uncommitted" blind child: results of intensive training of children formerly committed to institutions for the retarded. Exceptional Child. 33: 301–307, 1967.

35. Feild, J. R., Corbin, K. B., Goldstein, N. P., and Klass, D. W.: Gilles de la Tourette's syndrome. Neurology (Minneap.) 16: 453–462, 1966.

36. Fernando, S. J. M.: Gilles de la Tourette's syndrome. Brit. J. Psychiat. 113: 607–617, 1967.

37. Freeberg, N. E., and Payne, D. T.: Parental influence on cognitive development in early childhood: a review. Child Develop. 38: 65–87, 1967.

38. Freeman, R. D.: Controversy over "patterning" as a treatment for brain damage in children. J.A.M.A. 202: 385–388, 1967.

39. Freeman, R. D.: Drug effects on learning in children: a selective review of the past 30 years. J. Special Education 1: 17–44, 1966.

40. Freeman, R. D.: The home visit in child psychiatry: its usefulness in diagnosis and training. J. Amer. Acad. Child Psychiat. 6: 276–294, 1967.

41. Frommer, E.: Treatment of childhood depression with antidepressant drugs. Brit. Med. J. 1: 729–732, 1967.

42. Gallagher, J. J.: Children with developmental imbalances: a psychoeducational definition. In: Cruickshank, W. M. (Ed.): The Teacher of Brain-Injured Children. Syracuse, N.Y., Syracuse Univ. Press, 1966, pp. 23–43.

43. Gardner, G. G.: The relationship between childhood neurotic symptomatology and later schizophrenia in males and females. J. Nerv. Ment. Dis. 144: 97–100, 1967.

44. Gardner, W. I.: Occurrence of severe depressive reactions in the mentally retarded. Amer. J. Psychiat. 124: 386–388, 1967.

45. Gay, M. J., and Tonge, W. L.: The late effects of loss of parents in childhood. Brit. J. Psychiat. 113:753–759, 1967.

46. Glaser, K.: Masked depression in children and adolescents. Amer. J. Psychother. 21: 565–574, 1967.

47. Gordon, N. (Chairman): The psychiatrist and the handicapped child: a report from a study group. Develop. Med. Child Neurol. 9: 506–510, 1967.

48. Green, A. H.: Self-mutilation in schizophrenic children. Arch. Gen. Psychiat. 17: 234–244, 1967.

49. Guerney, B., Jr., Stover, L., and Andronico, M. P.: On educating disadvantaged parents to motivate children for learning: a filial approach. Commun. Ment. Health J. 3: 66–72, 1967.

50. Guess, D.: Mental retardation and blindness: a complex and relatively un-explored dyad. Exceptional Child. 33: 471–479, 1967.

51. Guess, D., and Rutherford, G.: Experimental attempts to reduce stereotyping among blind retardates. Amer. J. Ment. Defic. 71: 984–986, 1967.

52. Haywood, H. C.: Perceptual handicap: fact or artifact? Child Study 28: 2–14, 1967.

53. Hertzig, M. E., and Birch, H. G.: Neurologic organization in psychiatrically disturbed adolescent girls. Arch. Gen. Psychiat. 15: 590–598, 1966.

54. Heston, L. L., Denney, D. D., and Pauly, I. B.: The adult adjustment of persons institutionalized as children. Brit. J. Psychiat. 112: 1103–1110, 1966.

55. Hewett, F. M., Mayhew, D., and Rabb, E.: An experimental reading program for neurologically impaired, mentally retarded, and severely emotionally disturbed children. Amer. J. Orthopsychiat. 37: 35–48, 1967.

56. Hill, O. W., and Price, J. S.: Childhood bereavement and adult depression. Brit. J. Psychiat. 113: 743–751, 1967.

57. Jensen, G. D., and Womack, M. G.: Operant conditioning techniques applied in the treatment of an autistic child. Amer. J. Orthopsychiat. 37: 30–34, 1967.

58. Korner, A. F., and Opsvig, P.: Developmental considerations in diagnosis and treatment. J. Amer. Acad. Child Psychiat. 5: 594–616, 1966.

59. Kurtis, L. B.: Clinical study of the response to nortriptyline on autistic children. Int. J. Neuropsychiat. 2: 298–301, 1966.

60. Lombroso, C. T., Schwartz, I. H., Clark, D. M., Muench, H., and Barry, J.: Ctenoids in healthy youths: controlled study of 14- and 6-per-second positive spiking. Neurology (Minneap.) 16: 1152–1158, 1966.

61. Lorand, S.: Adolescent depression. Int. J. Psychoanal. 48: 53–60, 1967.

62. Lovaas, O. I., Freitas, L., Nelson, K., and Whalen, C.: The establishment oι imitation and its use for the development of complex behavior in schizophrenic children. Behav. Res. Ther. 5: 171–181, 1967.

63. Lucas, A.: Gilles de la Tourette's disease in children: treatment with haloperidol. Amer. J. Psychiat. 124: 243–245, 1967.

64. Magder, D., and Werry, J. S.: Defection from a treatment waiting list in a child psychiatric clinic. J. Amer. Acad. Child Psychiat. 5: 706–720, 1966.

65. Mann, L., and Phillips, W. A.: Fractional practices in special education: a critique. Exceptional Child. 33: 311–319, 1967.

66. Masterson, J. F.: The symptomatic adolescent five years later: he didn't grow out of it. Amer. J. Psychiat. 123: 1338–1345, 1967.

67. McDermott, J. F., Jr., and Finch, S.: Ulcerative colitis in children: reassessment of a dilemma. J. Amer. Acad. Child Psychiat. 6: 512–525, 1967.

68. McDermott, J. F., Jr., Harrison, S. I., Schrager, J., Lindy, J., and Killins, E.: Social class and mental illness in children: the question of childhood psychosis. Amer. J. Orthopsychiat. 37: 548–557, 1967.

69. Menkes, M. M., Rowe, J. S., and Menkes, J. H.: A twenty-five year follow-up study on the hyperkinetic child with minimal brain dysfunction. Pediatrics 39: 393–399, 1967.

70. Menolascino, F. J.: Mental retardation and comprehensive training in psychiatry. Amer. J. Psychiat. 124: 459–466, 1967.

71. Mogel, S., and Schiff, W.: "Extinction" of a head-bumping symptom of eight years' duration in two minutes: a case report. Behav. Res. Ther. 5: 131–132, 1967.

72. Myerson, L., Kerr, N., and Michael, J. L.: Behavior modification in rehabilitation. In: Bijou, S. W., and Baer, D. M. (Eds.): Child Development: Readings in Experimental Analysis. New York, Appleton-Century-Crofts, 1967.

73. Noshpitz, J. D.: Training the psychiatrist in residential treatment. J. Amer. Acad. Child Psychiat. 6: 25–37, 1967.

74. Oettinger, L., Jr., Nekonishi, H., and Gill, I. G.: Cerebral dysrhythmia induced by reading (subclinical reading epilepsy). Devel. Med. Child Neurol. 9: 191–201, 1967.

75. Offord, D. R., and Aponte, J. F.: Distortion of disability and effect on family life. J. Amer. Acad. Child Psychiat. 6: 499–511, 1967.

76. O'Leary, K. D., O'Leary, S., and Becker, W. C.: Modification of a deviant sibling interaction pattern in the home. Behav. Res. Ther. 5: 113–120, 1967.

77. Patterson, G. R., and Brodsky, G.: A behaviour modification programme for a child with multiple problem behaviours. J. Child Psychol. Psychiat. 7: 277–295, 1966.

78. Philips, I.: Problems of training the professional in the field of mental retardation. J. Amer. Acad. Child Psychiat. 5: 693–705, 1966.

79. Philips, I.: Psychopathology and mental retardation. Amer. J. Psychiat. 124: 29–35, 1967.

80. Phillips, C.: Interviewing the blind child. Dis. Nerv. Syst. 28: 727–730, 1967.

81. Pinkerton, P.: Correlating physiologic with psychodynamic data in the study and management of childhood asthma. J. Psychosom. Res. 11: 11–15, 1967.

82. Pollack, M., Woerner, M. G., Goodman, W., and Greenberg, I. M.: Childhood development patterns of hospitalized adult schizophrenic and nonschizophrenic patients and their siblings. Amer. J. Orthopsychiat. 36: 510–517, 1966.

83. Powell, G. F., Brasel, J. A., and Blizzard, R. M.: Emotional deprivation and growth retardation simulating idiopathic hypopituitarism. I. Clinical evaluation of the syndrome. New Eng. J. Med. 276: 1271–1278, 1967.

84. Powell, G. F., Brasel, J. A., Raiti, S., and Blizzard, R. M.: Emotional deprivation and growth retardation simulating idiopathic hypopituitarism. II. Endocrinologic evaluation of the syndrome. New Eng. J. Med. 276: 1279–1283, 1967.

85. Rafferty, F. T.: Child psychiatry service for a total population. J. Amer. Acad. Child Psychiat. 6: 295–308, 1967.

86. Rie, H. E.: Depression in childhood: a survey of some pertinent contributions. J. Amer. Acad. Child Psychiat. 5: 653–685, 1966.

87. Risley, T., and Wolf, M.: Establishing functional speech in echolalic children. Behav. Res. Ther. 5: 73–88, 1967.

88. Robbins, M. P.: Test of the Doman-Delacato rationale with retarded readers. J.A.M.A. 202: 389–393, 1967.

89. Robins, L. N.: Deviant Children Grown Up: A Sociological and Psychiatric Study of Sociopathic Personality. Baltimore, Williams and Wilkins, 1966.

90. Ross, J. R., Jr., Braen, B. B., and Chaput, R.: Patterns of change in disturbed blind children. Children 14: 217–222, 1967.

91. Rutter, M., Greenfield, D., and Lockyer, L.: A five to fifteen year follow-up study of infantile psychosis. II. Social and behavioural outcome. Brit. J. Psychiat. 113: 1183–1199, 1967.

92. Rutter, M., and Lockyer, L.: A five to fifteen year follow-up study of infantile psychosis: I. Description of sample. Brit. J. Psychiat. 113: 1169–1182, 1967.

93. Sak, H. G., Smith, A. A., and Dancis, J.: Psychometric evaluation of children with familial dysautonomia. Amer. J. Psychiat. 124: 682–687, 1967.

94. Santostefano, S., and Stayton, S.: Training the preschool retarded child in focusing attention: a program for parents. Amer. J. Orthopsychiat. 37: 732–743, 1967.

95. Schaffer, H. R.: Activity level as a constitutional determinant of infantile reaction to deprivation. Child Develop. 37: 595–602, 1966.

96. Schonfeld, W. A.: Adolescent psychiatry: an appraisal of the adolescent's position in contemporary psychiatry. Arch. Gen. Psychiat. 16: 713–719, 1967.

97. Scott, P. M., Burton, R. V., and Yarrow, M. R.: Social reinforcement under natural conditions. Child Develop. 38: 53–63, 1967.

98. Scott, R.: Head start before home start? Merrill-Palmer Quart. 13: 317–321, 1967.

99. Stephens, W. E., Cunningham, E. S., and Stigler, B. J.: Reading readiness and eye-hand preference patterns in first-grade children. Exceptional Child. 33: 481–488, 1967.

100. Stevens, D. A., Boydstun, J. A., Dykman, R. A., Peters, J. E., and Sinton, D. W.: Presumed minimal brain dysfunction in children: relationship to performance on selected behavioral tests. Arch. Gen. Psychiat. 16: 281–285, 1967.

101. Swift, C. R., Seidman, F., and Stein, H.: Adjustment problems in juvenile diabetes. Psychosom. Med. 29: 555–571, 1967.

102. Sylvester, E., and Cooper, S.: Truisms and slogans in the practice and teaching of child psychotherapy. J. Amer. Acad. Child Psychiat. 5: 617–629, 1967.

103. Tate, B. G., and Baroff, G. S.: Aversive control of self-injurious behavior in a psychotic boy. Behav. Res. Ther. 4: 281–287, 1966.

104. Tennes, K. H., and Lampl, E. E.: Some aspects of mother-child relationship pertaining to infantile separation anxiety. J. Nerv. Ment. Dis. 143: 426–437, 1966.

105. Tessman, L. H., and Kaufman, I.: Treatment techniques, the primary process, and ego development in schizophrenic children. J. Amer. Acad. Child Psychiat. 6: 98–115, 1967.

106. Vernon, M.: Relationship of language to the thinking process. Arch. Gen. Psychiat. 16: 325–333, 1967.

107. Weiss, H. H., and Born, B.: Speech training or language acquisition? A distinction when speech is taught by operant conditioning procedures. Amer. J. Orthopsychiat. 37: 49–55, 1967.

108. Wenar, C., Ruttenberg, B. A., Dratman, M. L., and Wolf, E. G.: Changing autistic behavior: the effectiveness of three milieus. Arch. Gen. Psychiat. 17: 26–35, 1967.

109. Werry, J. S., and Wollersheim, J. P.: Behavior therapy with children: a broad overview. J. Amer. Acad. Child Psychiat. 6: 346–370, 1967.

110. Wilson, I. C., Alltop, L. B., and Buffaloe, W. J.: Parental bereavement in childhood: MMPI profiles in a depressed population. Brit. J. Psychiat. 113: 761–764, 1967.

111. Wolff, S.: Behavioral characteristics of primary school children referred to a psychiatric department. Brit. J. Psychiat. 113: 885–893, 1967.

112. Wood, A. C., Friedman, C. J., and Steisel, I. M.: Psychosocial factors in phenylketonuria. Amer. J. Orthopsychiat. 37: 671–679, 1967.

113. Zigler, E.: Familial mental retardation: a continuing dilemma. Science 155: 292–298, 1967.

114. Zrull, J. P.: The psychotherapy of a pair of psychotic identical twins in a residential setting. J. Amer. Acad. Child Psychiat. 6: 116–130, 1967.

BEHAVIOR THERAPY WITH CHILDREN:
A REVIEW AND EVALUATION OF RESEARCH METHODOLOGY

DONNA M. GELFAND AND DONALD P. HARTMANN

As compared to adults, children have become an increasingly popular client population for behavioristically oriented therapists. Some reasons for the widespread use of learning-theory-based therapy for children's problems may be the comparative brevity of the treatment, the relative ease with which children's social environments can be controlled, and the types of maladaptive behaviors for which children are often referred for treatment. An important element of most behavioristic treatment interventions is the manipulation of the client's environment so that undesirable behavior patterns are eliminated and prosocial responses are positively reinforced (Ullmann & Krasner, 1965, Ch. 1). The requisite environmental control is often easier to achieve for children in their homes and schools than in the typically more complex and varied social interactions of noninstitutionalized adults. Since the young child spends the major part of his time either among his family or at school, the therapist can effectively manipulate the child's social experiences by instructing a fairly small group of people, the teacher and parents. Moreover, these people have considerable control over the child, and are specifically responsible for the child's welfare and for teaching him appropriate behavior patterns. When treating adults, it is usually more difficult to find and solicit the cooperation of persons who can serve as equally powerful reinforcement-dispensing or controlling agents, and it is highly unlikely that they would have the degree of authority over the adult client that adults typically possess with respect to children.

In addition, children are often referred for professional help for maladaptive behaviors which have proved among the most amenable to behavior-therapy techniques. When parents or school personnel refer children for treatment, the presenting complaint is often a well-defined behavior such as bedwetting, a phobia, or temper tantrums, the types of problems which, as Grossberg (1964) has pointed out, behavior therapy most successfully treats. It has also been suggested (Krasner & Ullmann, 1965, p. 57) that the type of specific and detailed instructions parents receive from behavior therapists more nearly meet the parents' initial treatment expectations than do the more general and vague directions, for example, to be demonstrative and accepting, traditionally given by children's therapists.

As a consequence, parents may be more likely to aid than to interfere with the therapeutic effort. Parental sabotage is thought to occur notoriously often in the more traditional play-therapy interventions, and it is not uncommon to hear a therapist state his belief that the parents do not sincerely want their child's adjustment to improve. To date, the same charge has not been made with any frequency by behavioristically oriented therapists who, by and large, report parents to be

23

cooperative and interested in aiding in the treatment process.

As used here, the term behavior therapy refers to treatment techniques derived from theories of learning and aimed at the direct modification of one or more problem behaviors rather than at effecting more general and less observable personality or adjustment changes. Because behavior therapists assume that both desirable and deviant social responses are learned, their treatment interventions consist of laboratory-derived learning procedures, for example, modeling and operant and classical conditioning.

Results of behavior therapy with a variety of subject samples have previously been reviewed (Bandura, 1961, 1967; Grossberg, 1964; Rachman, 1962; Werry & Wollersheim, 1967) and critically evaluated (Breger & McGaugh, 1965; Weitzman, 1967). It is the purpose of this paper to survey the behavior-therapy literature for subjects between infancy and 18 years of age, examine the range of problems treated, the methods used, and to critically review the adequacy of the therapy-evaluation attempts. This literature review is limited to reports of the clinical application of behavior-modification techniques.

Behavior-therapy studies can conveniently be classified in terms of the desired effect on rates of children's emission of both undesirable and prosocial behaviors.[1] Some treatment interventions aim to decrease the production of problem behaviors, others attempt to enhance the variety and likelihood of occurrence of desirable responses such as adequate language and motor skills, while a third approach combines acceleration of rates of prosocial behaviors with elimination of problem behaviors. This classification schema may have an advantage in clarity over those more commonly employed (e.g., Bandura, 1961; Rachman, 1962) in which learning mechanisms have often been confounded with treatment procedures, for example, extinction and negative practice (Grossberg, 1964). Moreover, a confusing variety of terms has been used to describe essentially identical manipulations; for example, desensitization, reciprocal inhi-

[1] This classification scheme was suggested by O. R. Lindsley in a workshop presentation, University of Utah, November 30, 1965.

bition, counterconditioning, deconditioning, and unconditioning have all been used to describe a single technique for the treatment of phobias. And finally, the sheer number of categories required by the use of previously employed descriptive terms plus the addition of new terms required by the increased use of operant techniques would be unwieldy.

It is recognized that in the case of some therapy reports the categories used in this paper do not include mutually exclusive techniques. A therapist who intends chiefly to use a deceleration technique may also informally include some social reinforcement of his client's prosocial behaviors. In such cases, the study will be categorized according to the therapist's stated intentions. Any classification system is somewhat arbitrary, and the schema used is designed simply to allow adequate description of a wide range of problems and treatment techniques.

DECELERATION OF MALADAPTIVE BEHAVIORS

Phobias

A large group of therapeutic interventions have as their aim a decrease in the magnitude and frequency of a variety of problem behaviors. Jones' (1924a, 1924b) elegant and long-neglected treatment of a child's fear of animals falls within this treatment classification. The technique used by Jones and others in the behavioristic treatment of phobias involves pairing incompatible experiences of relaxation and enjoyment with the presentation of anxiety-evoking stimuli so the previously fear-provoking stimuli become associated with pleasurable feelings (Bandura, 1961). Modifications of techniques developed for use with adults by Wolpe and his colleagues (Wolpe, 1958; Wolpe & Lazarus, 1966) are most often used in the treatment of children's phobias. Briefly, the procedure involves inducing feelings of relaxation in the child by the therapist through suggestion, hypnosis, or drugs. An anxiety hierarchy is constructed with items ranging from least to most fear-provoking situations, and the child is helped to imagine progressively stronger fear items under uninterrupted relaxation. This treatment technique has been used to combat irrational fear of water (Bentler, 1962), fear of hospitals and ambulances (Lazarus & Rachman, 1957), school phobia (Garvey & Hegrenes, 1966; Lazarus & Abramovitz, 1962), and dog phobia (Lazarus, 1959). Patterson (1965b) has also treated school phobia with a shaping procedure, direct praise and candy reinforcement given to a child for tolerating separation from his mother and for making statements about a boy doll's bravery in a structured doll-play situation. An interesting and methodologically sophisticated variation in the treatment of dog phobia has been described by Bandura, Grusec, and Menlove (1967) who demonstrated that exposure to a fearless peer model displaying approach responses produces stable and generalized reduction in children's avoidance behavior. The Bandura et al. study was particularly impressive because the authors: (a) precisely identified the active therapeutic ingredient through the inclusion of several matched treatment and control groups, (b) developed a specialized performance scale to measure the strength of avoidance responses, and (c) included pretests and posttests as well as follow-up measures.

Antisocial and Immature Behavior

Behavior therapists have also reported considerable success in the treatment of aggressive, antisocial, and immature behaviors. In a relatively early study, Williams (1959) controlled temper tantrums in a 21-month-old child through extinction. The customary reinforcement the parents had accorded the child for his refusal to sleep was abruptly discontinued, and his crying was effectively controlled at the tenth extinction trial. Periods of time out from positive reinforcement have been used to decrease rates of thumbsucking (Baer, 1962), vomiting (Wolf, Birnbrauer, Williams, & Lawler, 1965), and stealing (Wetzel, 1966). A combination of mild punishment and time-out techniques was successfully used to control the generalized negativism of a 5-year-old child truly gifted as a trouble maker (Boardman, 1962), while aggression in a nursery school class was controlled by instructing the teachers not to attend to either physical or verbal aggression and instead to reward cooperative behavior (Brown & Elliott, 1965).

Hyperactivity

The hyperactivity often associated with neurological deficit has long been thought unamenable to psychological manipulation and has been treated chiefly by administration of a variety of tranquilizing drugs. Patterson (1965a) and Patterson, Jones, Whittier, and Wright (1965), however, have used positive reinforcement in a classroom setting to control hyperactivity in 9- and 10-year-old boys diagnosed as brain damaged. Observing that the boys' inappropriate activities frequently earned them the acclaim of their classmates, Patterson reinforced the entire class for the subjects' desirable responses with a consequent increase in their attending behaviors. Doubros and Daniels (1966) also reported success in controlling children's overactive behavior through positively reinforcing low-magnitude responses in a playroom setting, while another group of investigators (Homme, deBaca, Devine, Steinhorst, & Rickert, 1963) imaginatively used the opportunity to engage in noisy play as a reinforcer for children's sitting quietly and attending to their nursery school teacher. James (1963) reported dramatic changes in a group of five hyperactive children by programming the teacher's behavior so that social reinforcers were made contingent upon the occurrence of socially acceptable behavior.

Tics

A popular technique for the control of tics is massed practice of the problem behavior voluntarily engaged in by the tiqueur. Massed practice has been used successfully with adults (Jones, 1960; Yates, 1958), and Yates predicted that it would be even more effective with child subjects because in their briefer learning histories the tic would not be overlearned so that, according to Hullian learning theory, massed practice would contribute more to growth of reactive inhibition than to habit strength. This expectation has, by and large, not been confirmed in the child-therapy literature. Although Walton (1961) effectively controlled multiple facial, arm, leg, and vocalization tics in an 11-year-old boy in only 36 treatment sessions and Ernest (1960) reported eliminating a girl's inspiratory tic, two recent studies have reported massed practice to be ineffective in controlling bizarre, repetitive rocking at night (Evans, 1961) and head-jerk and eyeblink tics (Feldman & Werry, 1966). In the latter study, both tics actually increased in frequency over base-line levels as a result of massed practice of the head jerk. A third tic which had previously disappeared also recurred concurrent with the treatment attempt. Feldman and Werry (1966) attributed their negative results to a probable buildup in the child's anxiety level which was thought to be responsible for the tics.

The conditions under which a massed-practice technique will be successful have not yet been well established, and consequently descriptions of therapeutic failures can provide valuable information regarding crucial controlling variables. Unsuccessful outcome may be related to difficulty in policing the massed-practice trials in that the experience is probably very fatiguing and aversive for the child who will attempt to avoid the practice session whenever possible, thereby defeating the treatment attempt. The therapist must also be careful not to inadvertently reinforce the tics, for example, by writing or marking a record sheet each time the tic occurs, thus increasing the rate.

Self-Destructive Behavior

Lovaas and his colleagues (Lovaas, Berberich, Perloff, & Schaeffer, 1966; Lovaas, Freitag, Gold, & Kassorla, 1965; Lovaas, Freitag, Kinder, Rubenstein, Schaeffer, & Simmons, 1964; Lovaas, Schaeffer, & Simmons, 1965) have treated self-injurious behaviors in schizophrenic children through administration of punishment via electric shock, critical comments, and slapping. Having in this manner focused the children's attention upon relevant social stimuli, their appropriate behaviors could then be more effectively positively reinforced. Both time out from reinforcement and electric-shock punishment were used to control a variety of self-destructive responses in a 9-year-old psychotic boy (Tate & Baroff, 1966). Not surprisingly, the shock procedure was the more powerful modification technique. In the course of the avoidance conditioning, the buzzing sound produced by the stock prod used to administer shock acquired secondary reinforcing properties and was used to promote the child's eating and to control his holding a lake of saliva in his mouth and his persistent clinging to people. Although the main techniques used by Tate and Baroff (1966) were time-out and punishment, praise was also given the child for his prosocial responses.

ACCELERATION OF PROSOCIAL BEHAVIORS

In some instances, therapists are faced not with the prospect of minimizing undesirable responses, but with increasing the extent of the child's behavior repertoire, which may be inadequate and restricted for his age group (Quay, Werry, McQueen, & Sprague, 1966). For example, Johnston, Kelley, Harris, and Wolf (1966) enhanced the development of motor skills of a generally awkward and inhibited nursery school boy by making his teachers' attention and approval contingent upon his using a play-yard climbing frame. The same group of investigators also eliminated regressed crawling in a 3-year-old girl through differential social reinforcement of her walking rather than crawling (Harris, Johnston, Kelley, & Wolf, 1964) and increased the frequency of peer as opposed to teacher interaction in a socially isolated nursery school girl (Allen, Hart, Buell, Harris, & Wolf, 1964). In an attempt to maximize the extratherapeutic maintenance of new behaviors, Ferster and Simons (1966) have emphasized the importance of capitalizing on natural reinforcers in dealing with behavioral deficits in disturbed children.

Toilet Training

Toilet training is another developmental task apparently facilitated through judicious use of positive reinforcement (Madsen, 1965; Pumroy & Pumroy, 1965). To increase training efficiency, Van Wagenen and Murdock (1966) have developed a transistorized device which is placed in training pants and automatically activates a tone signal when the child has urinated or defecated, thus allowing parents to shape appropriate toilet use through the method of successive approximations. On successive trials the infant is positively reinforced for elimination closer and closer to the proper location.

26

The Mowrer electric-alarm method (Mowrer & Mowrer, 1938) and later modifications have seen considerable recent use in the treatment of enuresis (Coote, 1965; Jones, 1960; Lovibond, 1963, 1964; Werry, 1966; Wickes, 1958). Well-controlled studies by De Leon and Mandell (1966) and Werry and Cohrssen (1965) have demonstrated the comparative superiority of the bed-buzzer method over unspecified psychotherapy-counseling techniques and no-treatment controls.

Making positive reinforcement contingent upon bowel movements has been reported to be an effective procedure in cases of encopresis with mental retardates (Dayan, 1964; Hundziak, Mauer, & Watson, 1965), psychotics (Keehn, 1965; Neale, 1963), and children with no other reported problems (Gelber & Meyer, 1965; Peterson & London, 1965). Peterson and London also used hypnotic-like suggestion and reasoning with the child to help promote behavior change.

Retardation

The instatement and acceleration of prosocial behavior have also been accomplished in children displaying severe retardation in the learning of necessary social and motor skills. As a dramatic example, Fuller (1949) trained a bedridden 18-year-old vegetative idiot to move his arm to earn a food reinforcer. Rice and McDaniel (1966) provided useful methodological suggestions for manipulating the motor behavior of profoundly retarded children. Psychotic and mentally retarded children have been successfully treated for poverty in generalized imitation tendencies (Metz, 1965), self-help behavior (Bensberg, Colwell, & Cassel, 1965), and speech deficiency (Commons, Paul, & Fargo, 1966; Cook & Adams, 1966; Kerr, Meyerson, & Michael, 1965; Salzinger, Feldman, Cowan, & Salzinger, 1965; Straughan, Potter, & Hamilton, 1965). The treatment techniques used in the latter group of studies were combinations of modeling procedures and positive reinforcement for imitation or correct responding.

MULTIPLE TREATMENT TECHNIQUES

The studies discussed in this section have combined manipulations designed to promote adaptive behaviors with attempts to decrease the occurrence of problematic behavior. The use of such technique combinations with individual clients appears to be growing in popularity among behavior therapists possibly because the child who displays a particular maladaptive behavior is likely also to have learned relatively few socially desirable means of acquiring the reinforcement which his deviant responses were intended to secure. Under such circumstances, it is possible that apparent "symptom substitution" will occur, with another problem behavior emerging after a treated deviant response has been successfully eliminated, simply because the child's response hierarchies include few prosocial behavior patterns (Bandura & Walters, 1963, p. 32). Thus the therapist can help prevent the appearance of additional problems through teaching the child alternative desirable responses which are likely to be maintained through positive reinforcement available in the child's social situation.

Delinquents

Delinquents typify a group exhibiting a number of undesirable response patterns (e.g., stealing, fighting, lying) in combination with a deficiency in prosocial responses such as cooperation with authorities, regular work habits, and sufficient self-control. Not surprisingly, behavior-therapy interventions with delinquents have frequently involved use of combined acceleration-deceleration techniques. For example, Burchard and Tyler (1965) used time out in an isolation room to control an institutionalized delinquent boy's antisocial behaviors, and at the same time positively reinforced his adaptive behaviors. He was awarded tokens which could be turned in for a number of reinforcing events for each hour he managed to remain out of isolation. Tyler (1965) has also reported successful use of time out in an isolation room for delinquents' misbehavior while playing pool. In the same paper, Tyler described promising pilot-study data indicating that reinforcing an adolescent delinquent's approximations to satisfactory academic performance will produce improvement in his school grades. Schwitzgebel (1967) has also demonstrated a significant increase in adolescent delinquents' cooperative and constructive behaviors when this class of responses was followed by positive consequences such as verbal praise or a gift. In a matched delinquent group, attempted punishment of hostile, antisocial statements through the therapist's disagreement or inattention failed to produce a corresponding decrease in deviant responding. Since Schwitzgebel's subjects were not institutionalized and engaged in the interview sessions on a purely voluntary basis, the experimenters were reluctant to jeopardize the boys' willingness to participate by exposing them to powerful aversive stimuli. Consequently, it is probable that the aversive consequences for deviant responses were simply too mild to have any effect, as Schwitzgebel himself hypothesized. In an earlier study (Schwitzgebel & Kolb, 1964), prosocial behavior was increased in adolescent delinquents through administration of positive reinforcers (small change and cigarettes) on a variable-interval schedule. The boys received reinforcement for keeping appointments, appropriately discussing and analyzing their feelings, and performing job-training tasks. Three years after termination of treatment, these subjects showed a significant reduction in frequency and severity of criminal offenses as compared to a matched-pair control group.

Autistic Behaviors

Simultaneous use of acceleration and deceleration modification techniques has proved to be a powerful approach to the treatment of particularly maladaptive and resistant behavior patterns, such as those often observed in psychotic children (Lovaas, Freitag, Gold, & Kassorla, 1965). For example, working with a severely autistic 3-year-old boy, Wolf, Risley, and Mees (1964) produced considerable positive behavior change through a combination of positive reinforcement (food) and a procedure described as "mild punishment and extinction" which involved isolating the boy in his bedroom contingent upon his having had a temper tantrum. Other investigators have described similar brief isolation sessions as time out from positive reinforcement (Hawkins, Peterson, Schweid, & Bijou, 1966). Similarly, Zimmerman and Zimmerman (1962) have combined extinction of bizarre

and tantrum behaviors with social reinforcement for appropriate responses in a special classroom situation, and Marshall (1966) has successfully used food reinforcement and mild punishment (slaps on the buttocks, extinguishing room lights) to toilet train an 8-year-old autistic child. Davison (1964) reported extinction of fear and aggressive responses as well as increased responsiveness to adult requests in a 9-year-old autistic girl through contingent application of candy, attention, and opportunities to look into a mirror and withdrawal of social reinforcement for undesirable behavior. Treatment of nonpsychotic children's aggression (Gittelman, 1965; Sloane, Johnston, & Bijou, 1966), storm phobia and anorexia nervosa (Hallsten, 1965; White, 1959), school phobia (Lazarus, Davison, & Polefka, 1965), and operant crying (Hart, Allen, Buell, Harris, & Wolf, 1964) seems also to be facilitated through simultaneous use of acceleration and deceleration techniques.

Parental Training

A new treatment technique which seems to have considerable promise is the training of parents to become appropriate reinforcement-dispensing agents. In some instances, parents are invited to observe reinforcement-treatment sessions, first, to see that the reinforcement contingency actually does control their child's problem behavior, and second, to learn how and when to dispense reinforcers, both tangible and social. Thus far, parents have been reported to have been successfully trained as behavior therapists for their children's antisocial behavior (Hawkins et al., 1966; Russo, 1964; Straughan, 1964; Whaler, Winkel, Peterson, & Morrison, 1965; Zeilberger, Sampen, & Sloane, 1966) excessive scratching and self-mutilation (Allen & Harris, 1966), and psychotic temper tantrums (Wetzel, Baker, Roney, & Martin, 1966). Patterson and Brodsky (1966) have recently ambitiously attempted the treatment of a child's multiple problem behaviors through the concurrent use of several conditioning programs including training the parents. The child's temper tantrums were modified through the use of an extinction-counterconditioning procedure, his separation-anxiety reactions were treated through another extinction-counterconditioning program, positive reinforcement was used to increase his positive interactions with peers, while his parents were trained to extinguish his negativistic and immature behaviors and to reward any evidences of cooperation and independence. Since there is some evidence that the environmental reinforcement contingencies to which delinquents (Buehler, Patterson, & Furniss, 1966) and adult psychotics (Gelfand, Gelfand, & Dobson, 1967) are exposed probably maintain their deviant behaviors, it is likely that the best hope for permanent positive behavior change rests in modifying the client's social environment. In the case of children, it may well prove more efficacious to modify the parents' child-rearing practices than to bring the child to the laboratory or clinic for direct interaction with the therapist. Parental education of this type may well have important preventive aspects also in that parents who are aware of the nature of their control of their children's behavior may be better able to prevent the occurrence of future problems and to promote appropriate interpersonal behavior.

RESEARCH METHODOLOGY

Paradigms for psychotherapy research using the more traditional treatment versus control groups designs have recently been discussed in detail by other writers (Bergin, 1966; Goldstein, Heller, & Sechrest, 1966; Kiesler, 1966) so this paper will deal only with evaluation of treatment with single subjects. As is the case with traditional play-therapy evaluation reports, the vast majority (96%) of the child-behavior-therapy papers reviewed here are case studies which describe modification of the behavior of individual subjects or of small groups of children displaying similar problem behaviors. Some writers have concluded that demonstrations of therapeutic efficacy with single cases represent no scientifically acceptable evidence at all. For example, Breger and McGaugh (1965) have argued that the behavior therapists' reliance upon single-subject therapy evaluations necessarily creates doubts about their claims of therapeutic success, and that, therefore, most of the reported successes "must be re-garded as no better substantiated than those of any other enthusiastic school of psychotherapy . . . [p. 351]." This criticism has application only insofar as the methods used by therapy researchers studying individual subjects fail to meet the criteria usually applied to laboratory "free operant" studies. The "single organism, within-subject design" (Dinsmoor, 1966) has been extensively described elsewhere (Bachrach, 1964; Honig, 1966; Sidman, 1960, 1962), so this paper will discuss only a few of the major features. The contention here is that use of this method in therapy evaluation can powerfully demonstrate behavior control if certain specified procedures are followed. For instance, adequate base-line measures of the occurrence of the problem behavior (and, when applicable, frequency of prosocial responses) should be collected over a period of time long enough to provide reliable rate information. Obviously, these data should be collected in a rigorous, planned manner and not retrospectively recounted by the child's parents or teachers, as is frequently done in both traditional and behavior-therapy case studies. The therapist-experimenter should also provide a specific and detailed description of the treatment procedures, which should include sufficient data to permit replication by other investigators. Included should be information on the total number of treatment sessions, the length of each session, description of their spacing over time, and the total time span of the therapeutic intervention. The nature and extent of contacts with parents, teachers, and other involved individuals also ought to be provided. This body of information allows the reader to make comparisons regarding the efficiency and power of various treatment techniques. The work of Paul (1966), Lang and Lazovik (1963), and Lang, Lazovik, and Reynolds (1965) provides a high standard regarding adequate description of treatment procedures. The former author also presented a useful analysis of problems and alternative strategies in the design of therapy-evaluation studies.

Therapy-process data on the rate of occurrence of the behavior under investigation should be collected during every treatment session. Continuous data collection during therapy aids both in precise identification of the variables controlling the child's behavior and in the evaluation of treatment efficacy (Reyna, 1964).

A technique refinement not often observed is the systematic variation of the treatment reinforcement contingencies. After substantial and apparently reliable behavior modification has taken place, the reinforcement contingencies should be altered temporarily, for example, reversed, so the problem behavior is once again reinforced, or a prosocial response, instated through positive reinforcement, is extinguished. Correlated changes in the observed response rate provide a convincing demonstration that the target behavior is unmistakably under the therapist's control and not due to adventitious, extratherapeutic factors. This design feature is extremely important, if not essential, when $N = 1$, as Sidman (1960) and Dinsmoor (1966) have pointed out. The problem of the feasibility of such reinforcement-contingency reversals in clinical research is a knotty one, but this procedure should have high priority when the report is presented as a research study and the method described is to be taken seriously as an effective treatment technique. If the problem behavior precludes the reinstatement of natural contingencies, a number of substitute techniques might be considered. Use of a yoked control treated identically to the treatment subject with the exception that the active therapeutic ingredient is not systematically administered should prove useful in desensitization studies where contingency reversal is not feasible. Demonstration of behavioral control also might be accomplished by breaking the target behavior into subunits, for example, on the basis of response magnitude or object, and independently manipulating the separate units.[2] Less desirable substitutes for complete contingency reversal include the following control techniques: contingency changes that have predictable effects on response emission, for example, schedule changes; contingency reversal for a limited aspect of the target behavior and/or for the target behavior under limited, discriminable conditions.

[2] This technique was suggested by Florence R. Harris in a workshop presentation, University of Utah, April 28, 1967.

Unfortunately, all of the previously discussed experimental control procedures are undermined if the accuracy of the rate measures is open to question. As in all psychotherapy research, extreme care must be taken to assure that truly objective behavior observations and measures are used. Since therapists are notoriously unobjective observers when the validity of their favorite treatment technique is in question, the best procedure would require either automatic recording of the target behaviors or the use of observers who are naive regarding the treatment procedure. Two additional refinements used by Brackbill (1958) in her study of the extinction of the smiling response in infants seem highly desirable for use in therapy evaluation also. First, sound-film recordings should be made at several points in the treatment process to permit independent and, if necessary, repeated observer reliability checks. Such a film record would also be useful to therapists wishing to learn the techniques which are often not adequately described in the published report. Another impressive design feature used by Brackbill was the establishment of high interobserver reliability prior to the inception of the study proper, a procedure rarely, if ever, followed in the child-therapy research literature where observer reliability is typically shaped while the behavior modification is proceeding. A possible result is that the observations made early in therapy lack reliability.

Lest the state of affairs in the reliability department look too black, it should be pointed out that the types of behaviors usually dealt with by behavior therapists are well defined, easily observed, and difficult to mistake, for example, the incidence of temper tantrums, enuresis, or speech deficit. Therefore, observer bias should less seriously affect the results than would be the case where the variables under investigation are less rigorously defined, such as lack of positive self-regard, covert hostility, and high anxiety. Nevertheless, investigators should not ignore Rosenthal's (1963, 1964) convincing demonstrations that experimenter bias can distort results even when seemingly very unmistakable response classes are under study.

One further therapy-evaluation procedure

which should be undertaken in single-case as well as in treatment versus control group designs is a follow-up analysis of the stability of the behavior modification. A series of follow-up evaluations over a period of time, perhaps several years, would provide much-needed information concerning "symptom substitution" and generalization effects and would be a highly desirable design feature. Naturally, it is proposed that any follow-up data collection be made in a form more rigorous than the all too typical therapist's phone call to the child's parents or teacher, a procedure very likely to be subject to the Hello-Goodbye effect (Hathaway, 1948), according to which the persons contacted for information feel it is only polite to assure the therapist that he had helped the child, whether or not any change in behavior is actually observable.

Unfortunately, many of the behavior-therapy studies reviewed in this paper fail to meet most of the assessment standards suggested in the evaluation paradigm and thus represent no improvement over the traditional clinical case study in terms of experimental rigor. Nevertheless, in contrast to the play-therapy case-study literature, there are a small but growing number of carefully designed behavior-therapy case studies which meet most, if not all, of the suggested evaluation criteria and which convincingly demonstrate the power and efficiency of behavioristic treatment approaches (Allen et al., 1964; Doubros & Daniels, 1966; Harris et al., 1964; Whaler et al., 1965). While it is still possible to argue the merits of the theoretical bases for behavior-therapy techniques, careful application of the "single organism, within-subject design" should leave little question about the method's effectiveness.

REFERENCES

ALLEN, K. E., & HARRIS, F. R. Elimination of a child's excessive scratching by training the mother in reinforcement procedures. *Behaviour Research and Therapy*, 1966, 4, 79–84.

ALLEN, K. E., HART, B., BUELL, J. S., HARRIS, F. R., & WOLF, M. M. Effects of social reinforcement on isolate behavior of a nursery school child. *Child Development*, 1964, 35, 511–518.

BACHRACH, A. J. Some applications of operant conditioning to behavior therapy. In J. Wolpe, A. Salter, & L. J. Reyna (Eds.), *The conditioning*

therapies: The challenge in psychotherapy. New York: Holt, Rinehart & Winston, 1964.

BAER, D. M. Laboratory control of thumbsucking by withdrawal and representation of reinforcement. *Journal of the Experimental Analysis of Behavior*, 1962, 5, 525–528.

BANDURA, A. Psychotherapy as a learning process. *Psychological Bulletin*, 1961, 58, 143–159.

BANDURA, A. Behavioral psychotherapy. *Scientific American*, 1967, 216, 78–86.

BANDURA, A., GRUSEC, J. E., & MENLOVE, F. L. Vicarious extinction of avoidance behavior. *Journal of Personality and Social Psychology*, 1967, 5, 16–23.

BANDURA, A., & WALTERS, R. H. *Social learning and personality development.* New York: Holt, Rinehart & Winston, 1963.

BENSBERG, G. J., COLWELL, C. N., & CASSEL, R. H. Teaching the profoundly retarded self-help activities by shaping behavior techniques. *American Journal of Mental Deficiency*, 1965, 69, 674–679.

BENTLER, P. M. An infant's phobia treated with reciprocal inhibition therapy. *Journal of Child Psychology and Psychiatry*, 1962, 3, 185–189.

BERGIN, A. E. Some implications of psychotherapy research for therapeutic practice. *Journal of Abnormal Psychology*, 1966, 71, 235–246.

BOARDMAN, W. K. Rusty: A brief behavior disorder. *Journal of Consulting Psychology*, 1962, 26, 293–297.

BRACKBILL, Y. Extinction of the smiling response in infants as a function of reinforcement schedule. *Child Development*, 1958, 29, 115–124.

BREGER, L., & McGAUGH, J. L. Critique and reformulation of "learning-theory" approaches to psychotherapy and neurosis. *Psychological Bulletin*, 1965, 63, 338–358.

BROWN, P., & ELLIOTT, R. Control of aggression in nursery school class. *Journal of Experimental Child Psychology*, 1965, 3, 102–107.

BUEHLER, R. E., PATTERSON, G. R., & FURNISS, J. M. The reinforcement of behavior in institutional settings. *Behaviour Research and Therapy*, 1966, 4, 157–167.

BURCHARD, J. D., & TYLER, V. Ó., JR. The modification of delinquent behavior through operant conditioning. *Behaviour Research and Therapy*, 1965, 2, 245–250.

COMMONS, M. L., PAUL, S. M., & FARGO, G. A. Developing speech in an autistic boy using operant techniques to increase his rate of vocal-verbal responding. Paper presented at the meeting of the Western Psychological Association, Long Beach, California, April 1966.

COOK, C., & ADAMS, H. E. Modification of verbal behavior in speech deficient children. *Behaviour Research and Therapy*, 1966, 4, 265–271.

COOTE, M. A. Apparatus for conditioning treatment of enuresis. *Behaviour Research and Therapy*, 1965, 2, 233–238.

DAVISON, G. C. A social learning theory programme with an autistic child. *Behaviour Research and Therapy*, 1964, 2, 149–159.

DAYAN, M. Toilet training retarded children in the state residential institution. *Mental Retardation,* 1964, 2, 116–117.

DE LEON, G., & MANDELL, W. A comparison of conditioning and psychotherapy in the treatment of functional enuresis. *Journal of Clinical Psychology,* 1966, 22, 326–330.

DINSMOOR, J. A. Comments on Wetzel's treatment of a case of compulsive stealing. *Journal of Consulting Psychology,* 1966, 30, 378–380.

DOUBROS, S. G., & DANIELS, G. J. An experimental approach to the reduction of overactive behavior. *Behaviour Research and Therapy,* 1966, 4, 251–258.

ERNEST, E. (Personal communication.) Cited by H. G. Jones, Continuation of Yates' treatment of a tiqueur. In H. J. Eysenck (Ed.), *Behavior therapy and the neuroses.* Oxford: Pergamon Press, 1960. P. 257.

EVANS, J. Rocking at night. *Journal of Child Psychology and Psychiatry,* 1961, 2, 71–85.

FELDMAN, R. B., & WERRY, J. S. An unsuccessful attempt to treat a tiqueur by massed practice. *Behaviour Research and Therapy,* 1966, 4, 111–117.

FERSTER, C. B., & SIMONS, J. Behavior therapy with children. *Psychological Record,* 1966, 16, 65–71.

FULLER, P. R. Operant conditioning of a vegetative human organism. *American Journal of Psychology,* 1949, 62, 587–590.

GARVEY, W. P., & HEGRENES, J. R. Desensitization techniques in the treatment of school phobia. *American Journal of Orthopsychiatry,* 1966, 36, 147–152.

GELBER, H., & MEYER, B. Behavior therapy and encopresis: Complexities involved in treatment. *Behaviour Research and Therapy,* 1965, 2, 227–231.

GELFAND, D. M., GELFAND, S., & DOBSON, W. R. Unprogrammed reinforcement of patients' behavior in a mental hospital. *Behaviour Research and Therapy,* 1967, 5, 201–207.

GITTELMAN, M. Behavior rehearsal as a technique in child treatment. *Journal of Child Psychology and Psychiatry,* 1965, 6, 251–255.

GOLDSTEIN, A. P., HELLER, K., & SECHREST, L. B. *Psychotherapy and the psychology of behavior change.* New York: Wiley, 1966.

GROSSBERG, J. M. Behavior therapy: A review. *Psychological Bulletin,* 1964, 62, 73–88.

HALLSTEN, E. A., JR. Adolescent anorexia nervosa treated by desensitization. *Behaviour Research and Therapy,* 1965, 3, 87–91.

HARRIS, F. R., JOHNSTON, M. K., KELLEY, C. S., & WOLF, M. M. Effects of positive social reinforcement on regressed crawling of a nursery school child. *Journal of Educational Psychology,* 1964, 55, 35–41.

HART, B. M., ALLEN, K. E., BUELL, J. S., HARRIS, F. R., & WOLF, M. M. Effects of social reinforcement on operant crying. *Journal of Experimental Child Psychology,* 1964, 1, 145–153.

HATHAWAY, S. R. Some considerations relative to nondirective counseling as therapy. *Journal of Clinical Psychology,* 1948, 4, 226–231.

HAWKINS, R. P., PETERSON, R. F., SCHWEID, E., & BIJOU, S. W. Behavior therapy in the home: Amelioration of problem parent-child relations with the parent in a therapeutic role. *Journal of Experimental Child Psychology,* 1966, 4, 99–107.

HOMME, L. E., DEBACA, P. C., DEVINE, J. V., STEINHORST, R., & RICKERT, E. J. Use of the Premack principle in controlling the behavior of nursery school children. *Journal of the Experimental Analysis of Behavior,* 1963, 6, 544.

HONIG, W. K. (Ed.) *Operant behavior: Areas of research and application.* New York: Appleton-Century-Crofts, 1966.

HUNDZIAK, M., MAUER, R. A., & WATSON, L. S., JR. Operant conditioning and toilet training of severely mentally retarded boys. *American Journal of Mental Deficiency,* 1965, 70, 120–124.

JAMES, C. E. Operant conditioning in the management and behavior of hyperactive children: Five case studies. Unpublished manuscript, Orange State College, 1963. Cited by G. R. Patterson, R. Jones, J. Whittier, & M. A. Wright, A behaviour modification technique for the hyperactive child. *Behaviour Research and Therapy,* 1965, 2, 218.

JOHNSTON, M. K., KELLEY, C. S., HARRIS, F. R., & WOLF, M. M. An application of reinforcement principles to development of motor skills of a young child. *Child Development,* 1966, 37, 379–387.

JONES, H. G. The behavioral treatment of enuresis nocturna. In H. J. Eysenck (Ed.), *Behaviour therapy and the neuroses.* London: Pergamon Press, 1960.

JONES, M. C. The elimination of children's fears. *Journal of Experimental Psychology,* 1924, 7, 382–390. (a)

JONES, M. C. A laboratory study of fear: The case of Peter. *Pedagogical Seminar,* 1924, 31, 308–315. (b)

KEEHN, J. D. Brief case-report: Reinforcement therapy of incontinence. *Behaviour Research and Therapy,* 1965, 2, 239.

KERR, N., MEYERSON, L., & MICHAEL, J. A procedure for shaping vocalization in a mute child. In L. P Ullmann & L. Krasner (Eds.), *Case studies in behavior modification.* New York: Holt, Rinehart & Winston, 1965.

KIESLER, D. J. Some myths of psychotherapy research and the search for a paradigm. *Psychological Bulletin,* 1966, 65, 110–136.

KRASNER, L., & ULLMANN, L. P. (Eds.) *Research in behavior modification.* New York: Holt, Rinehart & Winston, 1965.

LANG, P. J., & LAZOVIK, A. D. Experimental desensitization of a phobia. *Journal of Abnormal and Social Psychology,* 1963, 66, 519–525.

LANG, P. J., LAZOVIK, A. D., & REYNOLDS, D. J. Desensitization, suggestibility, and pseudotherapy. *Journal of Abnormal Psychology,* 1965, 70, 395–402.

LAZARUS, A. A. The elimination of children's phobias by deconditioning. *Medical Proceedings*, South Africa, 1959, **5**, 261–265.

LAZARUS, A. A., & ABRAMOVITZ, A. The use of "emotive imagery" in the treatment of children's phobias. *Journal of Mental Science*, 1962, **108**, 191–195.

LAZARUS, A. A., DAVISON, D. C., & POLEFKA, B. A. Classical and operant factors in the treatment of school phobia. *Journal of Abnormal Psychology*, 1965, **70**, 225–229.

LAZARUS, A., & RACHMAN, S. The use of systematic desensitization in psychotherapy. *South African Medical Journal*, 1957, **31**, 934–937.

LOVAAS, O. I., BERBERICH, J. P., PERLOFF, B. F., & SCHAEFFER, B. Acquisition of imitative speech by schizophrenic children. *Science*, 1966, **161**, 705–707.

LOVAAS, O. I., FREITAG, G., GOLD, V. J., & KASSORLA, I. C. Experimental studies in childhood schizophrenia: Analysis of self-destructive behavior. *Journal of Experimental Child Psychology*, 1965, **2**, 67–84.

LOVAAS, O. I., FREITAG, G., KINDER, M. I., RUBENSTEIN, D. B., SCHAEFFER, B., & SIMMONS, J. B. Experimental studies in childhood schizophrenia: Developing social behavior using electric shock. Paper presented at the meeting of the American Psychological Association, Los Angeles, September 1964.

LOVAAS, O. I., SCHAEFFER, B., & SIMMONS, J. B. Building social behavior in autistic children by use of electric shock. *Journal of Experimental Research in Personality*, 1965, **1**, 99–109.

LOVIBOND, S. H. The mechanism of conditioned treatment of enuresis. *Behaviour Research and Therapy*, 1963, **1**, 17–21.

LOVIBOND, S. H. *Conditioning and enuresis.* Oxford: Pergamon Press, 1964.

MADSEN, C. H., JR. Positive reinforcement in the toilet training of a normal child: A case report. In L. P. Ullmann & L. Krasner (Eds.), *Case studies in behavior modification.* New York: Holt, Rinehart & Winston, 1965.

MARSHALL, G. R. Toilet training of an autistic eight-year-old through conditioning therapy: A case report. *Behaviour Research and Therapy*, 1966, **4**, 242–245.

METZ, J. R. Conditioning generalized imitation in autistic children. *Journal of Experimental Child Psychology*, 1965, **2**, 389–399.

MOWRER, O. H., & MOWRER, W. M. Enuresis: A method for its study and treatment. *American Journal of Orthopsychiatry*, 1938, **8**, 436–459.

NEALE, D. H. Behavior therapy and encopresis in children. *Behaviour Research and Therapy*, 1963, **1**, 139–150.

PATTERSON, G. R. An application of conditioning techniques to the control of a hyperactive child. In L. P. Ullmann & L. Krasner (Eds.), *Case studies in behavior modification.* New York: Holt, Rinehart & Winston, 1965. (a)

PATTERSON, G. R. A learning theory approach to the treatment of the school phobic child. In L. P.

Ullmann & L. Krasner (Eds.), *Case studies in behavior modification.* New York: Holt, Rinehart & Winston, 1965. (b)

PATTERSON, G. R., & BRODSKY, G. A behavior modification programme for a child with multiple problem behaviors. *Journal of Child Psychology and Psychiatry*, 1966, **7**, 277–296.

PATTERSON, G. R., JONES, R., WHITTIER, J., & WRIGHT, M. A. A behaviour modification technique for the hyperactive child. *Behaviour Research and Therapy*, 1965, **2**, 217–226.

PAUL, G. L. *Insight versus desensitization in psychotherapy.* Stanford: Stanford University Press, 1966.

PETERSON, D. R., & LONDON, P. A role for cognition in the behavioral treatment of a child's eliminative disturbance. In L. P. Ullmann & L. Krasner (Eds.), *Case studies in behavior modification.* New York: Holt, Rinehart & Winston, 1965.

PUMROY, D. K., & PUMROY, S. S. Reinforcement in toilet training. *Psychological Reports*, 1965, **16**, 467–471.

QUAY, H. C., WERRY, J. S., McQUEEN, M., & SPRAGUE, R. L. Remediation of the conduct problem child in the special class setting. *Exceptional Child*, 1966, **32**, 509–515.

RACHMAN, S. Learning theory and child psychology: Therapeutic possibilities. *Journal of Child Psychology and Psychiatry*, 1962, **3**, 149–163.

REYNA, L. J. Conditioning therapies, learning theory, and research. In J. Wolpe, A. Salter, & L. J. Reyna (Eds.), *The conditioning therapies.* New York: Holt, Rinehart & Winston, 1964.

RICE, H. K., & McDANIEL, M. W. Operant behavior in vegetative patients. *Psychological Record*, 1966, **16**, 279–281.

ROSENTHAL, R. On the social psychology of the psychological experiment. *American Scientist*, 1963, **51**, 268–283.

ROSENTHAL, R. Experimenter outcome orientation and the results of the psychological experiment. *Psychological Bulletin*, 1964, **61**, 405–412.

RUSSO, S. Adaptations in behavioral therapy with children. *Behaviour Research and Therapy*, 1964, **2**, 43–47.

SALZINGER, K., FELDMAN, R. S., COWAN, J. E., & SALZINGER, S. Operant conditioning of verbal behavior of two young speech-deficient boys. In L. Krasner & L. P. Ullmann (Eds.) *Research in behavior modification.* New York: Holt, Rinehart & Winston, 1965.

SCHWITZGEBEL, R. Short-term operant conditioning of adolescent offenders on socially relevant variables. *Journal of Abnormal Psychology*, 1967, **72**, 134–142.

SCHWITZGEBEL, R., & KOLB, D. A. Inducing behavior change in adolescent delinquents. *Behaviour Research and Therapy*, 1964, **1**, 297–304.

SIDMAN, M. *Tactics of scientific research.* New York: Basic Books, 1960.

SIDMAN, M. Operant techniques. In A. L. Bachrach (Ed.), *Experimental foundations of clinical psychology.* New York: Basic Books, 1962.

SLOANE, H. N., JR., JOHNSTON, M. K., & BIJOU, S. W. Successive modification of aggressive behavior and aggressive fantasy play by management of contingencies. Unpublished manuscript, University of Utah, 1966.

STRAUGHAN, J. H. Treatment with child and mother in the playroom. *Behaviour Research and Therapy*, 1964, **2**, 37–41.

STRAUGHAN, J. H., POTTER, W. K., & HAMILTON, S. H. The behavioral treatment of an elective mute. *Journal of Child Psychology and Psychiatry*, 1965, **6**, 125–130.

TATE, B. G., & BAROFF, G. S. Aversive control of self-injurious behavior in a psychotic boy. *Behaviour Research and Therapy*, 1966, **4**, 281–287.

TYLER, V. O. Exploring the use of operant techniques in the rehabilitation of delinquent boys. Paper presented at the meeting of the American Psychological Association, Chicago, September 1965.

ULLMANN, L. P., & KRASNER, L. (Eds.) *Case studies in behavior modification*. New York: Holt, Rinehart & Winston, 1965.

VAN WAGENEN, R. K., & MURDOCK, E. E. A transistorized signal-package for toilet training of infants. *Journal of Experimental Child Psychology*, 1966, **3**, 312–314.

WALTON, D. Experimental psychology and the treatment of a tiqueur. *Journal of Child Psychology and Psychiatry*, 1961, **2**, 148–155.

WEITZMAN, B. Behavior therapy and psychotherapy. *Psychological Review*, 1967, **74**, 300–317.

WERRY, J. S. The conditioning treatment of enuresis. *American Journal of Psychiatry*, 1966, **123**, 226–229.

WERRY, J. S., & COHRSSEN, J. Enuresis: An etiologie and therapeutic study. *Journal of Pediatrics*, 1965, **67**, 423–431.

WERRY, J. S., & WOLLERSHEIM, J. P. Behavior therapy with children: A broad overview. *American Academy of Child Psychiatry Journal*, 1967, **6**, 346–370.

WETZEL, R. Use of behavioral techniques in a case of compulsive stealing. *Journal of Consulting Psychology*, 1966, **30**, 367–374.

WETZEL, R. J., BAKER, J., RONEY, M., & MARTIN, M. Outpatient treatment of autistic behavior. *Behaviour Research and Therapy*, 1966, **4**, 169–177.

WHALER, R. G., WINKEL, G. H., PETERSON, R. F., & MORRISON, D. C. Mothers as behavior therapists for their own children. *Behaviour Research and Therapy*, 1965, **3**, 113–124.

WHITE, J. G. The use of learning theory in the psychological treatment of children. *Journal of Clinical Psychology*, 1959, **16**, 227–229.

WICKES, I. G. Treatment of persistent enuresis with the electric buzzer. *Archives of Disease in Childhood*, 1958, **33**, 160–164.

WILLIAMS, C. D. The elimination of tantrum behavior by extinction procedures. *Journal of Abnormal and Social Psychology*, 1959, **59**, 269.

WOLF, M. M., BIRNBRAUER, J. S., WILLIAMS, R., & LAWLER, J. A note on apparent extinction of the vomiting behavior of a retarded child. In L. P. Ullmann & L. Krasner (Eds.), *Case studies in behavior modification*. New York: Holt, Rinehart & Winston, 1965.

WOLF, M. M., RISLEY, T., & MEES, H. Application of operant conditioning procedures to the behavior problems of an autistic child. *Behaviour Research and Therapy*, 1964, **1**, 305–312.

WOLPE, J. *Psychotherapy by reciprocal inhibition.* Stanford: Stanford University Press, 1958.

WOLPE, J., & LAZARUS, A. A. *Behavior therapy techniques.* Oxford: Pergamon Press, 1966.

YATES, A. J. The application of learning theory to the treatment of tics. *Journal of Abnormal and Social Psychology*, 1958, **56**, 175–182.

ZEILBERGER, J., SAMPEN, S. E., & SLOANE, H. N., JR. Modification of child problem behavior in the home with the mother as therapist. Unpublished manuscript, City College of New York, 1966.

ZIMMERMAN, E. H., & ZIMMERMAN, J. The alteration of behavior in a special classroom situation. *Journal of Experimental Analysis of Behavior*, 1962, **5**, 59–60.

Conditioned Learning for the Brain Damaged Child

Behavior Modification in the Mentally Retarded

Application of Operant Conditioning Principles

SIDNEY W. BIJOU, Ph.D.

The application of behavior principles to training and treatment programs offers new hope for the mentally retarded child and those concerned with his welfare. It is now apparent that a child at any level of retardation can be helped to improve his personal, social, and intellectual behavior through proper instructional programming. In addition to enhancing the retarded child's potential, the same behavior principles have been applied to counseling parents of the retarded. Here, parent counseling takes the form of instructing the parent in behavior modification techniques, carrying out prescribed programs, keeping simple records, etc.

What is behavior modification? Originally, behavior modification referred to psychotherapy based on the application of behavior principles (sometimes referred to as learning theory). Recently, the definition has been expanded to mean the application of behavior principles to practically all remedial procedures, including rehabilitation, speech correction, remedial reading, classroom management, counseling, and guidance. We shall follow the current practice and use the term in the global sense. It is hoped that in the future there will be a specific label for the application of behavior principles to each remedial endeavor, a label which refers to the specific aspect of the deviant behavior remediated, or the normal behavior enhanced.

What do we mean by behavior principles? Behavior principles are general statements about the relationships between environmental events and changes in behavior. A teacher asks her class a question, and a child responds with a verbal statement; a mother kisses her little boy good-bye, and he leaves the house to go to school. At present, various sets of behavior principles are being applied in behavior modification programs. The principles followed in this paper are those developed by Skinner and his colleagues (Skinner, 1953 and 1968; Bijou and Baer, 1961; Ferster and Perrott, 1968), and are characterized by the systematic use of empirical and functional concepts; that is to say, all conditions, processes, and relationships are defined in objective terms. We should also point out, in the hope of eliminating confusion, that in our discussions we shall refer solely to behavior principles rather than to a variety of terms which have special meaning only for psychologists—terms such as learning principles, social learning principles, operant principles, and reinforcement principles.

Since behavior modification is a procedure for the application of behavior principles to the treatment of problem behavior, in this case the problem behavior of the retarded child, we cannot discuss this approach meaningfully without commenting on its implications for etiology, diagnosis, and prognosis. Hence, a brief analysis of retardation will be followed by a discussion of diagnosis and prognosis.

BEHAVIORAL ANALYSIS OF ETIOLOGY AND RETARDATION

Retardation, ranging from mild to profound, evolves through the genetic history and the individual developmental history of a child. Normal development is generated in the same way. However, progressions in the acquisition of abilities and skills and in the accumulation of knowledge proceed at a slow pace when the anomalies in a child's biological make-up adversely affect his interaction with physical objects and people. Development is also decelerated when essential physical objects and people are lacking, or when these are present but do not interact in ways that establish and maintain culturally useful behavior in the child. For example, his caretakers may be nonresponsive, punishing, or frustrating. The heart of the matter is: the anatomy and the physiology of the retarded child and the kinds and frequencies of his interactions with physical objects and people (his history) may all serve to restrict the *opportunities* for him to develop the essential repertories of behavior at a normal rate.

We shall develop this concept of retardation by first seeing how pathologic anatomy and physiology may serve as conditions restricting behavior and personality development. Then we shall consider how a child's interaction with environmental events (organic, physical, and social) from birth onward may retard the development of behavioral repertories. These interactions will carry such labels as inadequate discrimination programming, inadequate reinforcement history, punishment, and frustration. The analysis of the interactions between environmental events and a child's behavior is presented separately only for the purpose of exposition. In reality they intermingle constantly in intricate ways throughout the course of development.

37

Pathologic Anatomical Structure and Physiologic Functioning

We focus on the interplay between the behavior (responses) of a child and observable environmental events (stimuli), for out of these interactions come new ways of behaving (skills and knowledge) and new supports (motivators) for the maintenance of behavior. In doing this, we see that a child's physiologic functioning can influence the range of his responses and the availability of stimuli essential to normal responding. Irregularities in anatomical structure and physiologic functioning include defects in gross anatomy, the structure and functioning of the sense organs, the musculoskeletal system, the neurologic and endocrine systems, and other systems and glands of the body. Such flaws may originate in genetic processes or in injurious chemical and mechanical events in the prenatal, perinatal, or postnatal phase of development. Since biological anomalies may range from mild to severe, their effects on behavior development may extend from inconsequential to devastating.

Obviously the *response* potentiality of a child may be affected by impairments of the reacting and coordinating systems. A child cannot learn a response if he does not possess the anatomical parts or physiologic functioning that make up that response. A child with impaired vocal cords cannot be trained to make all the sounds necessary for normal speech. He may, of course, be trained to make different responses that will serve the same purpose in the sense that they will affect the environment in the same way. Whether he acquires compensating behavior depends on the nature of his defect and the effectiveness of the therapy.

Not so obviously, but just as truly, the *stimulus* aspect of interactions of the child and environmental events may also be affected adversely by his biological impairment. When skills in body management and locomotion are inadequately developed, the number and type of physical and social stimuli available for contact are curtailed; similarly, restricted mobility limits opportunities for the development of behavioral repertories. A child restricted to lying on his back can experience only stimuli that are above his body or those that are brought into his line of vision; the child who can roll from side to side and can sit up, can interact with stimuli above, below, and at his side; and the child who can move about on his own, can become involved in all sorts of novel physical and social situations. Depending upon the type and extent of biological impairment, some stimuli will never be accessible to certain children; others will be available on a delayed time schedule.

There is still another way in which organic impairment retards development. The physically impaired child may have restricted opportunities because of the way he *looks* to people. His physical appearance may be repugnant or offensive, causing people to avoid him, to leave him as quickly as possible, or to behave toward him in an altogether indifferent manner. Avoidant, abbreviated, and dutiful social relationships can *deprive* a child of the basic intellectual and social interactions that only people can provide. In this case, the condition responsible is organic; in others, it may be social.

Reinforcement Histories

"Reinforcement" refers to a stimulus event following a response which increases the strength of that response in a similar situation in the future. Behaviors which are strengthened (i.e., conditioned) by such consequent stimulus events are called *operants* by Skinner (1937). It has been experimentally demonstrated that operant behavior includes verbal, motor, social, and intellectual behavior, and a large component of emotional reactions. The event which follows operant behavior is designated as a "stimulus event" to emphasize that some observable environmental change has occurred after that behavior. An environmental change may consist of adding something to the situation (giving a glass of orange juice to a child after her request, "Mother, may I have a glass of orange juice?") or removing something from it (taking off a child's sweater in response to, "My sweater itches"). Stimulus events which strengthen operant behavior by presenting or withdrawing something are called *reinforcing* stimuli.

A defective reinforcement history is one of the conditions that retards the formation of adequate behavioral repertories. It may develop in a situation in which reinforcement is given only minimally by parents and others for motor, social, and intellectual behaviors. Under such circumstances appropriate social behavior (which includes language) may not develop. The required social reinforcements (e.g., attention, praise, affection) are absent, or are too weak to be effective. Another kind of situation which might generate a defective reinforcement history is one characterized by infrequent and small amounts of reinforcement. Such may be the case in an understaffed child care institution, and another example is the kind of cursory attention given to a biologically unattractive child. Still another kind of situation is one in which reinforcements are given indiscriminately, so that many behaviors are barely strengthened. For example, parents of a chronically sick, disabled, or incapacitated child may, in an effort to be helpful, react to each and every one of the child's needs and demands, reasonable and unreasonable.

A history of reinforcement which develops strong and persistent problem behavior may also lead to retardation. Highly reinforced problem behavior may become the child's way of responding to practically all situations. If he is constantly screaming or tantruming, his opportunities for strengthening new socially and educationally desirable behavior would, of course, be slow, or even static. The other consideration is that strong and persistent problem behavior may well discourage adults and peers from approaching and engaging in educational and social interactions with him, a situation which is similar to that of a child who is avoided because of his repellent physical appearance or functioning.

Presumably, no parent "in his right mind" would *want* to develop problem behaviors in his child. But problem behaviors may evolve precisely because the parent dislikes them, whereas paying attention to them naturally reduces or eliminates them. This type of understand able reaction strengthens both the problem behavior of the child and the parent's way of handling the problem; the child is positively reinforced by the parent's action and the parent is negatively reinforced by the termination of the aversive characteristics of the child's problem behavior. A familiar example of this interaction is the child who gets what he wants by having a temper tantrum. The chances are that temper tantrum behavior was established in the first place by the parents' compliance with the condition that instigated the tantrum. The chances are also that the parent "gave in" to terminate the distasteful or even alarming behavior displayed by the child. So the parental act of responding to the temper tantrum strengthens both tantruming on the part of the child and "giving in" on the part of the parent.

A final point about reinforcement history and retardation: a reinforcement history which involves the constant use of negative reinforcers (aversive contingencies) to control a child's behavior can eventually lead to almost exclusive and persistent escape and avoidance behavior. A child so equipped, usually described as a nervous or neurotic child, has little opportunity to engage in situations which generate a wide range of social and intellectual acts, skills, and bits of knowledge.

Discrimination and Perception History

If there are few or no occasions for a child to interact with responsive people and interesting things, or if the situations in which he can participate are not programmed for him, there will be few opportunities for him to acquire and retain such serviceable behaviors as: (1) skills in body management, manual dexterity, crawling, running, jumping, skipping, climbing, and skating; (2) the transformation of sounds into words, phrases, and sentences; and (3) the relating of words, spoken or written, to things, symbols, and other words. Thus it is more than likely that a child living in an opportunity-deprived environment of this sort will remain grossly uncoordinated, unskilled, and uninformed.

Well known to all are any number of situations in which poor programming leads to retarded development. Particularly familiar are the following: (1) A child is treated as though he were abnormal or chronically sick. Gross infantilization may forestall the development of speech and may impair motor coordination to the point where a child is unable to move about effectively. (2) The environment is thinly populated with stimulating people and interesting things. Not only are friendly people an essential component of an environment, but they are necessary for arranging the environment so that a child can acquire intellectual skills, learning manners, values, interests, and attitudes, all essential for community living. (3) The ordinary physical and cultural components of the environment are absent because of economic and social circumstances. In these days, when research findings stemming from such programs as Head Start, Job Corps, and Youth Opportunities literally pour out information on the effects of economic and social deprivation, it is unnecessary to elaborate further on this restrictive kind of history.

Severe Aversive Stimulation

In addition to reinforcement and discrimination, another kind of history which may retard development is one characterized by "contingent aversive stimulation." This phrase refers to the inflicting of strong punishment, either to make a child stop certain behaviors, or to protect his health and welfare, and refers also to injuries sustained in accidents. The emphasis here is on "strong" rather than mild punishment for behaviors known to almost every parent, e.g., a child who accidentally breaks a knick-knack he has been told not to touch; a child who runs into the road although he has been repeatedly told of the danger; and a child who, either through carelessness or no fault of his own, sustains painful or serious injuries in an accident. The consequences of contingent aversive events have been the subject of extensive research with animals. We shall limit our discussion to only a few of the findings. First, aversive stimulation may stop ongoing behavior—have suppressive effects. If the stimulation is moderate, it is likely that the suppressed behavior will reappear in settings similar to the one in which the stimulation occurred. A skinned knee from running too fast serves only to slow down the active youngster for a matter of minutes. If the aversive stimulation is severe, however, it is likely that the suppressive effects will remain for some time. There is more than one clinical account of a young child who would not talk for weeks, months, or years after traumatic punishment by an intoxicated or severely disturbed parent. Second, the setting in which aversive stimulation occurs may become aversive in itself; formerly neutral situations can become distasteful or frightening. (After being thrown from his favorite horse, the youngster now reacts to the animal with fear.) Third, aversive stimuli may evoke physiologic responses, such as gastric reactions to a traumatic event, which can be detrimental to the biological functioning of the child.

41

While the consequences of strong aversive stimulation are usually matters for psychopathologists, they are included here because they can retard development. Strong avoidant reactions, like certain biological anomalies, foreclose many occasions for the child to make new responses.

BEHAVIOR ANALYSIS AND DIAGNOSIS

A diagnosis of retardation is a statement of the severity of the retardation and its presumed causes, and is based on the history and current status of the child. For many years it has been the practice to classify the presumed causes in terms of endogenous, exogenous, mixed, and familial or unknown factors. More recently, this overly simplified and misleading system of classification has been replaced by one which ascribes causes to organic factors (prenatal, perinatal, and postnatal), sociocultural factors (socioeconomic status, father's occupation, parents' education, etc.), and psychological factors (frustrations, anxieties, perceptions, abnormal social behaviors, etc.). Now, advances in behavior analysis indicate the need for a further revision. The formulation would be somewhat like this: The presumed causes of retardation generate from defective organic (prenatal, perinatal, and postnatal) and sociocultural factors which interact with the behavior of the child in ways to produce retarded development. It will be recalled from the previous section that histories which lead to retardation include interactions with inadequate sensory and motor equipment, inadequate reinforcement contingencies and discrimination programming, and severe aversive contingent stimulation.

Regardless of the analytical basis of a diagnosis, it is indisputable that an accurate diagnosis requires sound information—clear-cut descriptive accounts of the specific interactions which constitute the child's history and his current ability. Admittedly, information of this sort is often difficult to gather; nevertheless, an effort should be exerted in every instance to obtain as much of it as possible. Hence a few comments on the gathering of information are in order.

Developmental History

Information about the child's history is usually obtained through interviews. As is well known, information collected this way sheds little light on the conditions that have produced the retardation. One reason: retrospective accounts are unreliable, especially when the informant is closely associated with the subject. Under such circumstances more is revealed about the behavior and personality of the informant than of the child.

A second reason for the limited value of information about a child's history obtained through interviews is that the statements obtained are most frequently not objective descriptions but conceptualizations and interpretations of behavior. For example, parents often say, "He was troublesome from the start;" "We did everything possible to get him to leave things alone;" "Toilet training was uneventful;" "He developed normally for the first year and a half of his life." These are *not* accounts of the child's behavior in relation to objects and people and the prevailing circumstances. For this reason they are less than ideal as a basis for an analysis of the conditions and the interactions that have generated the retardation.

A third reason for the limited value of interview information is that much of the material is an account of behavioral sequences isolated from their biological, social, and physical contexts. They are merely rough norms of development, such as, "He said his first words when he was 13 months old, and he walked when he was 14 months old." (It has been said that there is a relationship between the remoteness of the event recalled and its similarity to the Gesell norms.) Adequate information would consist of descriptions of the behavior and the conditions that prevailed. For example, a description of locomotor development should include not only the age at which the child lifted his head, turned over, sat in an upright position, and crawled about, but also the child's concurrent weight and health status, the actual opportunities for physical movement, the practices and responses of members of the family with respect to the child's movements, and so on.

At this point, the reader may ask: Given the limitations of the usual pediatric situation, what can be done to obtain better information on the child's history? Here are a few suggestions. First, take a brief history in the usual way, not so much in the hope of getting an accurate account of the occurrences that took place during development, but to learn something about the child-rearing practices of the parents: what they have probably done or not done in the past, and what they will probably do in the future. The information gathered would further serve to reveal aspects of the child's development which appear to require detailed investigation. Second, designate a nurse or some other available person to gather medical, sociological, economic, and educational reports and then use the facts to make guesses about past events in the child's life as well as what might be likely to occur under different treatment regimens. Third, review psychological test results for the purpose of ascertaining what the child's history has produced in terms of academic and social achievements, since the results of intelligence tests can be considered a rough indication of academic achievement. The subject of tests will be discussed in the next section.

Current Status

As with a child's history, so information concerning the child's current status is usually obtained from interviews, reports, and psychological tests. An additional source is direct. observation. In most cases, interview information would not be expected to give an adequate

43

account of a child's current behavior repertories, but it may provide valuable leads for additional sources of information and may indicate the need for special examinations. Descriptions of what the child can do in the way of personal care, locomotor skills, social skills, peer and adult interactions, verbal and academic skills, and the like, could later be modified and extended on the basis of direct observation, special reports, and test results.

Although it is frequently difficult to arrange, direct observation of current behavior can be extremely valuable. Ideally, observations should be made by a nurse, social worker, or visiting teacher in the home, school, or clinic. From a practical point of view, the pediatrician must settle for information from observations in whatever setting is available, and this is usually his office, reception room, or a playroom adjacent to his office. As we mentioned earlier, information from limited observations can often be supplemented. The doctor may instruct the child's mother to observe and record the child's behavior at lunchtime, naptime, bedtime, etc., and bring the report to him on her next visit; he may ask the teacher to observe the child's intellectual and social behavior in the classroom and send him a report; or he may request a public health nurse or a social worker to observe the child in the home. It will probably be necessary to instruct these people on specifically which behaviors are to be observed, how to record the events, and how to prepare a report which separates the actual events observed from their interpretations. A word of caution: If the worker is determined to find fixed traits or characteristics which transcend all situations, he is bound to be disappointed. There are none; behavior is related to the situation in which it occurs.

Nothing need be said about the use of medical, school, and social service reports to assess the child's current status; it is a well-established practice among pediatricians to obtain and use all such available reports. The problem is primarily one of integration and interpretation.

Psychological tests used to evaluate a child's intellectual and social behavior fall into two groups. One type classifies the child with respect to other children of the same age in terms of mental age, I.Q., achievement age, percentile, or standard score. From the point of view of a clinical study, scores from these tests may be interpreted as indicating achievement in the tasks sampled, as a consequence of a child's history. However, this type of test is also used by many to make an *actuarial* prediction of a child's future achievement. A prediction of this sort has the following meaning: The chances are X in 100 that a child with a score of Y on the test will perform at Z level in a specific, practical situation (such as schoolwork) if the environmental conditions remain about the same. It should be apparent that this type of group prediction is not helpful to a pediatrician who is primarily interested in the future development of a specific child.

The other class of psychological tests is an inventory of a child's skills and acquired knowledge. Inventories assess the specific things a child can or cannot do in the essential activities of living, like walking, sitting in a chair, paying attention, making speech sounds, putting on clothing, discriminating colors, reading, and engaging in cooperative play with peers. Hence results of these tests show precisely what the child can do and are often used as the first steps in a training program.

DIAGNOSIS AND PROGNOSIS

It is customary to think of a retarded child's future development as a kind of unfolding process with a consistent rate and a low terminal point. Undoubtedly this conception has evolved from Gesell-type normative studies and from data indicating constancy of the I.Q. for large populations of children. The unfolding metaphor of development is a reasonable one for the infancy years, the period in which behavior is strongly influenced and restricted by biological maturational factors; it does not describe development after infancy. From early childhood on, it is more consistent with the facts to estimate future development on the basis of the child's history, his current status, and the best possible estimate of his future mode of living. If the indications are that his basic biological condition, health status, and social and physical situations will remain much the same, then the best guess is that the child's future development will continue at about the same rate as previously. If, on the other hand, it is believed that because of probable changes or events (divorce and remarriage, new occupation for the father, moving to a different home, attendance at a special school, new training or treatment programs, including behavior modification programs, etc.) his situation will deteriorate or improve, then his rate of development can be expected to slow down or accelerate accordingly.

The total findings from the diagnostic work-up on a child's current status suggest the starting places in the training and treatment programs for that child. Admittedly, there are relatively few well worked-out programs at present, but many are being developed. Until the time comes when a variety of sound, effective programs is available, we must depend on research for leads and suggestions on how to help the child by working with the mother and others who are in direct, daily contact with him. A discussion of selected research in behavior modification follows.

BEHAVIOR MODIFICATION

Examples of Research

Research based on behavior principles has one objective: to determine whether a class of behavior that is weak or nonexistent can be strengthened (e.g., verbal behavior), or whether a class of behavior that is strong can be weakened (e.g., head banging), by a systematic alteration of a child's living conditions. This type of investigation does not aim to find a "cure" for mental retardation, childhood schizophrenia, autism, and the like. Nor does it seek new ways of helping a child acquire greater insight and understanding of himself and his parents. Studies devoted to either of these lines of inquiry invariably incorporate vaguely defined concepts such as constitutional make-up, innate mental ability, and inner tranquility. A natural science approach has no room for such terms.

Described below are some examples of research in behavior modification, selected because they deal with problems occurring frequently among retarded children.

Body Management and Locomotion. To train the profoundly retarded child to coordinate his muscles so that he can move about is often thought of as an impossible task. In some cases it is, as when the child's anatomical and physiologic equipment is seriously defective. In other cases, training is by no means impossible, especially when the defects are in the child's discrimination and reinforcement histories. Research on four such cases has been reported by Meyerson, Kerr, and Michael (1967). The first involved lack of motivation in a traumatic quadriplegic adolescent; the second, fear of falling in a cerebral-palsied child; the third, inability to walk in a mentally retarded child; and the fourth, self-destructive behavior in an autistic child. Their study of the nonambulatory mentally retarded child is of particular interest here. The subject was a 9-year-old girl, Mary, classified as congenitally retarded, who neither walked nor talked and was not toilet trained. She was reported to have crawled when she was 2 years old, but had never progressed beyond that. The diagnostic analysis stated that:

She was somewhat bow-legged, as if she had rickets at the age when most children begin to walk, but there were no other physical abnormalities now that would tend to interfere with walking or standing unsupported.

Mary, except for her very thin legs, and lack of muscular development in the calf, seemed physically capable of walking. Her primary mode of locomotion, however, was scooting across the floor on the buttocks by pushing with her feet and hands. She could be pulled to a standing position if the experimenter supported most of her weight, but she could not be induced to move her legs, and she would drop to the floor as soon as support was removed or relaxed.

The objective of the research was to devise procedures that would enable Mary to stand unsupported and walk independently. Since she ate and enjoyed popcorn, raisins, crackers, nuts, and ice cream, those foods were used to initiate walking, and the effects of the walking process itself would be used to maintain this behavior on the ward. Biweekly sessions lasted from 20 to 45 minutes, with long rest periods in the early stages of the training.

Training was conducted in three phases. In Phase 1, consisting of one session, Mary was lifted to her feet and given an edible while standing. At the end of that session she could stand from 5 to 15 seconds without support. In Phase 2, she was placed on the floor between two chairs standing back to back, 30 inches apart. The experimenter stood behind one chair and encouraged Mary to pull herself to her feet by grasping the back of one chair, turn around, and grasp the back of the other chair, first with one hand, and then with both hands. When Mary was standing upright the experimenter would say, "Mary, come over here." If she complied she was given a treat. Over the seven sessions of Phase 2 the distance between chairs was increased to 45 inches, requiring the girl to take more steps. In Phase 3 the chairs were removed. One experimenter held Mary's hands while another experimenter, several feet away, held out a "goodie." The first experimenter withdrew his hands after Mary had taken a few steps and the second experimenter backed slowly away. Initially she was given a reinforcer for every three or four steps, but this requirement was gradually increased in each session. By session 12, at least 25 steps were required to obtain a reinforcer. In the last three sessions, sessions 13, 14, and 15, the two experimenters stood at opposite sides of the room, and Mary walked from one to the other. During the training period, she took a total of 4600 steps, with and without support. A progress report 6 months after the termination of training showed that Mary was walking freely and frequently throughout the institution.

Feeding Behaviors. A profoundly retarded child, with or without auxiliary handicaps, who can control the movements of his fingers, arms, head, and mouth, can be trained to use eating utensils and to behave acceptably at the table. This generalization is based on the results of studies conducted in a children's psychiatric hospital (Wolf, Risley, and Mees, 1964) and in a child's home (Coyne, Peterson, and Peterson, 1965). The study by Coyne, Peterson, and Peterson has special significance since the subject was a visually handicapped girl, Julie, who at the age of 3 could not feed herself, despite efforts at training by the parents and by professionals. Although she did not have other physical impairments, she was developmentally retarded in that she was not toilet trained, did not dress herself, and had no speech behavior.

The research was conducted in four parts. In part one, which consisted of four sessions, the child's feeding behavior was observed by the mother and a nurse. A record was kept of the number of appropriate responses—the number of times the child placed the spoon in the food bowl, drew it to her mouth, and returned it to the bowl—and the number of inappropriate feeding responses—the number of times she ate with her fingers and banged the spoon on the high chair. This baseline information revealed three appropriate responses and 153 inappropriate feeding responses. Part two of the study, which consisted of three phases, is described as follows:

47

In phase I the nurse stood behind the chair and tapped a spoon filled with food on the tray of the high chair. She then grasped Julie's hand, placed it over the spoon, and drew it to the child's mouth. When the spoon reached her lips, the nurse said, "Good girl." These procedures were repeated a number of times. Subsequently the nurse began to reduce her assistance in lifting Julie's arm. After a time she placed her hand on Julie's wrist and somewhat later, on her elbow. Ultimately she gave no assistance whatever.

In phase II a bowl filled with food was added to the setting. A spoon laden with food was placed in the bowl and the subject was taught to pick up the spoon from the bowl and bring it to her mouth.

In phase III a larger bowl was substituted. The bowl and spoon remained on the tray and the child was taught to dip the spoon in the bowl, bring it to her mouth, return it to the bowl, and repeat this sequence.

During all phases of the first reinforcement period, Julie was never allowed to pick up food with her fingers or bring the bowl of food to her mouth. Whenever she attempted to do so the food was removed from her hand and the bowl taken off the tray for a brief interval.

Inappropriate behavior was eliminated after 12 sessions and independent, appropriate behavior occurred at a high and steady rate (about eight responses per minute) after 44 sessions.

The third part of the study, the reversal period, was designed to evaluate the effectiveness of giving praise for eating with a spoon. Instead of praising Julie for eating with a spoon, praise was now given for *inappropriate* eating behavior. Julie's rate of appropriate eating behavior decreased significantly. The aim of the fourth part of the investigation was to ascertain whether the high rate of appropriate eating responses achieved during the first experimental period could be reestablished by replicating the earlier condition of praising self-feeding with a spoon. Here, in only one session, the rate of appropriate eating behavior increased from 4 to 10 responses per minute.

At the completion of the study, the parents were given instructions for maintaining their child's new eating skills. Two months later, the parents reported that Julie continued to feed herself with little or no assistance.

Toilet Training. Many articles have been written about the toilet training of children, and mentally retarded children in particular. Much of the literature stresses the need for patience and understanding and adherence to the concepts of readiness, repetition, and reward, and much of it advocates procedures that involve changing the child's regimen and keeping a record of his eliminations. A few investigators have reported on the use of mechanical aids, especially for enuresis (e.g., Mowrer and Mowrer, 1938; Van Wagenen and Murdoch, 1966). Recently, reports have appeared which describe the results obtained when behavior principles are applied in the child's home (Wolf, 1965), in an institutional setting (Giles and Wolf, 1966), and in the nursery school (Wolf, Risley, Johnston, and Harris, 1967). Wolf's study of bowel movement training carried out in the home consisted of instructing the mother in keeping records of the time and frequency of bowel movements before starting training (these records constitute baseline data) and continuing to keep records until the desired behavior was well established. She was also instructed in using contingencies that would strengthen toilet behavior and weaken interfering behavior, and in using auxiliary procedures to enhance the probability of a response at the proper time and place. Finally she was given guidance in shifting from contrived to natural contingencies, and in stabilizing the new toilet behavior.

Speech Development. Since most retarded children are deficient in speech development, analyses of the conditions that facilitate verbal communication have been given considerable research attention (Sloane and MacAulay, 1968). One set of problems has focused on starting normal verbal interchange with a child whose verbal skill is limited to mimicking verbal responses. With such a child, the training techniques analyzed are designed to weaken mimicking behavior and to strengthen verbal responses to questions and requests.

Another set of research problems has centered around training techniques for the child who is completely devoid of verbal behavior. Here, the emphasis has been on procedures which (1) strengthen the relationships between phonemes in the repertory and the names of things which approximate them ("wah-wah" and water), (2) facilitate progressive refinements in pronunciation (from "wah-wah" to "water"), and (3) link words in short chains to make phrases and sentences (from "water" to "glass of water").

A third set of problems has been concerned with remediating the verbal behavior already developed, extending the vocabulary, and increasing the complexity of verbal structures (Sloane, Johnston, and Harris, 1968).

Self-Destructive Behavior. One of the startling findings in research on behavior modification indicates that many forms of self-destructive behavior, even those producing extreme tissue damage, can be reduced or eliminated by the proper management of reinforcement contingencies (Wolf, Risley, and Mees, 1964; and Lovaas, Freitag, Gold, and Kassorla, 1965).

The procedures used for body management and locomotion, feeding behaviors, toilet training, and speech development are similar in that positive reinforcement is used both to establish and to maintain new desirable behavior. However, in dealing with self-destructive behavior, as well as with aggressive behavior and temper tantrums, the aim is to eliminate a class of behavior. To do so involves the use of one set of contingencies to weaken the undesirable behavior, and at the same time, another set of contingencies to strengthen a competing class of desirable behavior. The technique is illustrated by a study by Peterson and Peterson (in press) of an 8-year-old institutionalized boy.

The child, Mark, was not toilet trained and did not talk, but he did respond to a variety of directions such as "Come here," and he could feed himself. A description of his self-destructive behavior follows:

> Most of the day Mark lay or rocked on his bed, wrapped in a small quilt. Often he carried a blanket with him when not on his bed. When not so engaged, Mark displayed violent self-injurious responses, slapping the side of his head or leg with either hand, hitting his hand against his teeth or banging his forehead against his forearm. Mark also struck his head and hands against chairs, tables, and walls. He cried loudly but tearlessly when behaving in this fashion. His responses were so forceful that Mark's face, arms, and legs were covered with bruises, scabs, abrasions, and on occasion, open wounds.

Sessions of about 15 minutes were held at mealtime, and portions of food were used as reinforcers. During the baseline period, the first 12 sessions, Mark struck his body an average of 27 times a minute. Throughout the first experimental period, reinforcement in the form of food and the experimenter's praise, "Good," was given contingent upon a 3- to 5-second period of no self-injurious responses. Whenever a self-injurious response did occur, the experimenter took the food from the table and turned away from the child. If no self-destructive behavior occurred for 10 seconds, the experimenter turned back to the child, said, "Good," and gave him a bit of food. In the course of the 10 sessions comprising the experimental period, the average number of self-destructive responses dropped from 27 to 14 per minute. To further reduce the rate of self-destructive responses, a change was made. Now Mark was given instructions to walk across the room (a distance of 12 feet) and to sit in a chair. If no self-injurious response occurred while he walked, the experimenter said, "Good," and gave him a bit of food. If, on the other hand, self-injurious behavior did occur, he was asked to walk across the room again. This procedure was continued until he walked across the room from one chair to the other without a self-injurious response. As a consequence, there was a gradual reduction in self-destructive behavior over the next 20 sessions, after which the responses disappeared completely. The next three sessions were used to test the effectiveness of the contingencies by reversing them. Under this circumstance, the self-destructive rate rose from zero to 23 per minute by the third session. The experimental conditions were reinstated (food and praise once again given for walking across the room without a self-injurious response) and all of the self-destructive behaviors dropped out after two sessions. Attendants reported that the child engaged in fewer self-injurious behaviors on the ward and spent more time with other children.

Characteristics of Behavior Modification Programs

Studies such as those described and cited in the previous section have provided an empirical basis for behavior modification programs that have been used by psychologists, teachers, child-care workers, mothers, nurses, social workers, and psychiatrists. The settings in which the programs have been carried out include the nursery school, special class-room, home, clinic, hospital, and residential school.

A behavior modification program includes three characteristics: (1) a specification, in behavioral terms, of the objective of the program, (2) a statement of the contingencies that will be used, and (3) an indication of the starting point and the steps, the latter tentative at first, which will enable the child to progress to the stated objective. Each feature will be discussed briefly.

A statement in behavioral terms of the objective of the program enables the worker and his professional supervisor to know precisely what new behavior is desired and at what point it is considered to be achieved. A program objective, often referred to as "terminal behavior," may be simple and require only a short period of training, such as teaching a child to sit quietly in his seat, or it may be complex and extend over many months, as in the case of training an adolescent in a vocational skill.

The recommended and usual procedure is to work on only one pro-gram at a time, despite the fact that it is often difficult to decide on priorities. Generally selected for initial attention is problem behavior that is most aversive to the mother or child-care worker (e.g., temper tantrums), or behavior that must first be strengthened or weakened in order to establish some other behavior (e.g., training a child to pay close attention to objects, pictures, and geometric forms before training him to read).

The second characteristic of a behavior modification program is the specification of a set of contingencies which will be *effective for that particular child.* Objects or events are often selected as reinforcers for a child because they are reinforcing to the adult who decides on them, or because the adult thinks they are reinforcing to most children, there-fore they ought to be reinforcing to this child. Neither of these considera-tions guarantees that the selected reinforcers will actually be reinforcing to the child. The only way to find out which objects and events will be effective is to present them to the child and observe his reaction. Objects and events that the child *shows* (not necessarily says) he likes, or those that will lead him to do things to acquire them, are reinforcing for him. But the best test is a demonstration that when the object or event is made contingent upon a class of the child's behavior, it strengthens that behavior. (It will be recalled that in the study in which a retarded child was being trained to walk, the number of steps she took was increased by giving snacks as contingencies.) Sometimes reinforcers may have to be a bit unusual. In a program designed to eliminate excessive self-scratching in a 5-year-old girl, the mother, under the guidance of a trained teacher, established a point system which made it possible, after she acquired a specific number of points, for the child to buy Barbie doll dresses (Allen and Harris, 1966). Points were at first given for short, then increasingly longer, periods of no scratching.

51

The third characteristic of a behavior modification program is two-pronged in that it has a starting point that ensures the child of immediate success in making correct responses, and thus of being reinforced at the outset, and it has steps that are designed with small increments to allow the child to progress smoothly from the initial training steps to the target or terminal behavior. The starting point is usually set on the basis of both informal and formal assessment procedures, as discussed in the section on diagnosis. Thus a program designed to control pants-wetting might start with reinforcing a child for retaining his urine for brief periods which are well within his demonstrated ability.

The steps in a program are always considered to be tentative. The best indicator of the appropriateness of the size and number of steps is the child's performance. Reasonable and steady progress means that they are suitable for the purpose. Small, irregular increments, plateaus, and regressions are signals to stop, assess, and revise the program. This kind of evaluation and procedural change was pointed out in the previous section in the study on self-destructive behavior when, in an effort to reduce further self-injurious responses, the requirement for the receipt of a reinforcer was changed from a lapse of time to walking across the room without a self-injurious response.

It should be apparent that records of the child's progress are essential for evaluating progress in a behavior modification program. As a minimum, two kinds of accounts are needed: (1) *counts* of the occurrences of the behavior to be modified (number of acts of aggression, or number of temper tantrums), or the duration of the behavior (length of a crying episode, or interval between bowel movements), and (2) *notations* of the kind of contingency given and when it was delivered. These records allow the person carrying out the program and the professional supervisor to monitor the program on a day-to-day basis, noting whether changes in the program appear necessary, and to continue to plan accordingly. Records of this sort are comparable to readings from a thermometer or an electrocardiograph, in that they give accounts of ongoing changes in different biological systems (Ayllon and Michael, 1959).

SUMMARY AND CONCLUSION

Behavior modification is defined as the application of behavior principles to the training and treatment of problem behavior in general. Here, these principles are applied to the specific problems of the retarded child.

The effective use of behavior modification techniques has implications for an analysis of retarded development. Hence a discussion of the research and the characteristics of behavior modification programs is prefaced with a brief review of a functional analysis of the etiology of retardation and with comments on gathering information for making a diagnosis and prognosis.

Examples of research with retarded children include the problem areas of body management and locomotion, eating behavior, toilet training, speech development, and self-destructive behavior.

Finally, the essential characteristics of behavior modification techniques are described. They include: (1) specification of the program's objective, (2) identification of the effective reinforcement contingencies to be used, and (3) an outline of the tentative steps in training that are designed to take the child from an appropriate starting point to the target behavior of the program. The need for simple but essential record keeping is emphasized in order that the child's progress can be evaluated day-by-day, or step-by-step.

The pediatrician who is interested in applying behavior modification principles to the problems of retarded patients and their parents can find articles dealing with specific problems in professional journals such as *Behaviour Research and Therapy* and the *Journal of Applied Behaviour Analysis,* and in a collection of studies by Krasner and Ullmann (1965). Basic and background material can be found in Bijou and Baer (1961) and Ferster and Perrott (1968).

By making inquiries at nearby universities or private and public agencies in his community, the pediatrician can learn which professional workers are using behavior modification techniques. These people—psychologists, nurses, social workers, teachers, and the like—can serve as treatment resources, and can assist the pediatrician by training and working with his personnel, as well as with his patients and their parents. There are, for example, an increasing number of nurses who are using behavior modification skills with extreme effectiveness (Whitney, 1966; Whitney and Barnard, 1966; and Peterson, 1967).

REFERENCES

Allen, K. E., and Harris, F. R.: Elimination of a child's excessive scratching by training the mother in reinforcement procedures. Behaviour Research and Therapy, 4:79–84, 1966.

Ayllon, T., and Michael, J. L.: The psychiatric nurse as a behavioral engineer. J. Exper. Anal. Behav., 2:323–334, 1959.

Bijou, S. W., and Baer, D. M. :Child Development: A Systematic and Empirical Theory. New York, Appleton-Century-Crofts, 1961, Vol. 1.

Coyne, P. H., Peterson, L. W., and Peterson, R. F.: The development of spoon feeding behaviors in a blind child. Unpublished manuscript, 1965.

Ferster, C. B., and Perrot, M. C.: Behavior Principles. New York, Appleton-Century-Crofts, 1963.

Giles, D. K., and Wolf, M. M.: Toilet training in institutionalized severe retardates: An application of behavior modification techniques. Amer. J. Ment. Defic., 70: 766–780, 1966.

Krasner, L., and Ullman, L. P., eds.: Research in Behavior Modification: New Developments and Implications. New York, Holt, Rinehart, and Winston, 1965.

Lovaas, O. I., Freitag, G., Gold, V. J., and Kassorla, I. C.: Experimental studies in childhood schizophrenia: Analysis of self-destructive behavior. J. Exper. Child Psychol., 2:67–84, 1965.

Meyerson, L., Kerr, N., and Michael, J. L.: Behavior modification in rehabilitation. *In* Bijou, S. W., and Baer, D. M., eds.: Child Development: Readings in Experimental Analysis. New York, Appleton-Century-Crofts, 1967.

Mowrer, O. H., and Mowrer, W. M.: Enuresis: A method for its study and treatment. Amer. J. Orthopsychiat., 8:436–459, 1938.

Peterson L. W.: Operant approach to observation and recording. Nursing Outlook, 15:28–32, 1967.

Peterson, R. F., and Peterson, L. W.: The use of positive reinforcement in the control of self-destructive behavior in a retarded boy. J. Exper. Child Psychol., in press.

Skinner, B. F.: Two types of conditioned reflex: A reply to Konorski and Miller. J. Gen. Psychol., 16:272–279, 1937.

Skinner, B. F.: Science and Human Behavior. New York, Macmillan, 1953.

Skinner, B. F.: The Technology of Teaching. New York, Appleton-Century-Crofts, 1968.

Sloane, H. N., Jr., Johnston, M. K., and Harris, F. R.: Remedial procedures for teaching verbal behavior to speech deficient or defective young children. *In* Sloane, H. N., Jr., and MacAulay, B. D., eds.: Operant Procedures in Remedial Speech and Language Training. Boston, Houghton Mifflin, 1968.

Sloane, H. N., Jr., and MacAulay, B. D., eds.: Operant Procedures in Remedial Speech and Language Training. Boston, Houghton Mifflin, 1968.

Van Wagenen, R. K., and Murdoch, E. E.: A transistorized signal-package for toilet training of infants. J. Exper. Child Psychol., 3:312–314, 1966.

Whitney, L. R.: Behavioral approaches to the nursing of the mentally retarded. Nursing Clin. N. Amer., 1:641–650, 1966.

Whitney, L. R., and Barnard, K. B.: Implications of operant learning theory for nursing care of the retarded child. Mental Retardation, 4:26–29, 1966.

Wolf, M. M.: Reinforcement procedures and the modification of deviant child behavior. *In* New Frontiers in Special Education. Council on Exceptional Children, National Education Association, 1965.

Wolf, M. M., Risley, T. R., Johnston, M. K., and Harris, F. R.: Application of operant conditioning procedures to the behavior problems of an autistic child: A follow-up and extension. Behaviour Research and Therapy, 5:103–111, 1967.

Wolf, M. M., Risley, T. R., and Mees, H. L.: Application of operant conditioning procedures to the behavior problems of an autistic child. Behaviour Research and Therapy, 1:305–312, 1964.

REINFORCEMENT PROCEDURES AND THE INCREASE OF FUNCTIONAL SPEECH BY A BRAIN-INJURED CHILD

R. VANCE HALL

A number of studies have demonstrated that verbal behavior can be established, maintained, or eliminated using operant conditioning techniques. Isaacs, Thomas, and Goldiamond (1960) used gum as a reinforcer in reinstating verbal behavior by mute psychotics. Similarly, vocalizations of a mute, retarded child were increased by the contingent delivery of "joggling" and singing (Kerr, Meyerson, and Michael, 1965), and vocalizations of normal infants were increased by the contingent delivery of smiling, tickling, and "clicking" (Rheingold, Gewirtz, and Ross, 1959). Sherman (1965) used positive reinforcement to reinstate verbal behavior in long-term, mute psychotics. Risley (1966) and Lovaas (1966) used reinforcement to establish speech in speech deficient children. Risley and Wolf (1967) developed verbal behavior in echolalic children by using food reinforcers to establish verbal imitative behavior and then used shaping and fading techniques to increase the complexity of the verbal behavior.

The studies reported above were largely carried out by skilled researchers, most of whom had extensive training in employing systematic reinforcement procedures, including laboratory work with lower animals. In contrast, the present study was carried out in a school setting by an experimenter with little experience in either speech training or operant procedures and no experience in an animal laboratory. Furthermore, the subject had been labeled as "brain injured" and had been termed "not ready" for speech training because of his extreme hyperactivity and inattention when speech testing had been attempted.

The primary purposes of this present study were to (1) examine the applicability of systematic reinforcement procedures to the speech training of a brain-injured child not deemed an appropriate subject for usual speech therapy sessions; and, (2) determine whether such training could be carried out in a school setting by an experimenter initially unskilled in either systematic reinforcement procedures or speech training techniques.

Jackie was a six-year-old boy who had been variously diagnosed as brain injured and autistic. According to psychological tests, his level of functioning was that of a youngster with moderately severe mental retardation.

When he entered school in the fall of 1963, he was hyperactive and often ran about flopping his hands. He liked making puzzles and playing records. He did not play with other children. His speech included unintelligible vocalizations. Most of his intelligible speech was inappropriate to the situation and echolalic in character.

After more than two years in school, Jackie still exhibited these behaviors. He chanted snatches of songs, rhymes, and nonsense syllables in jargon with occasional clearly articulated words appropriate to the situation. He seldom responded to verbal directions. He sometimes wrote from memory titles of songs he had seen on records, and had a surprisingly large reading vocabulary. He still was not playing with other children.

The school speech clinician had recorded occasional appropriate use of speech during extensive observations of Jackie prior to the experiment. Within a two-hour period, the amount of appropriate intelligible speech ranged from none to three or four words or phrases. Jackie's teachers reported that he was unresponsive to adult verbalizations. Furthermore, when adults attempted to contact him or give him approval, he often responded by running from them and making bizarre gestures and vocalizations. His mother and teachers also reported that he liked to play records and to color in coloring books. Although he was described as a poor eater, he liked peanuts, Fritos, raisins, cookies, and apple juice. The parents reported great difficulty in getting him to go to bed and to eat properly. They also reported many temper tantrums and that he used little appropriate speech at home. In spite of his age and the fact that he had been enrolled in school over two years, he had made little progress in speaking or responding to speech appropriately and was considered "not ready" for the usual speech therapy program available at the school.

PROCEDURES AND RESULTS

Physical Arrangements

Experimental sessions were held in a 9′ × 10′ room which contained a large desk, two chairs, a filing cabinet, and two bookcases. The room was not sound-proof and the noise of a typewriter and the sound of voices from the adjacent office and hallway could be heard intermittently.

Prior to the first session, Jackie's parents agreed to furnish a daily snack of apple juice and foods such as peanuts, Fritos, potato chips, candy, or raisins. No provisions were made for control of Jackie's food intake at breakfast, although his mother reported that this usually consisted of a slice of buttered toast and fruit juice.

No changes were made in Jackie's regular school sessions during the experiment, except that he did not receive the snack usually given members of the group near the end of the school session. He was picked up and brought from class to the experimental room by the experimenter at approximately 10:30 each morning.

Recording Data

Jackie's verbal responses were tallied by the experimenter. Simultaneously, a tape recording was made of each 30 to 35 min session to allow for a reliability check. An independent observer scored tape recordings of various sessions throughout the experiment and tallied the number of various types of verbal responses made by the subject during a session. This tally was then compared to the scores obtained by the experimenter. The number of responses on which there was agreement was divided by the total number of responses to find the percentage of agreement. The percentages ranged from 87% to 95% on data taken directly from the tape by both the experimenter and the second observer. Agreement between data taken live during the sessions and those on tape ranged from 82% to 89%.

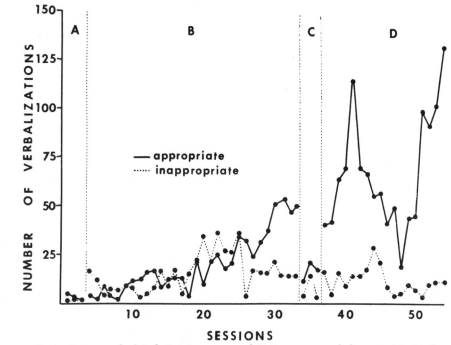

FIGURE 1. A record of Jackie's appropriate and inappropriate verbalization. (A. Baseline period, prior to contingent reinforcement. B. Reinforcement period, verbalizations reinforced by food, play materials and the E's attention. C. Reversal period, return to baseline conditions of noncontingent reinforcement. D. Second reinforcement period, return to procedures of contingent reinforcement.)

57

The Baseline Period: Sessions 1 Through 3

During the three baseline sessions, no attempt was made by the experimenter to reinforce Jackie's verbal behavior. He was allowed to play records, to color, was fed bites of snack, and was freely given verbal approval by the experimenter.

During the baseline sessions, 10 appropriate intelligible verbalizations (a mean of 3.3 per session) were recorded (Figure 1, Section A.) Jackie made only 2 appropriate and 1 inappropriate, intelligible responses to the experimenter's 296 questions, statements, commands, greetings during the sessions. Thus, the percentage of appropriate response for these sessions was less than 1% (see Section A of Figure 2).

Although he frequently "talked" in jargon or made other unintelligible sounds during these initial sessions, there was relatively little clapping, or other bizarre behavior. No tantrum behavior was encountered.

The Reinforcement Period: Sessions 4 Through 33

Beginning with Session 4, bits of snack and access to play materials were made contingent on intelligible and appropriate verbalizations by the subject. Bites of food also were given when Jackie obeyed the experimenter's verbal commands, even though they did not require verbalizations. These changes in conditions resulted in an increase in his general activity during the

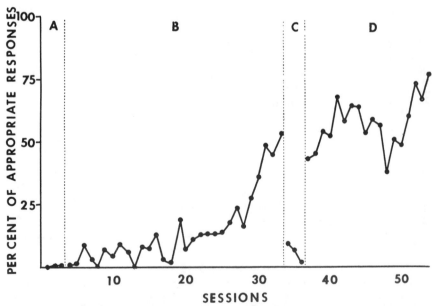

FIGURE 2. A record of the percentage of Jackie's appropriate responses to the Experimenter's verbal S^{D}s. (A, B, C, D, same as in Figure 1.)

first two sessions, with a display of a considerable amount of clapping, crying, bizarre laughing, pacing, and jargon. There was also an increase in the amount of intelligible but inappropriate speech. Often Jackie would point to the food or play object and would cry, scream, clap his hands, and emit a wracking cough if the experimenter did not give the item to him. While Jackie was engaged in this bizarre behavior, the experimenter asked what he wanted or named the desired object, waiting for Jackie to answer appropriately or imitate the name of the object. Very often, however, Jackie would cover his ears with his hands.

In Sessions 6 and 7, the experimenter turned away from Jackie when he engaged in bizarre behavior. This was done on the assumption that the experimenter's attention and verbalizations during tantrums might be maintaining them. Attention was also withdrawn when he was off the chair, whether or not he was engaging in bizarre behavior. This resulted in a decrease in bizarre verbalizations by the subject, with periods of long silences while Jackie was off the chair, and not attending to the experimenter.

In Session 8, Jackie had largely quit attending to the experimenter and spent a great deal of time pacing the room or lying on the floor. He received very little of his snack since there was almost no appropriate speech. Therefore, after Session 8, it was decided that the criterion of reinforcing only appropriate verbal responses should be altered, since these were occurring at a very low rate and Jackie was not receiving enough reinforcement to maintain responding.

Beginning with Session 9 (point A in Figure 1), all intelligible verbalizations, whether appropriate or inappropriate, were followed by a bite of snack, verbal approval, or access to a desired play material. Verbalizations (both appropriate and inappropriate) increased in frequency during this procedure.

In Session 14, there was a drop in appropriate verbal responding which coincided with two temper tantrums lasting a total of more than eight minutes. These occurred when the experimenter refused to help put one of Jackie's shoes back on his foot until he said, "shoe." Following this session, as the experimenter took the subject outside to his mother, Jackie addressed the experimenter and clearly enunciated, "I want to kiss you," and did so.

Beginning in Session 19 (point B in Figure 1), an effort was made by the experimenter to follow intelligible verbalizations more quickly with the words, "Good boy," and a bite of snack or access to desired materials; an analysis of the recordings of the previous sessions indicated there was often a delay between the time of Jackie's response and the reinforcement given by the experimenter. This decrease in latency resulted in an increase in rate of verbalization which was maintained and generally accelerated in the remaining experimental sessions.

During the conditioning sessions, Jackie came to repeat the experimenter's responses of "Good boy," and "That's a good boy," with high frequency. In Session 20, the experimenter discontinued reinforcing the phrases "Good boy," or "That's a good boy," when Jackie uttered them inappropriately. This attempt at extinction resulted in a temporary increase in the subject's inappropriate vocalizations ("That's a good boy," occurred 25 times in Session 20), and a decrease in rate of appropriate vocalization. In the sessions which followed, however, the rate of these utterances declined and then extinguished completely by the fortieth session, while the rate of appropriate responding accelerated.

In Session 24, the experimenter introduced Jackie to a tracing book which had pictures of the cartoon characters "Mush Mouse," and "Punkin Puss." Tracing copies of the pictures in the book with a pen provided by the experimenter proved to be an effective reinforcing activity to Jackie. When using the pen was made contingent on saying, "a pen," this vocalization became an imitative response to the command, "Say, a pen," and an answer to the question, "What is this?" Once this response was controlled by the experimenter's questions, "What is this?" and "What do you want?", the rate of naming other objects and pictures of objects appropriately in answer to these questions was accelerated.

Since by Session 27 Jackie was responding appropriately 30 or more times per session, reinforcement (in the form of bites of snack, use of the record player, or the opportunity to trace in a tracing book) was discontinued for all inappropriate verbalizations. When this was done in Sessions 4 through 8, the subject received so little reinforcement that his verbal behavior almost ceased; at this point (Session 27) appropriate responding continued at higher rates while inappropriate responding decreased. By the last session of the reinforcement period Jackie was responding appropriately to the experimenter's questions, statements, commands, and imitative S^Ds more than 50% of the time.

During the 30 sessions comprising the reinforcement period, 601 appropriate intelligible vocalizations were recorded for Jackie, a mean rate of 20.0 per session. As can be seen by an examination of Section B of Figure 1, inappropriate vocalizations had also increased, but by the twenty-fifth session, inappropriate vocalizations were fewer than appropriate vocalizations and the difference increased after Session 25.

Reversal Period Sessions 34 Through 36

Beginning with Session 34, a brief return to baseline conditions was instituted in order to observe the effect of noncontingent reinforcement. During these sessions, no reinforcing consequences were provided following Jackie's intelligible verbalizations. Rather bites of snack and access to materials were given on a noncontingent basis. This change in conditions brought about marked changes in rates of responding to the experimenter's verbal cues. Whereas, in the preceding three sessions, Jackie had responded appropriately to verbal cues given by the experimenter 48.3%, 44.8%, and 53.7% of the time, in the three reversal sessions, the rates were 9.6%, 6.7%, and 1.6%. Thus, he responded appropriately to but 10 of the 175 verbal cues given by the experimenter; the mean rate for the three sessions was 5.7% (see Section C, Figure 2).

During reversal, 37 of the 48 appropriate verbalizations recorded were free, verbal operants and their character was restricted. In the last two sessions of reversal, all of the 31 appropriate free, verbal operants consisted of the three phrases, "a pen," "the green pen," or, "a book."

Near the end of the last reversal session, Jackie began substituting a jargon expression for his requests for the above objects when they were not supplied as a consequence of naming them appropriately. The rate of jargon and other bizarre behaviors also increased in the sessions. Hand clapping, lying and sitting on the floor, and jumping (behaviors which had largely been extinguished) reappeared.

The Second Reinforcement Period: Sessions 37 Through 54

In the first session of the second reinforcement period, Jackie did not respond appropriately to the first few of the experimenter's questions, imitative cues, or commands. Several times he repeated jargon sounds. Once an appropriate vocal response occurred and was reinforced, however, the number of intelligible vocalizations and the rate of appropriate responding to the experimenter's verbal cues rose quickly. Total intelligible vocalizations for the session rose from 20 in the previous session to 55. The appropriate responses to the experimenter's verbal cues rose from 1.6% to 43.7%.

In Session 38, the experimenter began reinforcing the subject's appropriate responses with food or access to desired play materials or activities on a variable ratio schedule in which reinforcement occurred about 70% of the time. In subsequent sessions, the rate of appropriate vocalizations rose rapidly.

In Session 40, the experimenter began teaching Jackie to preface his requests with "I want." This was accomplished by having him imitate the experimenter's vocalization "I want a record." When this was being imitated consistently, the experimenter would hold up a favorite record. Jackie would say, "a record." The experimenter would say, "I want a record," and Jackie would imitate. When he was responding consistently, the experimenter would hold up a record and say, "I want," and Jackie would say, "a record." Then the experimenter would say, "I," and prompt him by forming the voiceless mouth movement for "want" and Jackie would say "want a record." Then the experimenter would do the same with the word "I" until the subject was saying, "I want a record" without any prompt. In later sessions, this same fading technique was used to teach Jackie to say, "I want the green pen," "I want the paper," and similar requests.

Following Session 43, Jackie's mother reported that he had begun, for the first time, to request things at home by prefacing them with "I want." Similar fading procedures had been used beginning in Session 39 to teach him to respond to "Hi, Jackie" with "Hi, Mr. Hall."

Beginning in Session 42, a fading technique, utilizing Jackie's reading skills, was used to teach him appropriate answers to such questions as "Who is your teacher?" "What is your name?" "Who is your sister?" "How old are you?" "What school do you go to?" Jackie would readily read the appropriate written

61

answers to these questions, which were then progressively removed until he was responding appropriately to the experimenter's questions without written prompts.

Just prior to Session 46, Jackie missed four days of school due to illness. During that session and the three following, he was listless and uninterested in bites of snack. He spent long periods lying on the floor. The total number of vocalizations for these sessions decreased. In Session 48 (point C in Figure 1), he was inactive; he would lie on the floor and moan. He drank juice several times but refused any bites of his snack. He requested the examiner to unlatch the door on four occasions. The session was terminated after approximately 16 minutes. The number of appropriate intelligible vocalizations and the percentage of appropriate responses to the experimenter's verbal cues were reduced. In Session 49, Jackie was still lethargic but the full session was held.

Session 50 occurred after a weekend. Jackie's mother reported he was feeling well again. Unfortunately, the tape recorder malfunctioned after 15 minutes of recording. In spite of the shortened session, the number of appropriate responses was greater than in the previous full session.

In the last four sessions (51 through 54), the number of appropriate responses increased, reaching 132 in the final session. The percentages of appropriate responses to the experimenter's verbal cues were also generally higher, reaching a peak of 78.5% in the final session.

In the last sessions of the experiment, very little jargon, clapping, crying, or other bizarre behavior was observed. In four of the last seven sessions, no inappropriate, free, verbal operants were recorded.

During the 18 sessions comprising the second reinforcement period, 1005 appropriate vocalizations were recorded, a mean rate of approximately 55.8 per session (Section D of Figure 1); 362 of the intelligible vocalizations were appropriate, free, verbal operants. Typically, these consisted not only of the appropriate naming of objects and the reading of words appearing on records (as was observed in the first reinforcement period), but also more complex phrases and statements, some of which were taught or shaped by the experimenter, and some of which were emitted without training.

Among the more complex phrases and sentences initiated by Jackie without verbal prompting were "I want a drink of apple juice," "I want a candy," "I want to play," "Oh, it's time to go," "Please open the door," "Loosen it," "Thank you," "I want you to take it off," "I want to write," "Get the lunch pail," "Be quiet," and "Mother is here." By the last experimental session Jackie was using speech as an appropriate means of communication and was increasing the complexity of his speech.

Evidence of Generalization of Speech Training at Home and in the Classroom

During the course of the speech training experiment with Jackie, there was some evidence that the increase in appropriate speech observed in the experimental setting generalized to the classroom and the home.

Jackie's mother recorded the number of intelligible vocalizations he made at home during a six-day period prior to the beginning of the experimental procedures. A total of 27 or 4.5 per day was recorded by the mother. Twenty of the 27 were 1-word vocalizations. During the first six days of reinforcement procedures, the mother recorded 69 or 11.5 vocalizations per day. Only 7 of these were 1-word responses. At a parent meeting on the day of the 16th session, Jackie's father stated to the experimenter, "I don't know just what you're doing, but Jackie is sure talking more."

In a five-day period corresponding to the nineteenth through the twenty-third sessions of the experiment, the mother recorded 94 or 18.5 verbalizations per day for Jackie. Of these, only 2 were 1-word responses. On the day of the 24th experimental session, Jackie's mother reported his verbal production was too great for her to record adequately and no further attempt to record home vocalizations was made until three months after the experiment had terminated. At that time, the mother recorded his vocalizations for one day from 3:30 p.m. until bed time. There was a total of 32 appropriate sentences and phrases, and no single words recorded. Among those in the repertoire were "A riding horse, giddy-up," "Sharpen the pencil," "Want a fig bar," "Wash a hands," "Hung up the towel," "Run up and to potty," "Mail a letter, put in a mailbox," "Bowl of potato chips," "A vacuum, put it together," "Turn it on," "Turn it off," "Mommy unplugged it," and "Plug it in." A record of the number of Jackie's verbalizations at home is shown in Figure 3.

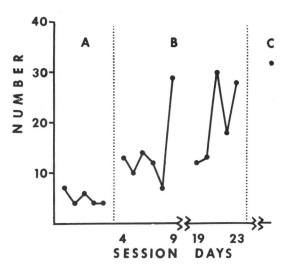

FIGURE 3. A record of Jackie's intelligible appropriate verbalizations at home. (A. Baseline period, prior to experimental procedure; B. Reinforcement period, on days of reinforcement procedure sessions; C. Postexperiment, three months after termination of the experiment—3:30 to 9:00 p.m.)

At the conclusion of the experiment, the mother reported that since the experiment began she had noticed a definite increase in the amount of Jackie's speech, the addition of sentences, and an increased willingness to respond to "Hi!" or, "Good-bye," from about 5% to 60% of the time, as well as a decrease in temper tantrums.

Jackie's father reported that his son's speech had developed from meaningless words and unintelligible syllables to sentences with "meaning." He also reported that there had been an increase in Jackie's asking for things and "his understanding of us."

Evidence of the effects on Jackie's behavior in the classroom was reported by the teachers at various times during the experiment. On several occasions, teachers noted that when the experimenter came to get Jackie for his sessions, he would verbalize appropriately in the experimenter's presence, saying such things as, "Hang up the coat," "Open the gate," "Open the door," "Good-bye." On the day of the 33rd (final reinforcement period) Session, Jackie's teacher volunteered that Jackie seemed to be beginning to listen and attend to what was being said. Subsequently, both she and the assistant teacher of the group reported that Jackie began to follow verbal directions consistently for the first time in the two years he had attended the school.

Both teachers reported toward the end of the experiment that Jackie began participating in the group activities in the classroom and responding verbally to the questions as the other children had been doing throughout the year. The teachers also reported more frequent appropriate verbal responses in other school situations.

A follow-up observation of the subject was made by the experimenter three months after the termination of the experiment. At that time, Jackie was enrolled in the outpatient clinic of the Child Psychiatric Ward at the University of Washington Hospital. Among the behaviors noted was that Jackie continued to obey vocal commands by adults to do things such as, "Come with me," "Read this page," and "Sit down."

A record was kept of his intelligible vocalizations and responses to the verbal cues of his teachers during approximately 4 hours and 15 minutes of observation on 3 different days. During this period, a total of 264 intelligible vocalizations was recorded. Of these, 205 were judged appropriate and 59 inappropriate to the situation. The appropriate vocalizations included reading from books in the classroom, naming objects and pictures, and sentences such as, "Hi, Mr. Hall," "Let's go see the fountain," "C'mon outside," "That's my folks," "Play a record," "Hey, it's time to go," "Play with the railroad track," "I want the green pen" (when he saw this in the experimenter's hands), "There's Mr. Hall." Generally, the data indicate that Jackie was emitting appropriate, intelligible vocalizations at a higher rate than before the experiment in speech training.

DISCUSSION

This study indicates that reinforcement procedures were effective in a speech training program for a boy diagnosed as brain injured or neurologically impaired. The study also calls into question the assumption that behavior of such children is inherently different from normal organisms (Strauss and Lehtinen, 1947; Lewis, Strauss, and Lehtinen, 1960). This assumption was questioned previously in relation to nonverbal behaviors of brain-injured children (Hall and Broden, 1967).

Although it is possible that the etiology of Jackie's inappropriate speech was related to brain damage, it is apparent that this speech behavior was subject to environmental control, and was amenable to modification using reinforcement procedures. This is not to say that the speech behavior of children diagnosed as brain injured is unrelated to their medical histories, but it does indicate that even with such an etiology reinforcement techniques for accelerating appropriate speech may be employed successfully.

The fact that the present experimenter was able to use reinforcement procedures to increase functional speech indicates that they can be used even though the person employing them lacks an extensive background of training in an experimental laboratory. The case of the successful use of reinforcement procedures in speech therapy is strengthened further because the experimenter did not have a background as a speech correctionist.

There seems to be little reason why speech correctionists should not experiment with reinforcement procedures. Of course, one would want to familiarize himself with the literature available and, to be sure, it would be most advantageous for anyone attempting operant speech training to consult with someone skilled in the application of reinforcement principles. The experimenter in this case did consult with a person (Donald M. Baer) who was quite knowledgeable regarding operant principles. One critical point of technical assistance came when, after hearing a tape recording of a session, the consultants suggested decreasing the latency between the time of Jackie's vocal response and the delivery of reinforcement. Except for this help, however, the experimenter developed techniques and modified procedures as the need arose during the session. The fading technique of using written cues which were gradually withdrawn, for example, had not been used previously and was devised during the experiment.

Another aspect of the study which was different from operant speech training studies reported previously was the extensive use of access to play materials and compliance to the requests of the subject as a reinforcing consequence. Homme et al. (1963) used the opportunity to engage in highly probable activities as reinforcement for engaging in less probable activities. It was discovered in the present experiment that giving Jackie the opportunity to use the experimenter's pen, or permitting him to play a favorite record or gain access to other objects were often more effective reinforcing consequences than were bites of snacks. Therefore, the experimenter utilized such consequences extensively, expanding them to include such things as holding Jackie aloft contingent on an appropriate request ("Up," or later "Up in air, Mr. Hall."), opening the door or the gate, giving him objects, unfastening the arm on the record player, turning the record player on or off, allowing him to trace pictures on onionskin paper, etc.

It is probable that food would have been more effective as a reinforcer if greater deprivation had been induced. This was not attempted, however, because the experimenter wished to maintain the conditions which existed in the school setting with as little change as possible. Another advantage of reinforcers other than food may be that generalization to the nontherapy environment may occur more rapidly. For example, very soon after Jackie was taught to preface requests for objects with the words, "I want," his parents reported that he had begun to ask for things at home using these words and they could reinforce his requests by giving him the desired object or by letting him engage in the desired activity.

In summary, the data from this study are evidence that reinforcement procedures offer promise for working with children who are deemed not ready for usual speech therapy. Secondly, the data suggest that speech correctionists should consider using reinforcement procedures in a systematic manner. Even though they have limited backgrounds in using reinforcement procedures, they are likely to find, as did the author, that self-training occurs very rapidly in the process of carrying them out. Finally, the data suggest that, in addition to food, access to desired play materials or the opportunity to engage in highly probable activities may be used advantageously as reinforcers during speech training.

ACKNOWLEDGMENT

R. Vance Hall (Ph.D., University of Washington, 1966) is a Research Associate with the Bureau of Child Research, University of Kansas; and Coordinator of Juniper Gardens Children's Project, Kansas City, Kansas. This study was supported in part by NICHHD grants HD 00870, HD 00870 04S1, 1P01 HD 03144-01, MR HDP, Bureau of Child Research, University of Kansas.

REFERENCES

HALL, R. V., and BRODEN, MARCIA, Behavior changes in brain-injured children through social reinforcement. *J. exp. Child Psych.*, 5, 463-479 (1967).

HOMME, L. E., DEBACA, P. D., DEVINE, J. V., STEINHORST, R., and RICKERT, E. J., Use of the Premack principle in controlling the behavior of nursery school children. *J. exp. Anal. Behav.*, 6, 544 (1963).

ISAACS, W., THOMAS, J., and GOLDIAMOND, I., Application of operant conditioning to reinstate verbal behavior in psychotics. *J. Speech Hearing Dis.*, 25, 8-12 (1960).

KERR, NANCY, MEYERSON, L., and MICHAEL, J., A procedure for shaping vocalization in a mute child. In Ullmann, L. P., and Krasner, L. (Eds.), *Case Studies in Behavior Modification.* N.Y.: Holt, Rinehart & Winston, 366-370 (1965).

LEWIS, R. S., STRAUSS, A. A., LEHTINEN, L. H., *The Other Child.* N.Y.: Grune and Stratton (1960).

LOVAAS, I. O., A program for the establishment of speech in psychotic children. In Wing, J. K. (Ed.), *Childhood Autism.* Oxford: Pergamon Press (1966).

RHEINGOLD, HARRIET, L., GEWIRTZ, J. L., and ROSS, HELEN W., Social conditioning of vocalizations in the infant. *J. comp. Phys. Psych.*, 42, 68-83 (1959).

RISLEY, T. R., The establishment of verbal behavior in deviant children. Unpublished dissertation, Univ. Washington (1966).

RISLEY, T. R., and WOLF, M. M., Establishing functional speech in echolalic children. *Behav. Res. Ther.*, 5, 73-88 (1967).

SHERMAN, J. A., Use of reinforcement and imitation to reinstate verbal behavior in mute psychotics. *J. abnorm. Psych.*, 70, 155-164 (1965).

STRAUSS, A. A., and LEHTINEN, L. E., *Psychopathology and Education of the Brain-Injured Child.* N.Y.: Grune and Stratton (1947).

A behavior modification approach to head banging

MORTON G. HARMATZ
WARREN A. RASMUSSEN

Head banging in institutionalized retarded and emotionally disturbed children is very difficult to control. The child may inflict serious physical injury on himself if the behavior is allowed to continue; on the other hand, the typical procedure for controlling it, complete restraint of the child, also produces problems. The result is confusion and frustration about how to handle this behavior.

A behavioral analysis of the head-banging response indicates that its function may be to produce social reinforcers. The head-banging response, in its initial stages, usually draws the attention and intervention (frequently physical intervention, such as holding and attempting to calm the child) of the caretaking staff. This is reinforcing for the child, especially in a situation in which social reinforcements from adults are at a premium, as is true in most institutions. Once staff members note that the child is banging his head, they may attempt to withhold social reinforcement; but, since each response means more danger of physical damage, the caretakers must eventually interfere. The result is that the behavior becomes more intense and more frequent.

The practice of tying the child down, although it interferes with the behavior, contributes to the strengthening of the reinforcer. The restraining procedure deprives the child of all social contacts, which increases the value of these reinforcers.[1] Thus, when the child is taken out of the restraints, the head banging is very likely to occur again, and the social reinforcement is likely to follow. It can be seen that the head-banging response, once initiated, becomes involved in a cycle that leads to greater frequency and intensity of the problem behavior until the only way of handling the child is complete restraint.

Behavior modification techniques should be applicable to such a disorder. The behavior therapist is faced with some major difficulties, however. The response obviously has to be extinguished; but, by the time it is referred, the behavior has reached a very high magnitude, and simple extinction (allowing the behavior to occur while withholding the social reinforcements) cannot safely be employed. Negative reinforcement has been attempted, but has the difficulties inherent in using noxious stimulation with children (objection of parents, nurses, administrators, etc.). This paper presents a procedure for extinguishing head banging, illustrated by a case study.

The procedure employed was to allow the child to bang his head yet prevent damage by making him wear a football helmet of the type used by linesmen. This is a well-padded, sturdy, plastic helmet with a face guard. An adult can hit his head with full force on a wall in such a helmet without damage to the helmet or the head. The face guard protects the forehead and face. The helmet was modified by replacing the snap-on chin strap with rawhide, which was knotted so that the child could not remove it. The helmet could be comfortably worn for long periods.

The behavior control procedures were quite simple. The child was placed in the helmet and released from his restraints. Staff members were instructed to attend to the child for any behavior other than head banging, paying particular attention to any social behaviors. Should the child bang his head, they were to turn away immediately and not attend to the child until they could hear no further head banging. When the child stopped, they were then to attend to him for any non-head-banging behavior. The staff's attention was also focused on any other self-destructive behavior that might develop (biting, etc.); such behavior was to be treated immediately in the same manner as the head banging. The staff was encouraged to give a great deal of reinforcement for appropriate behavior, at the early stages, that could later be shaped to schedules more appropriate to their regular duties with the children.

Case Study

Background information

B. entered the state school at the age of one and a half years. At the time of the investigation he was eight years, one month old. His mental age, tested two months prior to this project, was two years, one month.

B.'s mother had spent some time in a state mental hospital, and he had a sister who was considered a mild retardate. His parents rarely visited him.

His chief behavior problem was reported to be head banging. Because of this, it was impossible to leave the child untied, except when in the firm grasp of an attendant. It was stated that he was kept tied to his bed except for meals and occasional walks outside in the company of a staff member. During meals he had to be restrained in order to prevent head banging. Also, he would refuse to eat unless he was accompanied and/or fed by an attendant.

It is not at all clear when the behavior was first noticed. Apparently he had not learned this response prior to admission. The problem, according to the nurses, had not been so severe in the past. It may have become more frequent because of a program instituted at the school that concentrated on increasing the amount of love and affection given to the children. B. was selected as needing more of this loving care than most of the other children and was given much attention and affection. After this had continued for some time, it was decided to reduce the amount of attention devoted to B. to a more even level. It was at about this time that his head banging became serious.

Observation session

An observation session was arranged to obtain a record of the eliciting stimuli and the frequency of the head-banging response. The therapist requested the nurse to untie B. and remove him from the bed while he observed and took notes. This was accomplished without the response being elicited. B. clung close to the nurse. She was then instructed to try and get the child to stand away from her a few feet. To this B. reacted with a pained expression and attempted to maintain his hold on the nurse. The therapist asked to see the same behavior performed in the dayroom in which the other thirty children were playing. B. banged his head twice when the nurse let go of him to open the door to the playroom.

As the nurse walked around the dayroom, B. clung either to her hand or her skirt. A crowd of other children also followed her. In order to free herself of B., the nurse briefly interested him in a toy. He let go of her and bent down to examine the toy more closely. As he placed the toy on the floor, he quickly looked up to see the nurse, now a few feet away, attending to another child, with her back to him. B. dropped the toy and ran straight for the wall, against which he banged his head. A second nurse ran over to him and grabbed him, telling him not to do that. He then clung to her as she walked about the room. The therapist then asked the second nurse to free herself of B.

As soon as he was made to stand alone, the child ran for the wall and again banged his head. An attendant ran over, and they grabbed each other; but, after B. was taken away from the wall, the attendant tried unsuccessfully to discourage him from hanging on to him. By this time B. was practically in tears and the first nurse had returned. B. was then returned to his bed and climbed obligingly into his restraint.

Four head bangs were noted in this brief observation. The functional connection of the head-banging response to attentional reinforcers from the staff was clearly demonstrated.

Procedure

As noted above, B. was always to be in the helmet when out of restraints. Head-banging behavior was to be responded to with a deliberate removal of any social reinforcement, i.e., the attendant was to turn away and not turn back until the behavior stopped. All other acceptable behaviors were to be reinforced with attention and affection.

In addition to the above, B. was also to receive reinforcement for any attempts to get attention from other children. This would facilitate the extinction of head banging and provide a source of social reinforcement that would be more available in the future.

A number of older and brighter children were chosen as substitute reinforcers. After a few sessions, however, it became clear that one child, J., was the strongest reinforcer for B. Furthermore, she followed the experimenter's instructions very well.

The following procedure was used in a variety of situations. B. was permitted to hold onto J. as long as he refrained from head banging. In order to make the sessions reinforcing to J. as well, both children were given candy approximately every two minutes. B. lost his turn for candy if he had banged his head in the previous two-minute interval. When he did bang his head, no matter who was with him, B. was ignored as much as possible.

Results and Discussion

This child's head-banging responses, after an initial rise in frequency, showed a marked decrease in the first few sessions in which these procedures were used. Although cumulative records were not possible on the ward, frequency counts during observation sessions showed a decrease from five to eight head bangs in a half-hour to none five weeks later. More importantly, during the final week of observation B. wore no helmet and didn't bang his head at all.

Both the time he spent in the playroom and number of children permitted in the playroom were slowly increased, and there was no return of the head-banging response. B.'s behavior at this point consisted of his staying with J. unless either nurse H. or nurse B. (who seemed to be his favorite) remained near him for more than a few seconds. Under these conditions, B. would run to the nurse, who would let him climb up into her arms. After he had received his hug, he would climb down and return to J. If the nurse still remained in the area, this would be repeated. The nurses were warned by the experimenter that they were potentially much greater reinforcers than J. and that they would have to be careful to avoid reshifting the balance of reinforcement. B. began to show some interest in other children besides J.

The results of this treatment procedure support the hypothesis that the head banging was maintained by social-attentional reinforcers and that extinction of the response was made possible by withholding that reinforcement. Ideally, the procedures should have been reversed in order definitely to establish the suggested functional relationship. However, because of the nature of head banging and its potential danger, the reversal procedure was not employed.

The establishment of other children as a source of social reinforcement for B. was felt to be a necessary addition to the extinction procedure. Too frequently, behavioral approaches to the removal of "high frequency" behavior do not pay attention to the "behavioral void" that may result from successful extinction. The organism cannot simply stop responding. If acceptable routes to reinforcement are not made available, behaviors may appear that are, again, problem behaviors. This can be thought of as a behavioral version of symptom substitution. In the present case, deliberate procedures were employed to ensure against any uncontrolled emergence of behavior reinforced by attention.

As a final note, the staff displayed some initial resistance to the procedures since the child was thought to "need" the head banging. Some thought of the behavior as representing a biological drive. Toward the end of the project, staff reaction was very positive. The relatively quick removal of a behavior problem that had worried and frustrated staff members for years was quite exciting to them and opened the way for further work with other children on the ward.

Summary

Self-destructive responses such as head banging are frequently maintained by social-attentional reinforcers they elicit from the environment. This study demonstrates the extinction of a head-banging response accomplished through the removal of social reinforcement in a retarded eight-year-old boy.

REFERENCE

1. Gewirtz, J. L., and Baer, D. M.: Journal of Abnormal and Social Psychology, 56:165, 1958.

THE COMPARISON OF MATCHING-TO-SAMPLE WITH DISCRIMINATION LEARNING IN RETARDATES [1]

Laird W. Heal and Malcolm L. Bransky

THERE has been considerable recent interest in the discrimination learning of children and mental defectives because of the important theoretical inferences that can be drawn when conditions are appropriately compared. (See, for instance, Lipsitt, 1961; Reiber, 1965.) The concentration has been upon the comparison of performance on successive and simultaneous discrimination problems, or variations of one type or the other. To the writers' knowledge, these two problem types have not yet been compared with the matching-to-sample mode usually employed in the card-sorting tasks given to college students. The comparison of simultaneous discrimination (Sim) and matching (M) seems to be particularly critical because inferences have been drawn in the literature that assume them to be testing comparable learning processes. For instance, over-training has been found to facilitate extradimensional shifts in matching-to-sample by college students (e.g., Grant & Cost, 1954) but to impair such shifts in simultaneous discrimination by rats (MacKintosh, 1962). Such contradictory findings might well reflect a difference in the problem solving requirements of the two tasks. The present experiment compared Sim and M, using a third condition, a successive discrimination (Suc), to assess the effect of partial reinforcement of approach-to-cue responses under the M condition.

METHOD—REPLICATION I

Subjects. The Ss were 30 mental defectives, selected at random from those patients who had demonstrated ability to learn a simple object quality discrimination in prior experiments. The IQ range from recent Stanford-Binet and WISC examinations was 25 to 61 and the CA was 16 to 30. Ss were assigned at random to the six treatment combinations, with the restriction that five Ss were assigned to each.

Apparatus. The face of the response unit of the apparatus measured 19 in. x 16 in. and

was tilted upward from the horizontal 30 degrees. Three Industrial Electronics displays (#10 N 83) were mounted in a triangle configuration beneath the response unit and projected cues from the rear onto $1\frac{1}{2}$ in. x 2 in. plexiglass panel. Two of these windows, positioned horizontally, had their inner edges $3\frac{1}{2}$ in. apart; the third was centered with its lower edge $3\frac{1}{2}$ in. above these two. Two stimulus dimensions were used, colors (1 in. green and white circles) and forms (1 in. crescent and $\frac{1}{4}$ in. dot.) The presentation scheme for the dimensions of color and form appears in Table I. A response button was positioned 1 in. below each of the bottom stimulus windows. The locus of the correct response and the presentation of stimuli upon which it was contingent were pre-programmed electronically in an unsystematic sequence.

Procedure. The S was seated before the response unit and given the following instructions. "Now, —————, we are going to play a game and win some candy. The lights will come on in these windows and I want you to push one of these buttons with one finger. The pictures will tell you how to ring the ding-dong. If you learn how to ring the ding-dong every time, you will win some candy. OK?" Minor departures were made from these instructions to insure that the Ss understood. The experimenter then administered treatments from an adjoining room, observing through a one-way window.

All Ss had the same pretraining task, which was given to eliminate position preferences and other irrelevant strategies. During pretraining a small square appeared in the left or right windows in a predetermined sequence. S's task was to press the button under the square. When S pressed the correct button in the presence of the stimulus, a door chime rang and, after a $\frac{1}{2}$ second delay, the stimuli were extinguished. If he pressed the wrong button, the lights remained lit until he corrected himself. After he reached a pretraining criterion of eight consecutive

TABLE I
PRESENTATION SCHEME FOR THE DIMENSIONS OF COLOR AND FORM ACROSS THE
THREE EXPERIMENTAL PROBLEMS

		M		Suc		Sim	
Color	Setting 1	G + G	— W	+	—	+ G	— W
	Setting 2	W — G	+ W	—	+	— W	+ G
Form	Setting 1	dot + dot	— crescent	+	—	+ dot	— crescent
	Setting 2	crescent — dot	+ crescent	—	+	— crescent	+ dot

correct responses, S was given one of the experimental treatments.

Three different discrimination problems were used as the experimental treatments: simultaneous, successive, and matching. For Simultaneous Discrimination (Sim), stimuli were presented in both lower windows at the same time and S's task was to push the button under the correct (same) stimulus each trial. The cue designated as correct was randomly assigned for each S. For Matching (M) three lights were projected before the subject on every trial, the left and right being invariant (e.g., green always left, white always right) and the third, centered above the other two, varying from trial to trial. The S's task was to push the button under the invariant light that matched the center light. For Successive Discrimination (Suc) the stimuli were presented one at a time in the upper window and the S's task was to push either the left or the right button depending on which stimulus was presented. Thus Suc differed from M only in that the cues in the lower windows were removed. In Replication I, the successive discrimination problem (Suc) was run after Sim and M as a control for the possible effect of partial reinforcement for approaching cues presented in the lower windows in the M condition.

The following experimental procedures were applied to each of the three conditions in Replication I: (a) each problem was continued to a criterion of eight consecutive correct responses or to a maximum of 99 trials;

(b) the pretraining task was readministered following the first error after each 33 trials; (c) a correction procedure was used for all problems, with incorrect responses leaving the cues unchanged; (d) the intertrial (post-reward) interval was programmed at a constant 6 sec., after which the lights were automatically presented for the next trial; (e) the position of the correct response varied from trial to trial in a 16-trial predetermined unsystematic sequence, restricted so that right and left were rewarded equally often and responses to the last rewarded position were rewarded 50% of the time; (f) a five cent bag of M & M candy was given to each S after his session.

METHOD—REPLICATION II

Thirty Ss were drawn at random from the same population as that specified for Replication I, with the restriction that no subject was used in both replications. The apparatus and procedure were changed in the following ways: (a) the lights were extinguished immediately following S's response; (b) no pretaining was given; S was given his treatment problem immediately after his instructions; (c) each S was instructed he would win a nickel if he rang the bell enough; (d) the experimenter re-entered the experimental room following the first error after each 33 trials to tell the S that he was doing well, but that he must try to ring the "ding-dong" every time he pushed a button; (e) the intertrial interval was reduced to a constant 3½

TABLE II
THE NUMBER OF LEARNERS, SUBJECTS WHOSE TRIALS TO CRITERION WERE ABOVE THE MEDIAN FOR THE
OVERALL SAMPLE, MEAN TRIALS TO THE LAST ERROR, AND ROOT MEAN SQUARES (RMS) FOR THE
SIX BASIC TREATMENT COMBINATIONS OF THE PRESENT EXPERIMENT

	Simultaneous Discrimination (Sim)				Successive Discrimination (Suc)				Matching (M)			
	Learners	Below Median	Mean Trials	RMS	Learners	Below Median	Mean Trials	RMS	Learners	Below Median	Mean Trials	RMS
R_1	8	7	33.5	42.14	5	5	55.4	31.64	3	2	77.6	40.70
R_2	6	6	54.1	38.79	8	7	54.6	47.36	5	3	68.0	39.85

Note: N in each treatment combination is 10.

sec.; (f) a different experimenter was used; (g) the Suc condition was run at the same time as Sim and M, S being randomly assigned to one of the three conditions immediately prior to his treatment; (h) a nickel was given to each S immediately after his session.

RESULTS AND DISCUSSION

For each of the basic treatment combinations, Table II shows the number of learners, the number of Ss below the median for the overall sample, the mean trials to the last error, and the root mean squares (RMS) of the trials to the last error. The summary of the data analysis is presented in Table III. Due to the bimodality of the data (14 Ss reached criterion in 10 trials while 25 failed to reach criterion in 99) a non-parametric analysis was performed. The partitioned chi square (Sutcliffe, 1957) had problems, replications and a median split as variables of classification. Data were collapsed over dimensions.

It appears that Matching (M) was more difficult than Simultaneous Discrimination (Sim), $X^2=6.40$, p<.05, and perhaps more difficult than Successive Discrimination (Suc) as well, $X^2=4.51$, exact p=.054. There is no indication that Sim and Suc differed from each other, or that any conditions interacted with replications. An analysis of variance of the trials to the last error led to exactly the same conclusions.

The finding that Sim is easier than M is consistent with the combined results of Hill (1965) and Scott (1964). Hill, using normal children, found a simultaneous discrimination (Sim) easier than an oddity (O) problem, and Scott, using retardates, found an oddity (O) problem not significantly different from a matching problem. Thus, although

they used different subject populations, the results of Hill (Sim>O) and Scott (O=M) are consistent with the finding that Sim is easier than M (Sim>M).

The failure to find a difference between Sim and Suc in this situation is in agreement with a considerable body of animal (e.g., Bitterman, Tyler, & Elam, 1955) and child (e.g., Lipsitt, 1961; Etzel & Wright, 1964; Reiber, 1965) literature, in which the relative difficulty of Sim and Suc seems to have been a function of the method employed to compare them. It has been shown that proximity of stimulus and response is associated with Sim superiority and separation of stimulus and response with Suc superiority. The present situation using stimulus-response proximity for Sim and stimulus-response separation for Suc would presumably produce maximal performance on both tasks.

Probably the major source of the relative difficulty of M over Sim lay in the solutions required in each case. Sim required S to approach a single cue consistently; M required him to ignore specific cues per se and respond to the relationship among cues. Thus, under M specific approach-to-cue responses were rewarded half the time; per-

TABLE III
PARTITIONED CHI-SQUARE FOR SUBJECTS SCORING
ABOVE THE OVERALL SAMPLE MEDIAN

	Median Analysis		
Source	df	x^2	2-Tailed Fisher Exact P's
P (Problems)	2	7.60*	....
D vs. M	(1)	6.40*	.024
DM vs. S	(1)	.10	....
M vs. S	(1)	4.51*	.054
DS vs. M	(1)	7.50*	.020
R (Replications)	1	.27	....
R x P	2	.93	....
Total (Sum. Sqs.)	5	8.60	....

* p.05.

haps this opportunity to make partially reinforced approach responses to the lower cues contributed to M difficulty. The Suc condition, which differed from M only in that the lower cues were removed, was run with the objective of testing this possibility. The finding that Suc was nearly as easy as Sim lends support to the interpretation just offered.

This interpretation of the results might be qualified by the fact that many of the Ss had learned a two-choice object quality discrimination using the Wisconsin General Test Apparatus from six to 12 months prior to the present experiment. Perhaps this experience transferred to the present task and specifically facilitated performance under the Sim condition. However, this alternative interpretation fails to account for the relative ease with which Suc was learned. Thus, it appears that the data are more completely in accord with the interpretation that M proved more difficult than Sim because the former involved partial reinforcement of approach-to-cue responses.

The chief reason for running the second replication was to test the possibility that a treatment bias might have been effected by the approach-to-cue pretraining, facilitating Sim and impairing M. The lack of interaction of treatments with replications in the face of considerable situational change indicates that the findings of the present study have considerable generality, being quite stable despite changes in pretaining, stimulus offset, incentive, or experimenter.

L.W.H.

Box 512
Geo. Peabody College for Teachers
Nashville, Tenn. 37203

REFERENCES

Bitterman, M. E., Tyler, D. W., & Elam, C. B. Simultaneous and successive discrimination under identical stimulating conditions. *Amer. J. Psychol.*, 1955, 68, 237–248.

Etzel, B. D., & Wright, E. S. Effect of delayed reinforcement on response latency and acquisition learning under simultaneous and successive discrimination in children. *J. exper. child Psychol.*, 1964, 1, 281–293.

Grant, D. A. & Cost, J. R. · Continuities and discontinuities in conceptual behavior in a card sorting problem. *J. gener. Psychol.*, 1954, 50, 237–244.

Hill, S. D. The performance of young children on three discrimination learning tasks in childrn. *Child Developm.*, 1965, 36, 425–435.

Lipsitt, L. P. Simultaneous and successive discrimination learning in children. *Child Developm.*, 1961, 32, 337–348.

MacKintosh, N. J. The effects of overtraining on a reversal and a nonreversal shift. *J. comp. physiol. Psychol.*, 1962, 55, 555–559.

Nissen, H. W., Blum, J. S., & Blum, R. A. Analysis of matching behavior in chimpanzees. *J. comp. physiol. Psychol.*, 1948, 41, 62–74.

Reiber, M. An analysis of simultaneous vs. successive stimulus presentation in children's discrimination learning. Paper presented at the biennial meeting of the Society for Research in Child Development. Minneapolis, 1965.

Scott, K. G. A comparison of similarity and oddity. *J. exper. child Psychol.*, 1964, 1, 123–134.

Sutcliffe, J. P. A general method of analysis of frequency data for multiple classification designs. *Psycholog. Bull.*, 1957, 54, 134–137.

Weinstein, B. Matching-from-sample by rhesus monkeys and by children. *J. comp. physiol. Psychol.*, 1941, 31, 195–213.

REWARD SCHEDULES AND INSTRUMENTAL CONDITIONING IN NORMAL AND RETARDED CHILDREN

BETTE M. JOHNSON

The performances of retarded and normal children, matched for MA, were compared in a simple instrumental conditioning situation under conditions of continuous and alternating partial reward. Acquisition and extinction series were administered in an attempt to discern the relative effects of differential cues and schedules of reinforcement. Speed of response was used as a measure of learning. A significant difference between speeds on reinforced and nonreinforced trials was demonstrated for both normals and retardates. Although absolute response speeds of retardates were significantly slower than those of normals, there appeared to be no difference in rate of acquisition. Both groups learned quickly to anticipate the reward schedule, and there was no difference in their rates of extinction.

Several investigators have noted a tendency for subjects in conditioning experiments to respond to a given trial on the basis of reinforcement conditions on the preceding trial or series of trials (Hake & Hyman, 1953; Nicks, 1959; Skinner, 1942). Capaldi, Turner, and Wynn (1962), using alternating partial reinforcement, found that rats ran more slowly on trials

This paper is adapted from a dissertation presented to the University of Houston in partial fulfilment of the requirements for the degree of Doctor of Philosophy. The investigation was supported, in part, by grant M-5671 (A) to Dr. Morton Rieber from the National Institute of Mental Health, U.S. Public Health Service. Appreciation is expressed to Mr. H. M. Landrum, Superintendent of Schools, Spring Branch, Texas, and to Dr. William Sloan of Austin State School, for making subjects and facilities available.

The author is presently a clinical psychologist in the Community Mental Health Division of San Diego County Hospital, 225 West Dickinson Street, San Diego, California 92103.

following nonreinforcement at the beginning of training. Because of the alternation of reward and nonreward, these trials were rewarded trials. As training progressed, the rats learned to anticipate rewards on trials following nonreinforcement, and running speeds on these trials exceeded the speeds on trials following reinforcement.

In the pretraining of young children, using partial delay of reward, Rieber (1964) and Rieber and Johnson (1964) found that overall response times were slower on trials following immediate reinforcement. The child was responding on the basis of the preceding trial rather than in anticipation of the immediate or delayed reward on the current trial.

Evidence from rat studies (Burt & Wike, 1963) indicates that anticipation of reward conditions takes place much more slowly when delayed and immediate reward are alternated rather than reward and nonreward. In the present study, the effects of alternating reward and nonreward on the response speeds of normal and retarded children were studied. It was expected that under these conditions the children would learn to anticipate reinforcement conditions and that at some point in training speeds on trials following nonreward would become faster than on trials following reward. Such anticipation would indicate that the child's response was no longer a simple consequence of events which had occurred on the immediately preceding trial. Instead, it may be assumed that he had conceptualized the schedule of reinforcement and responded on the basis of a predicted continuation of that schedule. The point at which responses on trials following nonreinforcement became faster than those on trials following reinforcement could be regarded as the point at which conceptualization took place.

The alternation of reinforcement with nonreinforcement provides a paradigm for studying simple concept formation. The major purpose of this study was to investigate the differences between normal and retarded children, matched for MA, in their ability to respond to alternation on the basis of a conceptualization of the reinforcement schedule. It was hypothesized that anticipation of reward conditions would be aided by the presentation of two distinctive stimuli, one always associated with reward and the other associated with nonreward.

Normal and retarded children of approximately equivalent MA were trained using four different learning conditions. Group I received partial alternating reinforcement, with different colors of light on rewarded trials as an aid to differentiation. Group II received partial alternating reinforcement, with the same color of light on every trial. Groups III and IV received continuous reinforcement. Group III received alternation of color of stimulus lights, which was irrelevant to reward. Group IV received a single color of light.

An extinction series was given to all groups. No rewards were dispensed during extinction.

METHOD

Subjects

The Ss used in this study were 96 normal children and 80 mentally retarded children. The normal Ss were enrolled in a public school kindergarten. It was assumed that the normal Ss' MA was approximately equivalent to their CA. The mean CA of the 96 normal children was 5 years, 8 months.

The retarded Ss were institutionalized in a state school for retarded children. The retardates' CA ranged from 8 years, 7 months to 15 years, 1 month, with an average CA of 12 years, 2 months. Their IQ's, as measured by the Stanford-Binet or WISC intelligence scales, ranged from 32 to 64 with an average IQ of 47. Their MA's ranged from 3 years, 7 months to 7 years, 8 months, with an average MA of 5 years, 7 months.

The overall normal group was assumed to have an average MA roughly equivalent to the average CA of 5 years, 8 months. The overall retarded groups had an average MA of 5 years, 7 months. Subgroups were not individually matched but were randomly assigned through alphabetizing all Ss' names, then assigning them, consecutively, to Group I, II, III, or IV prior to training.

Apparatus

The apparatus consisted of two rectangular wooden boxes, the stimulus box and the control box. The S was seated facing the stimulus box. The control box was placed behind the stimulus box and was largely out of view of S. The E was seated behind the control box so that she was also out of view of S during the actual conditioning. The S could be observed by E, however, by means of a mirror placed behind and to one side of S.

The stimulus box was 18½ × 18½ × 10 inches and had a 17 × 7½-inch glass panel on the top front which could be lighted red or yellow. There was a 7½ × 1-inch wooden lever below the glass panel and a 3 × 2-inch reward receptacle below the lever. When the front panel was lighted red by E, a red light glowed in the reward chute and a small red light was illuminated beside the reward receptacle. When the panel light was yellow, the chute light was yellow and a small yellow bulb was lighted near the reward box.

The control box was 44 × 16 × 9½ inches. It contained the switches, timers, and reward dispenser. The control box was joined to the stimulus box through electrical connections and by a chute through which the rewards of small toys and trinkets traveled from the dispenser to the reward receptacle. The E determined whether a reward would follow S's response on any particular trial by setting a switch. Another switch controlled the color of the light presented to S, either red or yellow.

There were two clocks on the control box. One clock recorded, in hundredths of a second, the time lapse between presentation of the stimulus (light) and the beginning of the lever press. This time was called "starting time." When S's hand touched the lever, the first clock was stopped and the second one activated. The second clock recorded, also in hundredths of a second, the amount of time lapsed in the completion of the lever depression. This second measure was called "movement time."

Procedure

The S was brought into the room and seated facing the stimulus box. He was told he was going to play a game where he would have a chance to win some prizes. The S was given a paper sack in which to put his prizes and told that he could keep all the prizes he won and take them with him. The S's hand preference was determined, and he was given the instructions. In the instructions, S was told to place his hand on a provided picture of a hand, until a light came on. When the light came on, he was to pull the lever down, and he might receive a prize.

All Ss were given thirty acquisition trials followed immediately by twenty extinction trials. No rewards were dispensed during extinction. Each group of Ss, normal and retarded, were divided into four treatment groups. Each of the four treatment groups for normals consisted of 24 Ss. Each treatment group for retardates contained 20 Ss.

Group I for both normal and retarded Ss received partial alternating 50 per cent reinforcement with alternation of lights. Lights and rewards were alternated simultaneously. Thus Ss in group I received a reward on trials in which one color of light was presented and no reward on alternate trials with another color of light. The lights continued to alternate during extinction trials. Group II received partial alternating 50 per cent reinforcement with a single color of light throughout acquisition and extinction. Group III received continuous 100 per cent reinforcement during acquisition but with alternation in the colors of the stimulus light. The light color continued to alternate throughout extinction. Group IV received continuous 100 per cent reinforcement with a single-color stimulus light. The same color of light was presented during extinction.

Color of light associated with reinforcement was counterbalanced, as well as reward or nonreward on the first trial. Light conditions, of course, remained consistant for each individual S.

RESULTS

Reciprocals were computed for the starting- and movement-time measures, yielding starting and movement speeds. The first trial of each S was omitted from computation since this experiment was concerned with response speeds on trials following reinforcement or nonreinforcement. The first trial, of course, followed neither.

Half of the Ss in the partially reinforced groups were rewarded on the first trial. The other half of the partially reinforced Ss received no reward on the first trial. For those Ss beginning with nonrewards, the first trial was number 2 so that in computations all even-numbered trials would be nonrewarded trials. For a more detailed explanation of the method of combining trials, see Rieber and Johnson (1964).

The thirty-first trial for all Ss was included in the acquisition data even though this was actually the first trial of extinction, because S was not aware that there would be no reward until after his response was made.

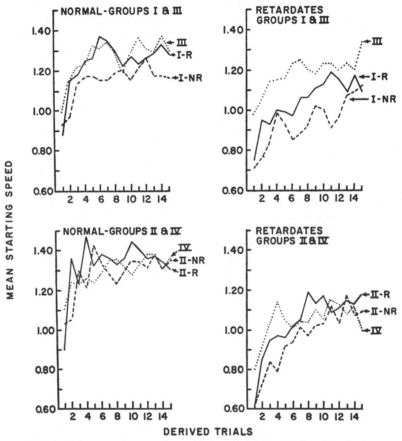

Fig. 1.—Mean starting speeds on reinforced and nonreinforced trials during acquisition.

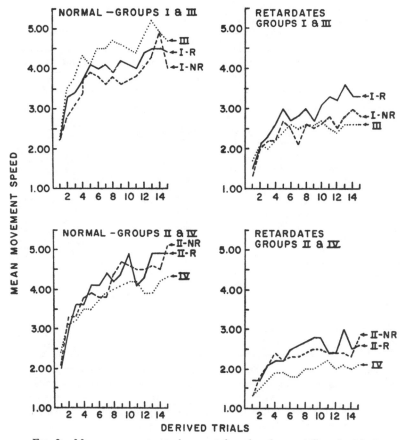

Fig. 2.—Mean movement speeds on reinforced and nonreinforced trials during acquisition.

Mean starting speeds over trials during acquisition are presented in Figure 1. Figure 2 contains the curves for mean movement speeds. In these figures, the data for partially reinforced groups are means of individual trials. For the continuously reinforced groups, each point represents the mean of two consecutive trials.

Table 1 summarizes the results of separate four-factor analyses of variance for starting and movement speeds. These analyses compared the speeds of reinforced and nonreinforced trials during acquisition.

The within-Ss variable was the average speed on reinforced as compared to nonreinforced trials. This was called the "reinforcement effect." For Ss receiving continuous schedules of reinforcement, alternate

79

TABLE 1
ANALYSES OF VARIANCE COMPARING REINFORCED AND NONREINFORCED
TRIALS DURING ACQUISITION

SOURCE	df	STARTING SPEED MS	F	MOVEMENT SPEED MS	F
Between:	175				
Intelligence (B)..........	1	3.562	19.67**	238.669	55.11**
Cues (C)................	1	.006	...	5.541	...
Schedules (D)...........	1	.444	2.45	.737	...
B × C................	1	.398	2.19	1.851	...
B × D................	1	.125	...	4.411	...
C × D................	1	.337	1.86	7.087	1.63
B × C × D..........	1	.035	...	2.289	...
Error (b)...............	168	.181	...	4.331	...
Within:	176				
Reinforcement (A).......	1	.014	2.00	.152	1.63
A × B................	1	.002	...	.021	...
A × C................	1	.006	...	.099	...
A × D................	1	.209	29.85**	.487	5.24*
A × B × C..........	1	.005	...	.036	...
A × C × D..........	1	.005	...	.123	1.32
A × B × D..........	1	.002	...	.009	...
A × B × C × D.....	1	.005	...	.019	...
Error (w)...............	168	.007	...	.093	...

* $p < .025$.
** $p < .001$.

trials were arbitrarily assigned to reinforced or nonreinforced categories for purposes of analysis, as all trials for these groups were actually reinforced.

One between-Ss variable compared the performance of normals to that of retardates. This was called the "intelligence effect." Another between-Ss factor was the average performance of those groups receiving an alternation of light as compared to those groups presented with a single color of light. This factor was called "cue." A third between-Ss factor pertained to differences in performances between those Ss receiving partial as opposed to those receiving continuous reinforcement. This variable was called "schedules."

The retarded Ss responded significantly more slowly than the normal Ss in both starting speed and movement speed. There was also a significant reinforcement × schedules interaction in both starting speed and movement speed. There were no other statistically significant main effects or interactions in the acquisition data.

Since there were no nonreinforced trials for the continuous group, the reinforcement × schedules interaction indicates that the overall starting and movement speeds were different on trials following nonreinforcement than on trials following reinforcement.

A three-factor analysis of variance was computed for the acquisition data using only those groups which received partial reinforcement. The within-Ss comparison in these analyses was the same as in the preceding analysis, that is, reinforced as opposed to nonreinforced trials. The between-Ss factors were intelligence and cues.

Table 2 is a summary of these analyses. As before, the speeds of the retardates proved to be significantly slower than those of the normals in both starting speed and movement speed. In this analysis, using only the partially reinforced groups, average speeds for reinforced trials were found to be significantly more rapid than speeds on nonreinforced trials.

TABLE 2

ANALYSES OF VARIANCE COMPARING REINFORCED TO NONREINFORCED
TRIALS DURING ACQUISITION FOR GROUPS RECEIVING
PARTIAL REINFORCEMENT

		STARTING SPEED		MOVEMENT SPEED	
SOURCE	df	MS	F	MS	F
Between:	87				
Intelligence (B).........	1	2.512	16.74**	89.095	20.57**
Cues (C)..............	1	.216	1.44	.048	...
B × C...............	1	.097	...	4.129	...
Error (b)..............	84	.150	...	4.331	...
Within:	88				
Reinforcement (A).......	1	.164	14.90**	.591	4.05*
A × B..............	1	.004	...	.029	...
A × C..............	1	.010	...	.222	1.52
A × B × C..........	1	.008	...	.054	...
Error (w)..............	84	.011	...	.146	...

* $p < .025$.
** $p < .001$.

An examination of Figures 1 and 2 reveals that speeds on reinforced trials were more rapid almost from the beginning of training. Both normals and retardates responded on the basis of anticipation of reward after the first few trials. The lack of an intelligence × reinforcement interaction in these analyses indicates that the retardates did not differ significantly from the normals in their ability to anticipate reward conditions.

The overall acquisition and extinction data for all groups are presented in Figure 3.

Table 3 is a summary of the analysis of variance for the extinction data. A four-factor analysis of variance was computed. The within-Ss factor was a comparison of the mean of each S's last six acquisition trials, with the mean of his last six extinction trials. This factor was called "extinction." The three between-Ss factors were the same as those used in the analyses of acquisition, that is, intelligence, cues, and schedules.

Overall speeds of the retardates were slower than speeds of the normals. A significant extinction effect was found in both starting and movement speeds. On movement speed, a significant extinction × cues interaction was found. This indicated that there was a greater extinction effect

81

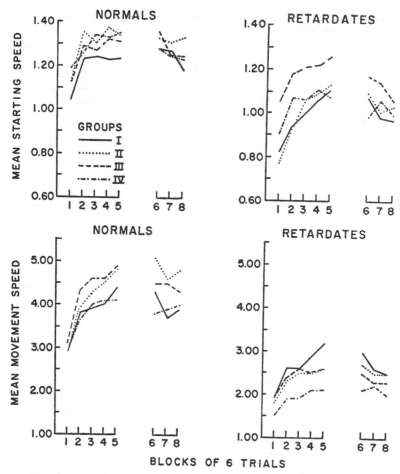

Fig. 3.—Overall response speeds during acquisition and extinction, plotted in blocks of six trials.

for those groups receiving alternation of lights than for those groups receiving a single color of light.

Though not statistically significant, the traditional PRE effect of greater resistance to extinction following partial reinforcement can be noted in the tendency toward an extinction × schedules interaction in starting speed.

There were no other statistically significant main effects or interaction in the extinction data.

TABLE 3

ANALYSES OF VARIANCE COMPARING THE MEAN OF THE LAST SIX
ACQUISITION TRIALS WITH THE MEAN OF THE
LAST SIX EXTINCTION TRIALS

SOURCE	df	STARTING SPEED		MOVEMENT SPEED	
		MS	F	MS	F
Between:	175				
Intelligence (B).......	1	3.178	17.09**	343.796	68.13**
Cues (C).............	1	.032	...	2.089	...
Schedules (D)........	1	.019	...	6.769	...
B × C............	1	.296	1.59	4.221	...
B × D............	1	.025	...	1.528	...
C × D............	1	.528	2.84	11.176	2.21
B × C × D.......	1	.030	...	6.876	...
Error (b)............	168	.186	...	5.046	...
Within:	176				
Extinction (A)........	1	.679	25.15**	8.068	13.51**
A × B............	1	.042	1.55	.072	6.06*
A × C............	1	.025	...	3.619	...
A × D............	1	.077	2.85	.003	...
A × B × C.......	1	.029	...	.067	...
A × C × D.......	1	.005	...	.177	...
A × B × D.......	1	.024	...	1.149	1.92
A × B × C × D...	1	.034	1.26	.149	...
Error (w)............	168	.027	...	.597	...

* $p < .025$.
** $p < .001$.

DISCUSSION

It was expected that early in training, Ss would respond more slowly following nonreinforcement. Due to alternation of reward and nonreward, this would mean slower speeds on reinforced trials in the beginning. When S began to conceptualize the reinforcement schedule, it was expected that he would begin to respond on the basis of anticipation of reward or nonreward, a reversal would occur, and speeds would become more rapid on reinforced trials and slower on nonreinforced trials.

Under conditions where delay of reward was alternated with immediate reward and a distinctive stimulus was paired with each of the reward conditions, Rieber and Johnson (1964) failed to find a reversal in starting speeds with continued training. Instead, starting speeds on trials following delay continued to be slower than those on trials following immediate reward.

In the present study, Ss receiving partial reinforcement with a different CS for rewarded and nonrewarded trials (Group I) showed significantly faster starting speeds on trials following nonreinforcement; the curves for reinforced and nonreinforced trials diverged during the first few trials. It appears that both the normal and retarded Ss learned the concept almost immediately. Under the more difficult nondifferential stimulus light condition (Group II), the differences are not as clear for the normal Ss, but the retardates anticipate reward conditions following the first trial and respond faster on trials following nonreward.

The findings with movement speed were similar to those with starting speed; speeds were faster following nonreinforcement except for the normal Ss under the more difficult condition (Group II) who showed little difference between the two types of trials.

The findings with Group I (different CS for rewarded and nonrewarded trials) can also be accounted for in terms of Amsel's (1958) discussion of the role of frustration in partial reinforcement. If it is assumed that the instructions given to S prior to the start of training are sufficient to establish anticipatory goal responses (rg-sg), then nonreinforcement resulted in anticipatory frustration responses (rf-sf) which became conditioned to stimuli associated with nonreward. For Group I, these stimuli were the color cues associated with reward and nonreward. This explanation, however, is not sufficient to account for the slower response speeds following reinforcement in Group II where Ss did not have a distinctive CS to signal nonreinforcement.

In an examination of the conditioning data as a whole (see Fig. 3), it appears that normal and retarded children matched for MA did not differ in their overall rates of acquisition and extinction of a simple instrumental response. The absolute response speeds did differ, however, for the two intelligence groups. In spite of the younger CA of the normal Ss (average CA 5 years, 8 months) as compared to retarded Ss (average CA 12 years, 2 months), both the starting and movement speeds of the normals were considerably more rapid. The lack of an interaction, however, between intelligence and any other variable, indicates that although retardates' overall speeds were at a slower absolute level, they learned the tasks under all conditions at a rate comparable to the normals.

The markedly slower overall response speeds of the retardates tended to give the impression that these Ss did not condition as well as the normals. The data, however, indicated that the retardates learned to respond on the basis of anticipation as rapidly as did the normals. Furthermore, while the absolute speeds were faster for the normals Ss, the slopes of the curves during acquisition and extinction did not differ for the two groups.

Data from the present study illustrated an overall extinction effect. Speeds became slower when reinforcement was withheld. A significant cues × extinction effect was found in movement speed. Examination of Figure 3 indicates that this was due primarily to Group II. Conditions for this group were those of the usual partial reinforcement training. This group, receiving partial reinforcement without differential stimulus cues, was highly resistant to extinction.

REFERENCES

Amsel, A. The role of frustrative non-reward in non-continuous reward situations. *Psychol. Bull.*, 1958, **55**, 102–119.

Burt, D. H., & Wike, E. L. Effects of alternating partial reinforcement and alternating delay of reinforcement on a runway response. *Psychol. Rep.*, 1963, **13**, 439–442.

Capaldi, E. J., Turner, L., & Wynn, W. Decremental and facilitative effects in the straight alley runway under partial reinforcement. *J. comp. physiol. Psychol.*, 1962, **55**, 545–549.

Hake, H., & Hyman, R. Perception of the statistical structure of a random series of binary symbols. *J. exp. Psychol.*, 1953, **45**, 67–74.

Nicks, D. Prediction of sequential two choice decisions from event runs. *J. exp. Psychol.*, 1959, **57**, 105–114.

Rieber, M. Delay of reward and discrimination learning in children. *Child Develpm.*, 1964, **35**, 559–568.

Rieber, M., & Johnson, Bette M. The relative effects of alternating delayed reinforcement and alternating nonreinforcement on response speeds of children. *J. exp. child Psychol.*, 1964, **1**, 174–181.

Skinner, B. F. The processes involved in the repeated guessing of alternatives. *J. exp. Psychol.*, 1942, **30**, 495–502.

GORDON F. JOHNSON

Programed Instruction and the Exceptional

ONE of the most difficult and challenging problems confronting special educators today is the development of effective and efficient teaching techniques. To further complicate the issue, conflicting viewpoints concerning the learning processes are supported by such scholars as Skinner (1959), Bruner (1961), and Rogers (1961). Contenders on the current scene have been classified as reinforcement/conditioning "therapists" and cognitive field theorists. Although literally worlds apart, they have some mutual threads of commonality, but rather than discuss these two major families, the author has chosen to discuss the reinforcement and conditioning position as documented in the research of Skinner (1959) and other "behavioral engineers."

The basic assumption, in reinforcement and conditioning, is that the organism, neutral-passive in nature, has needs which are accompanied by drive stimuli. Early investigators required their subjects to pull a lever or engage in some other comparable motor activity before receiving tangible reinforcement. As a basis for transfer of learning, Skinner (1959) advocated reinforcing or conditioning the responses. Recent investigations have been conducted by Homme (1965) and Dunn and Smith (1965).

Regardless of name or form, programed instruction consists of presenting a carefully prepared sequence of content material through small, appropriate steps. As the learner works independently, he is able to establish his own pace. Often a question accompanies each of the steps in the learning sequence, requiring the learner to actively respond. In addition, a great deal of motivation results from the reinforcement provided to the learner when he discovers how he is doing. Programing is careful, time consuming work, and it can also be expensive. Stolurow (1964) indicated that a one semester course in elementary arithmetic, in addition to the many man hours involved, would cost in excess of $50,000.

A Case of Conditioning

To illustrate the principles involved in programing, Mednick (1964) provided a classic example that has often been repeated. In a Massachusetts hospital for mentally disturbed patients, experiments were conducted in specially equipped basement rooms. A university student, interested in the conditioning theory, decided to attempt to bring a male patient, invested with long standing mental illness, to one of the therapy rooms. The prolonged illness had reduced this patient to animal like behavior; he had little or no control over his body processes, he frequently bit people, and his vocal utterances were barely human. Due to his antisocial behavior, he had been placed in virtual isolation.

To move his patient downstairs, the therapist used "shaping," an operant conditioning technique. In this method, the experimenter rewards the behavior approximating that which is desired. In this case, the therapist waited until his subject turned his head toward the door leading to the basement, and rewarded him with a small piece of candy, which had previously been proven to be a positive reinforcer for this subject. After a number of such incidents, the patient was standing before the open door. When this phase of condition was completed, the therapist withheld the candy until the patient took his first step toward the door. When this step was accomplished, the therapist again withheld the candy reinforcement until the patient took steps in the direction of the stairs leading down to the therapy rooms in the basement.

After a number of days, during which there were numerous reversals and disappointments, the patient walked down the stairs, entered a basement room, and commenced his therapy program. This was the first time, in many years, that this patient had behaved in what could be termed an organized fashion.

Recent Studies in Programed Instruction

Smith and Quackenbush (1960) used a mathematics program in a Devereux teaching machine. When the learner pushed a button adjacent to what he considered to be the right response, a buzzer sounded if his response was correct. After a year's instruction, the resultant average gain of .5 a year was indicated by the California Achievement Test. Corresponding gains by similar groups during the preceding year, without benefit of programed instruction, had been less than .2 a year.

Measuring the effectiveness of programed materials developed at Partlow State School and Hospital in Tuscaloosa, Alabama, Price (1963) presented addition and subtraction to three groups of institutionalized retardates whose IQ's ranged from 40 to 66. His programs involved simple counting, addition, subtraction, and arithmetic signs; the teaching machines used were Ferster Tutors, a simple device which presents programed material on paper scrolls.

When the amount of time working on the course material was considered, automated teaching appeared to hold a considerable overall advantage over the more traditional approaches. This study suggests that automated teaching is a useful supplementary approach to teaching arithmetic to mentally retarded individuals. Pines (1964) expressed an interest in the activities of O. K. Moore, a Yale sociologist who believed that appropriate programing techniques could assist the exceptional child in learning. She reported that Moore taught five retarded children, rejected by the public kindergartens because of their behavior problems, to read simple material within a year through the use of programed typewriters.

At the Johnstone Training and Research Center, a state residential school for retardates in New Jersey, studies conducted by Blackman, Capobianco, East, and Hoats (1964) revealed that programed instruction in arithmetic and phonics, via teaching machines, obtained significant gains in achievement; even more meaningful was the improvement noted in both in and out of school behavior. The investigators implied that programed instruction with retardates inculcates improved general habits of attention and application.

Recently, Johnson (1966) conducted a study in Oregon's central Willamette Valley to examine the effectiveness of teaching methods in arithmetic for mentally retarded subjects. The sample consisted of 72 subjects in public school special classes with IQ's of 49 through 80, chronological ages of 108 through 166 months, and mental ages of 71 through 130 months. The sample was divided into three groups: one group studied a program designed by the investigator, another studied from a commercially developed program (TMI-Grolier's *Elementary Arithmetic: Addition and Subtraction Facts*), and the third group studied from teaching lessons. During the ten weeks of study, two groups alternated programed textbook sessions with teaching lessons throughout the week. The results tended to lend credence to the premise that this curricular combination can produce substantial gains in academic achievement for the educable mentally retarded child.

The retarded child appears to adapt to programed instruction and seems to make as much or more progress through these approaches as he does through conventional teaching methods. Stolurow (1964) contended that the comparative study of programed instruction versus the live teacher is (and should be) on the way out. The important issue is the comparison of methods, techniques, and conditions which will maximize learning opportunities while promoting the development of favorable attitudes.

Programing for the Individual

Skinner (1959) has repeatedly demonstrated that there must be only a few seconds' time lapse between the response and the reinforcement for learning to be effective; however, in the typical classroom frequently extended periods of time elapse before reinforcement can occur. Skinner's basic premise has been that since an organism tends to do in the future what it was doing when reinforced, the educational engineer can use programing to lead the organism to do what he wishes. When we consider that in the present arithmetic curriculum alone there may be as many as 50,000 contingencies in the first four years of school that are taught in large blocks with infrequently planned reinforcement, it is truly amazing that this system produces any results at all.

One of the most fascinating studies of recent date used the application of operant techniques in teaching reading, writing, and arithmetic to retarded children in residence at the Rainier School in Buckley, Washington (Birnbrauer, Bijou, Wolf, Kidder, and Tague, 1965). A typical daily procedure followed by a pupil in the advanced learning group included getting his class folder with a specially prepared assignment sheet, setting his watch, and recording the starting time. Next, he worked on the assignments, entering answers in the designated places and noting the beginning and completion times for each exercise. The outstanding features of this program were:

1. Programing was individualized for each child.
2. No teacher or other significant adult was available in the immediate study area.
3. Programing was continuous, on a day to day basis.
4. Rewarding was both continuous and delayed.

The assigned work provided each child with immediate indications of how well he was doing. When he had completed his last assignment sheet, marks were made in the child's booklet and his errors were corrected. Throughout the sessions, the teachers and their assistants also gave marks for desirable behavior. A sheet full of marks could be cashed in at the end of the day for candy, toys, or other desired items. Completed pages of marks could also be saved for larger items or for special outings.

The principal investigators stated that it was difficult to realize that these were the same children who had started the program. The study strongly suggests that retarded children can learn academic subjects far beyond the level that was previously thought possible. Equally important is the fact that when the learning environment is appropriate, not only will the retarded child learn but also will reveal improved behavior patterns that cannot help but swell the pride of any teacher or parent.

Implications for Education

Certainly it cannot be implied that programed instruction is or can be the panacea for all educational endeavors. It is encouraging to note, however, that the programed instruction movement is not a transitory, magical, or momentary fad, but is vital and growing. One reason that programed instruction has survived is that learning theorists and behavioral psychologists have offered a working model for efficient learning. Programed instruction has been tested; it has been found to be effective with disadvantaged students because the students are doing something, they are being reinforced, and they are meeting success.

Special class teachers have a direct effect on the amount pupils learn from programed instruction; learning from these materials is not automatic. When pupils are permitted to progress at their own rates, one can look for accelerated learning. Motivation to learn is of tremendous importance; with programed instruction the teacher's role can be maximized. The work of Birnbrauer and his colleagues (1965) indicates that the outlook for the mentally retarded can be optimistic. With the present knowledge of programing and computers, and the study of basic metabolic processes and the balancing of body chemistry by synthetic means, it should be possible to develop appropriate procedures and techniques to enhance capacities for mental growth that were once considered incapable of further development.

In principle, any process that can be objectified can be broken down into steps and programed for instruction. Bruner (1961) has stated that anything can be taught to anyone, providing it is appropriately programed.

Research and the Classrooms

Programing methodology is essentially curriculum planning on a small scale. In the course of programing it is necessary to analyze course content in considerable detail. The programing movement performs valuable service in causing educators to express what they wish children to learn, and analyzing how children can most efficiently learn it. Inservice education is the graduate school of the profession.

We must encourage research and investigation in the empirical arena of the special class. Such efforts can be expected to produce more detailed and extensive procedures for motivating the exceptional child and for programing the basic academic tasks for survival training. Teachers need to obtain the programing skills which will enable them to utilize the results of research, to design their own programs, and to evolve effective teaching techniques and procedures. To accomplish these important tasks, both financial and human resources need to be provided.

Research should be developed using a diagnostic therapeutic design in which learners are first evaluated to determine the level of their present skills. On the basis of this information, programs specifically designed to meet the level of learning would be provided for each child on a unique N of one approach. Future assessments and planned programs would direct the progression and the teacher would function as a professional learning engineer.

More of the efforts for program development should be placed on the growing edge of the art rather than at the safe and conservative commercial center. Special educators should be involved in designing programs for the child with learning disabilities. Extensive experimentation is needed to determine which personality types learn more effectively through which methods of instruction. Combinations of teaching methods should be examined for effectiveness.

Teachers must be taught how to use programed materials effectively. The possibilities of making and using programs require knowledge in the areas of learning and child development. These must be areas of concern for all special educators. Additional avenues of approach, such as television, textbooks, typewriters, recorders, continuous loop films, and other audiovisual material should be examined to determine how they can be used to enhance the principles of programed instruction.

Computerized Instruction and the Future

It is already apparent that programed instruction, although still in the stages of infancy, has made a breakthrough in education with practical dimensions that must be assessed. In the immediate future we will see a flurry of activity surrounding automation and its implications for special education. Some of the most profound changes in education will be wrought through computerized instruction and microteaching. More than merely assisting the learner to solve problems, it will fundamentally improve and enrich the entire learning process. The learner's educational level and achievement can be analyzed by the computer; diagnostic teaching will become increasingly possible.

In the school of the future each child will progress with his own program of instruction at his own speed, limited only by his own capabilities. In place of traditional classrooms will be instructional units dealing with various areas of learning designed to modify behavior in a predictable way.

One approach to modifying behavior which appears to be compatible with the motivational system is computerized education—the application of a system analysis through electronic computers. Computers, with their vast storage capacities, are uniquely compatible with contingency management and the individualization of instruction in accordance with the child's rate of learning, his interests, and his style of learning. Computerized instruction which integrates programed instruction and operant conditioning offers a most promising system of effective learning.

During the past ten years, the typical electronic data processor has become ten times smaller, 100 times faster, and 100 times less expensive to operate. These trends will undoubtedly continue, and we will soon see additional innovative programs available to special classes throughout the country; technology will eventually enable each child to learn at his own rate, will maintain accurate records on him, and will provide suggestions concerning the future steps in his development.

In the past, educators have found that it takes from 25 to 75 years for a new educational concept or innovation to filter from the minds of the originators into actual teaching practice. Although the new school revolution is less than a dozen years old, experiments are rapidly becoming more widespread as the pace of change in accelerated. The present educational ferment is largely a "home brew" in spite of its emergence throughout the nation. The amount of involvement and the direction for the future is in the hands of the special educators; in the final analysis, they are the program.

References

Birnbrauer, J. S., Bijou, S., Wolf, J., Kidder, J., and Tague, C. Programmed instruction in the classroom. In L. P. Ullmann and L. Krasner (Editors), *Case studies in behavior modification.* New York: Holt, Rinehart and Winston, 1965.

Blackman, L. S., Capobianco, R. J., East, M. J., and Hoats, D. *The development and evaluation of a curriculum for educable mental retardates utilizing self-instructional devices or teaching machines.* Bordentown, New Jersey: Research Department of the Edward R. Johnstone Training and Research Center, 1964.

Bruner, J. S. *The process of education.* Cambridge, Massachusetts: Howard University Press, 1961.

Dunn, L., and Smith, J. *Peabody Language Development Kit manual for level #1.* Minneapolis: American Guidance Service, 1965.

Homme, L. A. *System for teaching English literacy to preschool Indian children.* Bureau of Indian Affairs, Final Report, 1965.

Johnson, G. F. *An investigation of programed procedures in teaching addition and subtraction to educable mentally retarded subjects.* Unpublished doctoral dissertation, University of Oregon, 1966.

Mednick, S. A. *Learning.* Englewood Cliffs, New Jersey: Prentice-Hall, 1964.

Pines, Maya. How three-year-olds teach themselves to read—and love it: In A. deGrazia and D. Sohn (Editors), *Programs, teachers and machines.* New York: Bantam Books, 1964. Pp. 205-217.

Price, J. E. Automated teaching programs with mentally retarded students. *American Journal of Mental Deficiency,* 1963, **68,** 69-72.

Rogers, C. R. *On becoming a person.* Boston: Houghton Mifflin, 1961.

Skinner, B. F. *Cumulative record.* New York: Appleton-Century-Crofts, 1959.

Smith, E. A., and Quackenbush, J. Devereux teaching aids employed in presenting elementary mathematics in a special educational setting. *Psychological Reports,* 1967, **7,** 333-336.

Stolurow, L. M. The future: zeal tempered by wisdom. In J. P. De Cecco (Editor), *Educational technology readings in programed instruction.* New York: Holt, Rinehart and Winston, 1964. Pp. 432-446.

STRENGTHENING SELF-HELP BEHAVIOR IN THE RETARDATE

Robert L. Karen and Sandra J. Maxwell

A NUMBER of workers have made important contributions to the understanding of operant behavior in the retardate. For example, data are available on retardate performance under single and multiple schedules of reinforcement (Orlando & Bijou, 1960, Ellis, Barnett & Pryer, 1960), temporal discrimination (Orlando, 1961), operant extinction and spontaneous recovery (Spradlin, 1961), amount of reinforcement (Ellis, 1962), conditioned reinforcement (Girardeau, 1962), operant discrimination and differentiation (Barrett & Lindsley, 1962) and instructions and reinforcement history (Headrick, 1963).

Derived from these basic studies on operant behavior is an increasingly effective technology of teaching the retarded basic social, intellectual and motor skills. For example, successful utilization of operant principles have been made in training retardates in socially acceptable behavior (Girardeau & Spradlin, 1964), toilet habits (Hundziak, Maurer & Watson, 1965), self-help skills (Bensberg, Colwell & Cassell, 1965), arithmetic and cursive writing skills (Birnbauer, Bijou, Kidder & Tague, 1965). Finally, it has been suggested that skill acquisition may be facilitated by combining principles of operant behavior with a "prosthetic environment" to accommodate to the sensory and motor defects often possessed by retardates (Lindsley, 1964).

The present report describes a set of procedures developed in teaching a seven year old boy what would appear to be a simple, self-help, motor skill, namely, buttoning a shirt. The procedures contain elements of operant conditioning through the utilization of differential reinforcement and successive approximation; task programming and "imitation."

METHOD

Subject

The S was a seven year old boy from a family of six children. All of the children in S's family have been characterized as "slow learners" but the S's repertoires were sufficiently poor to disqualify him from attendance in special education classes in the public schools. Lack of financial resources prevented S's parents from enrolling him in a private school. His day to day activities consisted solely of outdoor play with himself. Although S could carry on conversation with ease, he could not read nor write nor was he toilet trained. S's parents reported that he was hyperactive and disruptive in the classroom and this resulted in his dismissal from school. On the Stanford-Binet, Form L, his IQ was 45. His inattention and perseveration during testing was noted by the examiner who reported possible organic impairment. Although a routine pediatric examination was negative, further neurological tests were never conducted.

Apparatus

A specially designed prosthetic training aid was used consisting of a vest which contained four buttons in graduated sizes (diameter) as follows: $1''$, $\frac{3}{4}''$, $\frac{1}{2}''$, and $\frac{1}{4}''$. The largest button was at the top of the vest while the remaining buttons were below the top button in rank order by size. S wore the vest over his shirt during training. Following practice and success with buttoning the buttons on the vest, the vest was removed. S then wore his shirt and buttoned the buttons on it. Reinforcing stimuli consisted of M and M's, verbal expressions of praise, and the ownership of the vest upon task completion. S was trained in his bedroom occupied only by E and S. Data sheets were used to record the time and performance ratings.

Procedure

At the beginning of the session, S was shown the vest and put it on unbuttoned. Through questioning, it was determined that S could identify the button and the buttonhole for the large button at the top of the vest. Each trial began when the E pointed to the appropriate button and told the S to button it. The trial was terminated 15 seconds later at which time E recorded the time S took if he completed the task before the end of the trial. E also recorded the rating assigned by E for S's performance at the end of each trial as follows: $+1$ button not placed in the buttonhole, $+2$ button part way through the buttonhole, and $+3$ button all the way through the buttonhole. Most trials began following a brief rest period. S unbuttoned the button after each trial.

Training consisted of a preliminary or baseline trial during which time S was told to button the large button on the vest and that if he could button all the buttons on the vest,

he could keep the vest. On the second trial, S was told that he would receive an M and M for each good try with the large button and that each try had to be better than the last. Prior to the second trial, E then showed S how to button the large button by putting the side of the button in the underside of the buttonhole first, then pulling it through to the right side of the buttonhole.

Beginning with the second trial, E gave S the unconditioned positive reinforcing stimulus (one M and M) and the conditioned positive reinforcing stimulus (praise) for any response to button. On later trials, reinforcers were given only for increasingly precise and/or shorter responses to button the button.

When E subjectively judged that S could easily button the $1''$ button (using time and performance measures), the $\frac{3}{4}''$, $\frac{1}{2}''$ and $\frac{1}{4}''$ button was presented to the S who worked with them each to the same criterion. Finally, S was given his own shirt to button.

RESULTS

Figure 1 shows the time in seconds S took to button the various size buttons on the vest while Figure 2 shows the ratings assigned to S's performance at the end of each trial. On the very first trial, S failed to button the large button and thus received a low performance rating and took the maximum time allowed (15 seconds). On later trials, progressive improvement was observed by the decrease in time to complete the task and the increase in task ratings. On the $\frac{3}{4}''$ and $\frac{1}{2}''$ buttons, comparable improvment was noted. S had particular difficulty with the $\frac{1}{4}''$ button on the first four trials. From then on, progress was noted until the seventh trial during which S took the maximum time for task completion and received the lower performance rating. Following this trial, performance again improved until the S was able to complete the task easily.

Not shown in the figures was S's highly satisfactory performance on his shirt buttons which were of comparable size to the smallest

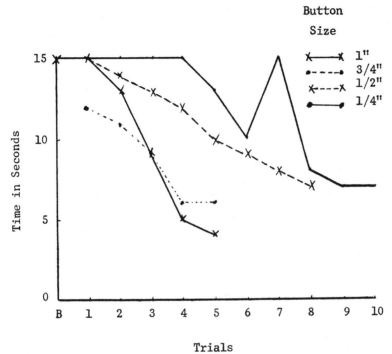

Button
Size

x———x 1"
●----● 3/4"
x---x 1/2"
●———● 1/4"

Time in Seconds

15

10

5

0

B 1 2 3 4 5 6 7 8 9 10

Trials

FIGURE 1. The time in seconds S took to button the 1", ¾", ½", and the ¼" buttons on each trial.

buttons on the vest. A follow-up a week later revealed that S was able to dress himself satisfactorily.

DISCUSSION

A number of factors contributed to the poor initial performance on each button of smaller size. In addition to greater precision of movement required to button the smaller buttons into their buttonholes, the initial attempt probably was more difficult because the buttonholes were tighter on the first trial requiring more force to pull the button through the hole. It was observed also that S could button the two larger buttons without looking at his fingers (through proprioceptive cues alone) while he studiously watched his own finger movements (visual cues) with the smaller buttons. Increased task difficulty also was observed during the trials with the smallest button which reached a climax during the seventh trial at which time S became upset and balked at further suggestions to complete the task. At this point, E suggested that they should take a brief rest period (amounting to fifteen minutes of chatting) and then the task was resumed to its completion.

From the procedures described, it is not possible to specify the exact conditions facilitating the acquisition on the above described self-help behavior, i.e., response contingent reinforcement or "imitation" through the contiguous association of sensory events provided by the demonstration given by E, S's responses to which were followed by rein-

Button Size

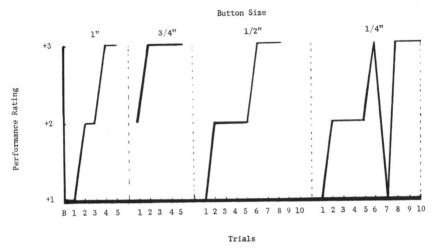

FIGURE 2. The performance rating S received at the end of each trial to button the 1″, ¾″, ½″, and ¼″ button.

forcement (Bandura, 1965). S's verbal reports during training seemed to emphasize the importance of the reinforcing stimuli (particularly the M and M's) and appeared to sustain S's behavior. However, E observed a distinct qualitative change in S's behavior following E's demonstration of how to button the large button. On the baseline trial, S attempted to push the face of the button through the buttonhole. After E's demonstration (prior to trial 2), S's attempts involved pushing the edge of the button through the buttonhole in a manner used by E. Finally, "programming" the task to insure greater probability of reinforcement was perhaps helpful.

It is interesting to note too, that prior to training, S had been given instructions to button his clothes by his parents but without success even though he could unbutton his clothes.

Robert L. Karen
San Diego State College
San Diego, California 92115

REFERENCES

Bandura, A. Influence of model's reinforcement contingencies on the acquisition of imitative responses. *J. personal. soc. Psychol.*, 1965, 1, 589–595.
Barrett, B. H., & Lindsley, O. R. Deficits in acquisition of operant discrimination and differentiation as shown by institutionalized retarded children. *Amer. J. ment. Defic.*, 1962, 67, 424–436.
Bensberg, G. J., Colwell, C. N., & Cassell, R. H. Teaching the profoundly retarded self-help activities by behavior shaping techniques. *Amer. J. ment. Defic.*, 1965, 69, 674–679.
Birnbauer, J. W., Bijou, S. W., Wolf, M. W., & Kidder, J. D. Programmed instruction in the classroom. In L. Ullmann and L. Krasner (eds.), *Case studies in behavior modification*. New York: Holt, Rinehart & Winston, 1965.
Birnbauer, J. W., Wolf, M. W., Kidder, J. D., & Tague, C. E. Classroom behavior of retarded pupils with token reinforcement. *J. exp. child Psychol.*, 1965, 2, 219–235.
Ellis, N. R. Amount of reward and operant behavior in mental defectives. *Amer. J. ment. Defic.*, 1962, 66, 595–599.
Ellis, N. R., Barnett, C. D., & Pryer, M. W. Operant behavior in mental defectives: exploratory studies. *J. exp. anal. Behavior*, 1960, 3, 63–69.
Girardeau, F. L. The effect of secondary reinforcement on the operant behavior in mental defectives. *Amer. J. ment. Defic.*, 1962, 67, 441–449.
Girardeau, F. L., & Spradlin, J. Token rewards in a cottage program. *Ment. Retard.*, 1964, 2, 345–351.
Headrick, M. W. Effects of instructions and initial reinforcement on fixed-interval behavior in retardates. 1963, 68, 425–432.

Hundziak, M., Maurer, R. A., & Watson, L. S. Operant conditioning in toilet training severely mentally retarded boys. *Amer. J. ment. Defic.*, 1965, 70, 120–124.

Lindsley, O. R. Direct measurement and prosthesis of retarded behavior. *J. Educ.*, 1954, 147, 62–81.

Orlando, R. Component behavior in a free operant temporal discrimination. *Amer. J. ment. Defic.*, 1961, 65, 615–619.

Orlando, R. Shaping multiple schedule performance in retardates: Establishment of baselines by systematic and special procedures. *J. exp. child Psychol.*, 1965, 2, 135–153.

Orlando, R., & Bijou, S. W. Single and multiple schedules of reinforcement in developmentally retarded children. *J. exp. anal. Behavior*, 1960, 3, 339–348.

Spradlin, J. Effects of reinforcement schedules on extinction in severely mentally retarded children. *Amer. J. ment. Defic.*, 1962, 66, 634–640.

TOILET TRAINING [1]

Werner Lohmann, B.A., Richard K. Eyman, Ph.D. and Emanual Lask, Ph.D.

SEVERAL attempts have been made recently to design toilet training programs for the severely retarded (Ellis, 1963; Dayan, 1964). However, before programs of this kind can be designed and evaluated effectively, the dynamics involved in changes of toilet skills must be investigated more closely. The present study is an attempt to investigate longitudinally changes of toilet training patterns as related to other patient characteristics.

Specifically, a stratified random sample of 90 cases was drawn from a total of 3,427 patients "on the books" at Pacific State Hospital between March, 1960 and May, 1964. These patients were studied longitudinally for five years (1964). The following questions were examined: (1) What changes in toilet skills took place in an institution for the mentally retarded with no intensive toilet training program at that time? (2) Was there a relationship between toilet skills over the five year study period and patient char-

acteristics such as age, IQ, length of hospitalization, illnesses, and behavior problems? (3) How useful are annual ratings of toilet training made by ward personnel relative to questions 1 and 2?

METHOD

An annual census questionnaire was completed over a five year period for the 3,427 resident and non-resident patients who were at Pacific State Hospital between 1960 and 1964. Patients who had died, were discharged, or transferred during the study period were not considered. There were 86 of them. One of the 60 items on this annual census questionnaire was concerned with toilet training skill. Ratings were made by ward personnel (psychiatric technicians) for resident patients and by social workers for non-resident patients. Each patient was rated as either not trained, partially trained, or fully trained.

An inspection of the five consecutive ratings available for each patient indicated nine mutually exclusive and exhaustive types of patterns of ratings. The nine patterns of ratings are as follows:

[1] Supported in part by the National Institute of Mental Health Grant No. MH-08667: Socio-Behavioral Study Center for Mental Retardation. Pacific State Hospital, Pomona, California. Appreciation for assistance is expressed to the Health Sciences Computing Facility, University of California, Los Angeles.

		Per cent of Total in Each Group
Group 1:	fully trained all years	57.6
Group 2:	partially trained all years	3.1
Group 3:	not trained all years	13.1
Group 4:	improved from not trained to partially trained	3.1
Group 5:	improved from partially trained to fully trained	4.6
Group 6:	improved from not trained to partially trained to fully trained	.8
Group 7:	regressed in toilet skills, e.g., 11223*	3.06
Group 8:	slightly irregular pattern in toilet skills, e.g., 22121*	13.6
Group 9:	very irregular pattern in toilet skills, e.g., 21313*	1.1

* 1 Bowel and bladder trained—patient uses toilet independently or makes toilet needs known.
2 Partially trained—patient responds to "trip" schedule but has some daytime untidiness.
3 Not trained at all—patient regularly soils and wets clothing.

A stratified random sample of ten cases was selected from each of the nine groups of patients, which gave a total sample size of 90 cases for this study.

Ward notes, medical records, information from punched cards, and personal interviews of the employees in charge of the particular patient all were used, alone or in combination, to obtain relevant information for the time period 1960 to 1964.[2]

The specific patient characteristics noted were: age at beginning of this study (1960), length of stay at hospital, IQ, age at time of improvement for those who improved, number of concomitant incidents[3] (subdivided into illness, behavioral, other) and total number of ward transfers over the five-year period. A distinction was made between ward transfers involving general type wards and changes

2 The number of concomitant incidents was determined from ward notes, medical records, and personal interviews, while all other information was available from punched cards.
3 Under these three subgroups, all incidents were listed which potentially affected the toilet training status of the patient.

involving wards into the acute unit of the hospital. This was necessary because moves into the acute unit are prompted by severe medical problems, while transfers between general case wards are generally dependent on aging and growth. Also noted was the ward on which each annual rating was made.

In order to determine differences between groups, separate one-way analyses of variance were conducted on each of the above variables. Duncan's multiple comparisons test was applied to those group means where the analysis of variance was significant at the .05 level. For the groups which improved over the five year period (4, 5, and 6), an extended median test and the Mann-Whitney U Test were applied to check whether these groups differed significantly in age at the time when this improvement took place.

RESULTS

One of the purposes of this study was to examine the utility of the annual ratings. Inconsistent ratings over the five-year study were, in particular, suspect, e.g., groups 8 and 9. There are three possible ways of explaining this variation: (1) changes in ratings are due to errors on the part of the rater, (2) changes in ratings are due to rating biases associated with different wards, and (3) changes in ratings represent actual variations in the patient's toilet training status. Evidence concerning reliability and validity of these ratings is reported elsewhere (WICHE)[4]. In all such investigations, the number of rating errors was judged as minimal in that inter-rater reliability was always greater than .90 and the number of patients found to be misclassified never exceeded 5 per cent.

However, a further check was made. This was done by examining the question of whether changes of ward, on which ratings

4 Data Collection and Utilization in Institutions for the Mentally Retarded. The Western Interstate Commission for Higher Education, Boulder, Colorado, October, 1964.

were made, is related to change in toilet training status. For example, if a change in toilet training status is related to the ward in which the rating was made, one would expect, that patients with a high number of rating locations also have a high incidence of rating change. An example of the specific method, which was used to answer this question, is given below:

ber of wards possible would be five per patient. If any relationship existed between changes in ratings and the location where these ratings were made, one would expect that those patients with the highest number of rating changes (Group 9) would also be high in the number of different wards on which these ratings were made. The results of the analysis of variance not only failed to

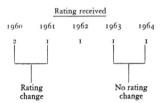

Patient X

This particular patient was rated four times (1960–1963) on Ward A and once (1964) on Ward B. The ratings, which were assigned to this patient on Wards A and B, indicate that the only change in toilet training status occurred between 1960 and 1961. Therefore, this particular patient was counted as follows:

Ward change; rating change	0
Ward change; no rating change	1
No ward change; rating change	1
No ward change; no rating change	2

Tabulation of these data showed that in 92 out of 274 instances of "no ward changes", there was a rating change. This is similar to 31 out of 86 occasions where a ward change was observed to be concomitant with a rating change. This seems to indicate that toilet training ratings are not biased by the location where they are made. In other words, all wards appear to be using the same criteria when evaluating the patient's level of toilet training.

Finally, a comparison was made of the nine different groups on the basis of the number of wards on which each patient, within any specific group was rated. Since each patient was rated once a year, the maximum num-

show significance, but it was observed that Group 9 (patients with the highest number of rating changes) was lower than any other group with respect to the number of wards on which ratings were made. Therefore, it is assumed that changes in toilet training ratings reflect actual changes in the patient's level of performance.

This, then, leads to the question why some patients fluctuated so greatly in their toilet habit while others remained fairly constant or changed systematically. One possible explanation is that patients who are unstable in toilet habits are also unstable in other behavior, e.g., aggressive, etc. Table I explores this possibility by presenting the number of concomitant incidents which could influence toilet training. It appears that patients who regressed in toilet training or were irregular in their training from year to year have relatively more behavior problems than other groups. A second possible explanation is that this extreme variation in toilet training is related to the patient being transferred from ward to ward due to severe medical problems or aging, etc., as indicated by Table II. It can be noted in Table II that the number of general transfers and acute hospi-

TABLE I

NUMBER OF CONCOMITANT INCIDENTS WHICH POTENTIALLY COULD INFLUENCE LEVEL OF TT

(Total Number 1960–1964)

	Illness [1]		Behavior [2]		Other [3]	
	N	%	N	%	N	%
1. Fully trained	16	100	0	0	0	0
2. Partially trained	43	91.4	3	6.3	1	2.3
3. Not trained	29	87.8	0	0	4	12.2
4. Improved from not trained to partially trained	19	95.0	1	5.0	0	0
5. Improved from partially trained to fully trained	25	96.1	0	0	1	3.9
6. Improved from not trained to partially trained to fully trained	34	97.1	0	0	1	2.9
7. Regressed	13	50.0	8	30.0	5	20.0
8. Slightly irregular	26	72.2	6	16.6	4	11.2
9. Very irregular	23	69.6	8	24.2	2	6.2

[1] Illness includes all medical problems which may have influenced the toilet training status of the patient, e.g., Shigellosis, severe seizures, etc.
[2] Behavior changes refer to incidents such as head banging, withdrawal from contact with patients and from employees, etc.
[3] All incidents that were not classified under illness or behavior were counted as "other": most of these were severe changes in handicaps, e.g., of ability to walk, loss of eyesight, etc.

tal moves were scattered among the nine groups so that no clear trend is evident.

Table III gives the median and interquartile range for each group with regard to chronological age at the beginning of the study, IQ, and hospital age. Hospital age is defined as the time the patient has been in the custody of the hospital, including one of the after-care programs. A separate one-way analysis of variables was conducted on each of the three variables.

The results of the analysis of variance on chronological age indicated that the groups differed beyond the .01 level of significance. Application of Duncan's Multiple Compari-

sons Method (Winer, 1962, pg. 85) to the group means showed that Group 6 is younger than either Groups 1, 7, 8, or 9, and that Group 1 is older than any other group (protection level $\leq$ .05).

The results of the analysis of variance of IQ indicated that the groups differed beyond the .01 level of significance. Duncan's Multiple Comparison Method applied to the group means identified (a) Group 1 as superior to any other group, (b) Group 5 as superior to Groups 2, 3, and 9, and (c) Groups 6 and 8 as superior to Group 3.

Analysis of variance for length of stay at the Hospital showed no difference of group

TABLE II

TOTAL NUMBER OF WARD CHANGES FOR ALL PATIENTS IN SAMPLE OVER THE FIVE-YEAR PERIOD

	Number of Acute Unit Moves [1]	Number of General Type Moves [2]	Per Cent of Acute Moves of Total Number of Moves
1. Fully trained	10	108	8.4
2. Partially trained	13	19	40.6
3. Not trained	13	26	33.3
4. Improved: not to partially	12	80	13.0
5. Improved: partially to fully	5	84	5.6
6. Improved: not partially to fully	18	77	18.9
7. Regressed	8	27	22.8
8. Slightly irregular	14	145	8.8
9. Very irregular	13	24	35.1

[1] Acute unit moves refers to transfers into the acute unit of the hospital because of serious illness.
[2] General type moves includes all ward changes not counted under acute unit moves.

TABLE III
SUMMARY TABLE OF MEDIANS AND INTERQUARTILE RANGES

	Age at Beginning of Study	IQ	Hospital Age 1960
Group 1	36*	41	15 *
Fully Trained	24–46	27–58	6–24**
Group 2	10	14	6
Partially Trained	9–25	10–15	3–12
Group 3	9	4	6
Not Trained	8–16	3–5	2–11
Group 4	15	11	9
Improved—Not Trained to Partially Trained	7–28	7–19	2–17
Group 5	18	19	5
Improved—Partially Trained to Fully Trained	10–22	14–34	2–8
Group 6	6	23	2
Improved—Not Trained to Fully Trained	5–7	17–28	1–5
Group 7	14	17	9
Regressed	11–33	14–18	6–18
Group 8	23.5	15	4
Slightly Irregular	12–25	7–35	1–18
Group 9	27	9	10
Very Irregular	17–30	9–12	4–16

* Medians.
** Interquartile Ranges.

means at the .05 level of significance. The age at which improvement was observed differed for those groups which improved consistently during the period of this study (see Table A). Groups 4 and 5 improved one step each over the five-year period, while Group 6 showed two improvements (from not trained to partially trained to fully trained) during the same time period. An extended median test indicated that the ages at time of improvements were not the same for Groups 4, 5, and 6 [5] (probability less than .05). Pairwise comparisons, using a Mann-Whitney U Test, showed that Groups 4 and 5 were not significantly different from each other, but that both were considerably older at their time

[5] The median test was conducted twice, once with Groups 4, 5, and 6, using the age at time of the first improvement for Group 6, and again with the age at the time of the second improvement.

of improvements than Group 6. In other words, retardates who improved fairly rapidly from not trained to fully trained were patients who were relatively young (mostly between 7–11 years).

DISCUSSION

One way of discussing the nine different patterns of Toilet Training is in terms of the type of care required of the institution. Obviously, patients considered "fully trained" (Groups 1, 5, and 6) require a minimum amount of physical care and are probable candidates, other factors being equal, for one of the out-patient programs. This point is demonstrated by a check on patient status in August, 1965, for the total cohort (3,427 patients), which revealed that over 40 per

TABLE A

	Age (Median)	Interquartile Range
Group 4 Improved from Not Trained to Partially Trained	16	12–29
Group 5 Improved from Partially Trained to Fully Trained	19	11–25
Group 6 Improved from Not Trained to Fully Trained	7.1△ 10 *	7–9△ 9–11 *

△ First improvement.
* Second improvement.

cent of the patients in Groups 1, 5, or 6 were on one of the aftercare programs. This is in contrast to the finding that under 20 per cent of the patients in other groups, representing an untrained or partially trained condition, were on an aftercare program, e.g., 7 per cent of Group 3, untrained patients, and 16 per cent of Group 2, the partially trained, were on such programs.

It can be seen from the results of comparing these patients by age and IQ that Groups 1 and 5 were among the higher patients in measured IQ and chronological age. Group 6 is significantly younger, which precludes the possibility of being hospitalized for a longer period of time. Length of hospitalization for Groups 5 and 6, where improvement was possible and fully trained skills achieved, was less than five years.

It is possible to hypothesize from these results, that retardates who are capable of mastering toilet training skills will do so within a relatively short time after admission, e.g., 5 or less years.

On the other side of the scale we find Groups 3, 7, 8, and 9. These three groups present a complex custodial problem due to the amount of physical care required by these patients. Also, the chances seem to be very poor that these patients will improve substantially at a later time. The patients in Group 3 (not trained) are probably mentally too low (median IQ 4) to be considered trainable by any standard. From the results in Table I, it appears that the patients in Groups 7, 8, and 9 are severely disturbed. These patients showed extreme amounts of behavior problems such as aggressiveness, acts of self destruction (e.g., head banging, biting), withdrawal from contact with other persons, etc. Although no specific diagnostic label is attached to this type patient, the possibility of these patients being psychotic must be considered.

The patients in Groups 2 and 4 are of particular interest because they seem to be representative of patients who are trainable, but who require a special effort in accomplishing this. The measured IQ for these groups is typically between 10–20, with the majority between 15–20. Groups 2 and 4 represent the patient who responds to some form of toilet training, such as the "trip schedule," e.g., partially trained. Under normal hospital conditions, this appears to be the maximum level of toilet training achievement of which these patients are capable. However, as shown by Ellis (1963), retardates in this category will respond to intensive training procedures, e.g., operant conditioning.

SUMMARY

It is possible that some of the extreme variation of toilet training skill is due, at least in part, to severe behavioral and medical problems. It is further indicated that patients who are young at the time of admission (about 6 years old) and have an IQ of 20 or more, however, will probably be fully toilet trained five years after admission.* On the other hand, patients who are somewhat older and have IQs between 10–20 (Groups 2, 4, and 5) are those who would benefit most from intensive toilet training programs. The toilet training of this group is likely to be accelerated considerably by special training methods.

Whether patients in Group 3 are trainable, at all, remains to be seen. These patients were of very low measured intelligence (median IQ 4) and were rated "not trained" for five consecutive years.

The findings supported the utility of the rating instrument, indicating that toilet training is a changing characteristic and highly related to patient ability and problems.

Definite possibilities exist for determining norms from which to evaluate patients' toilet skills over time. Such a system currently is being attempted at Pacific State Hospital.

---

* Exceptions to this are patients who were noted to have a large number of behavior problems.

It is hoped that an alerting can assist in identifying patients who appear to be not up to their potential in terms of hospital norms and facilities available.

Box 100
Pomona, Calif.

REFERENCES

Dayan, M. Toilet training retarded children in a state residential institution. *Ment. Retard.*, 1964, 2, 2, 116–117.

Ellis, N. R. Toilet training the severely defective patient: An S-R reinforcement analysis. *Amer. J. ment. Defic.*, 1963, 68, 1, 98–103.

Winer, B. *Statistical principles in experimental design.* McGraw-Hill, New York, 1962.

GARRY L. MARTIN
RICHARD B. POWERS

Attention Span: An Operant Conditioning Analysis

CONTEMPORARY literature suggests that the concept of attention span refers to two different phenomena. Under "span of attention," English and English (1958) list: (a) The number of distinct objects that can be perceived in a single momentary presentation; and (b) the length of time a person can attend to one thing. The first of these two definitions has historical precedent over the second. It relates to one of the oldest questions in the field of experimental psychology, namely, how many things can we attend to in a single instant of time?

The second definition, the more recent and frequent usage of the concept, is the one with which this paper is concerned. The length of time a person can attend to one thing was initially referred to as voluntary attention (James, 1890; Angell, 1904). More recently, the length of time a subject concentrated on a task has been referred to variously as interest span (Herring and Koch, 1930), sustained attention (Schacter, 1933), occupation interest (Bridges, 1927), perseveration (Cushing, 1929), or, most usually, as attention span (Cockrell, 1935; Bott, 1928; Van Alstyne, 1932; Gutteridge, 1935; Moyer and von Haller Gilmer, 1955).

With respect to special populations, it was suggested as early as 1904 that, "alienists and specialists in nervous disorders inform us that mental disease is commonly accompanied by disturbance in the power of attention" (Angell, 1904, p. 80). The concept of short attention span was suggested by Kuhlman (1904) as a way of accounting for the retardate's apparent difficulty in discrimination learning. Recently, Strauss and his associates (1947, 1955) have been influential in stressing the difficulty of brain injured children in attending to a task for any length of time, and references to the short attention span of retardates are common in the contemporary literature (Blodgett and Warfield, 1959; Goldstein and Seigle, 1961; Cromwell, Baumeister, and Hawkins, 1963; Weber, 1964; Garton, 1964).

Although the attention span concept appears to be widely employed in psychological and educational literature on special populations, current usage of the term is not entirely consistent. Some of these inconsistencies will be discussed briefly in the following section.

Current Usage

The concept seems to be used currently in at least three major ways. First, empirical evidence indicates that "attention span" is task specific. Measurements with normal children have yielded values ranging from seconds to forty-five minutes (Moyer and von Haller Gilmer, 1955). Moyer and von Haller Gilmer concluded that to speak of the concept of a "mean attention span" for children was meaningless because its measure depended so much on selecting the right task for the right age child. They proposed the notion of attention spans to replace that of attention span. Their point is well taken and might profitably be applied to the concept of *a* short attention span for retardates. That is, it seems reasonable that attention span measures of retardates are also task and child specific, and not a characteristic of retardation per se.

Second, although several authors have talked as though short attention span, distractibility, and hyperactivity refer to different phenomena, differences among the behavioral referents of these concepts are often difficult to specify. For example, concerning the brain injured child, Strauss and Kephart wrote:

He finds it impossible to engage in any activity in a concentrated fashion, but is always being led aside from the task at hand by stimuli which should remain extraneous but do not. . . . Under these conditions it would be expected that the individual would tend to respond to a variety of extraneous stimuli and lose track of the task at hand. We would describe such behavior as "distractibility" (1955, p. 135).

In their report on research in activity level, Cromwell et al. (1963) stated:

Another paramount problem is that activity level, owing to its lack of clarity in definition, can be confused with other variables. For example, the subject with a short attention span who shifts quickly from one goal-directed activity to another may appear to the observer to have a higher rate of activity than a subject fixated at one task but exerting the same amount of activity (1963, p. 634).

In view of such statements, a reader might refer to a child who engages in a task for a brief period of time as having a short attention span, or being easily distractible, or showing superactivity. Yet the concepts are discussed as though they were distinct phenomena. For example, in their article on activity level, Cromwell et al. wrote:

According to their (Strauss' and his associates') conception of the brain-injured child, an environment of overstimulation should exaggerate

the symptoms of distractible behavior, short attention span, and superactivity (1963, p. 641).

If these concepts do refer to different behavioral phenomena, the differences are not always obvious.

Third, attention span is sometimes discussed as though it were a faculty or process and the observed behaviors are considered as symptoms of the underlying short attention span. A consequence of this approach is the tendency to refer to short attention span as an absolute, unchanging characteristic of mental retardation. In some cases, a very short attention span is simply cited as a characteristic of the mentally retarded with no elaboration offered (Weber, 1964). In other cases, it is used as a diagnostic device to distinguish categories of mental retardation (Blodgett and Warfield, 1959).

A major consequence of these usages of short attention span is that they tend to impede the education of the retarded. A "rigid attention span" can be easily invoked as a way of accounting for poor attending behavior. But paying attention is a prerequisite in all classroom situations. Thus, as others have observed (Lewis, Strauss, and Lehtinen, 1960), various educational activities are often not attempted with a particular retarded child simply because his short attention span is thought to interfere with the necessary task attendance.

An Operant Conditioning Analysis of Attention Span

An operant conditioning analysis of attention span suggests an alternative view. This approach offers powerful tools which can be used to manipulate the length of time a child attends to a particular task. The most important single principle of operant conditioning is the empirical principle of reinforcement. The principle refers to the observation that there are certain environmental events (commonly called rewards) that we will work to produce. We influence others with these events when we reward any behavior that we wish to make more frequent. These rewarding events are more technically referred to as reinforcers. A reinforcer is defined as a stimulus, the presentation of which, following a response, increases the probability of future occurrence of that response. The common sense notion of reward is certainly not new. What is new is the precise specification of several variables that are crucial to the success of the reinforcement procedure.

The first crucial variable is the contingent relationship between the response and the reinforcer. The contingency is a logical if-then relationship, which is to be distinguished from a simple pleasant or rewarding situation in which a person might find himself. A pleasant situation typically doesn't require the person to do anything. The reinforcement procedure, however, requires the occurrence of some specified response prior to the presentation of a reinforcer. The second crucial variable is the immediacy of reinforcement. To be most effective, the reinforcer must follow the response without delay. A more extensive discussion of operant conditioning techniques may be found in Sidman (1962) and Michael (1964).

In this framework, the term "attention span" refers to nothing more than the behavioral events to which the name is attached. These behavioral events are explained in terms of environmental variables in the presence of which the behavior occurs. This interpretation places emphasis upon behavior that interferes with attending to a task, as well as the attending behavior itself. Thus, task perseverance, or a long attention span, is primarily a function of presenting reinforcement contingent upon attending behavior, and allowing incompatible behavior to go unreinforced. On the other hand, short attention span is observed when reinforcement is contingent upon behavior that is incompatible with attending to the task of interest, and attending behavior goes unreinforced. A similar analysis has been made by Michael (1963) in a discussion of the relevance of animal research to problems of learning in the retarded.

An experiment conducted by the authors supports this analysis. The purpose of the experiment was to study the effects of novel human stimuli upon an operant response in retarded children (Martin and Powers, 1965). The experimental chamber was divided into two cubicles separated by a plexiglass partition that allowed visual and auditory feedback. Each cubicle contained a lever mounted on a table. The children were conditioned individually to

operate a lever; that is, when the child pressed the lever, a token fell into a token cup. The token could then be exchanged for either salty foods (popcorn, pretzels, peanuts, etc.) or juice immediately after its receipt. Gradually, the number of lever presses required was increased until the schedule of reinforcement was a fixed ratio 10 (every tenth response was reinforced). The subjects were exposed to this schedule until they achieved a stable performance for five consecutive sessions. Each daily session lasted 20 minutes or until the subject received 50 reinforcements.

At this point, a confederate was introduced into the opposing cubicle with instructions to do one of three things: A, sit quietly and read a book; B, operate the lever and receive food or juice on a fixed interval 30 second schedule of reinforcement (the first response after 30 seconds produced the reinforcement); C, operate the lever and receive a token for every 30th response (fixed ratio 30). The token was then exchanged for food or juice.

These three conditions of the confederate were introduced on the assumption that each varied with respect to the frequency and intensity of the auditory and visual stimuli they provided to the subject. Two subjects were exposed to condition C; one was given condition A and B in that order; and the other subject was exposed to the sequence A, B, C. When more than one condition was used, the subject was returned to the control condition (fixed ratio 10) for a session prior to the onset of each new test condition.

In all three test conditions, the introduction of the confederate produced a temporary disruption of the stable pattern of responding that was observed under the control conditions. However, this stable pattern of responding was recovered, indicating that adaptation to the stimuli presented by the confederate had occurred.

Observations made during the initial conditioning sessions and during the test sessions have direct relevance to the issue of attention span. During the first four conditioning sessions, no subject earned the 50 reinforcements within the allotted time of 20 minutes. Failure to earn all available reinforcements appeared to be due to the frequent occurrence of responses that were incompatible with lever pressing such as climbing, crouching, banging on the door, lying on the floor, and so on. In other words, the subjects might have been described as shifting quickly from one goal directed activity to another, and many persons undoubtedly would have been willing to use the notion of a short attention span as an explanation for the subject's failure to respond in a consistent manner on the lever. Yet, by the fourth session, the subjects came to "pay attention" to the task for the duration of the session, earning their 50 reinforcements within the 20 minute period. This was accomplished by reinforcing only the task of concern and ignoring other incompatible behavior.

Some authors have suggested that subjects with a short attention span for a certain event or activity often invent activities with greater appeal to them (Goldstein and Seigle, 1961). Relevant to this suggestion are the observations taken during the test sessions. The disruption of the stable pattern of responding in the presence of the confederate was due to the occurrence of activities that are incompatible with lever pressing, such as staring, pointing, laughing at the other person, or tapping on the plexiglass partition. It might be suggested that the subjects invented these activities because of their greater appeal, since the only evidence ever offered for this explanation is the fact of their occurrence. However, such an explanation adds nothing in the way of correction procedures. By ignoring these activities and reinforcing only the lever pressing task, the subjects came to pay attention even in the face of the variety of visual and auditory stimuli provided by the confederate. A recent report indicates that even the occurrence of an earthquake in the middle of an experiment failed to disrupt the attending behavior of a retarded subject when that behavior was reinforced (Sloane and Harper, 1965).

Observations reported by other authors support this analysis. Kerr (1962) worked with two brain injured girls who supposedly had short attention spans and were irresponsible and hyperactive in the classroom (the hospital staff had reported the girls to have such short attention spans that they could not attend to a particular task for longer than three to six minutes). Kerr devised the task of folding 2 by 5 cards along a dotted line and placing each folded card in a container. During the first session the usual or traditional technique of urging the child to continue was used whenever a lag in productivity occurred, i.e., the experimenter would say such things as, "Come on, you can do better than that," and approximately ten minutes of productive behavior was obtained. During the next two sessions, experimenter attention was made contingent upon task performance, in the maner dictated by the empirical principles of reinforcement, and a full hour of work was obtained each time. Two more sessions of the traditional technique and two more reinforcement sessions replicated these effects. In discussing these results, Kerr reported:

> The significance of a demonstration that attention span of brain damaged children can be increased through manipulation of reinforcement variables is quite obvious. Procedures which induce a child to attend to a task facilitate education, therapies, and even physical examination. For example, a question about the eyesight of one of the children in this study had been raised by other staff members. An attempt to have her eyes examined was unsuccessful, "because of her short attention span." However, in the present experiment, it was easily determined that she could discriminate the fine printed line along which the paper was to be folded. Had the goal been to test her vision, other visual tasks could have been presented (1962, p. 118).

So far, emphasis has been placed upon the reinforcement of attending behavior. In addition, an operant analysis also stresses a concern for environmental variables that maintain behavior incompatible with a long attention span. For example, several staff members from the institution where the authors' research was conducted had commented upon the short attention spans of their students as a major barrier to their education. However, observation of these students in their respective classrooms revealed that they received attention from the teacher only when they left their desks, cried, or, in short, emitted behavior that was incompatible with a long attention span.

Evidence supporting the importance of reinforcement principles in eliminating behavior that is incompatible with attending to a task comes from two recent experiments. Zimmerman and Zimmerman (1962) eliminated unproductive classroom behavior in two emotionally disturbed boys by removing social consequences of the behavior. In both cases, the student would respond to a teacher's request by emitting behavior that was incompatible with the task of concern (such as having temper tantrums, emitting irrelevant verbal behavior, and talking baby talk). The experimenter initially responded to such behavior, giving the subject much attention and encouragement to respond appropriately. As this approach proved unsuccessful, the experimenter next proceeded to give attention (reinforcement) in the form of smiling, chatting, and physical proximity only after the emission of desired classroom behavior, or some approximation of it in the desired direction. As a result of this treatment, the students soon came to attend to the teacher's questions and classroom tasks.

Birnbrauer, Bijou, and Wolf (1963) selected eight boys from the youngest and educationally most naive educable children from the Rainier School for Retarded Children in an effort to teach them for a school year, using programed instruction and reinforcement techniques exclusively. With these techniques, the investigators had a great deal of success in teaching primary academic subjects and related practical skills. Relevant to this discussion, they report:

> Behavior problems did arise frequently and were handled almost exclusively with extinction; i.e., they were simply ignored. The physical arrangement of the room and the staggered schedules permtted temper tantrums, for example, to "wear themselves out" without overly affecting the other pupils. Shortly after the pupil stopped the inappropriate behavior, he received attention. In other words, adult attention was reserved for socially acceptable behavior (1963, p. 3).

Under these conditions, the retarded students came to read for 20 minutes at a time with the teacher, work quietly at their desks at various tasks, and even do homework.

An operant conditioning approach considers attention span only in terms of the time spent engaging in a task, and uses reinforcement variables in accounting for task persistence. This approach provides teachers with a powerful tool with which to strengthen good attending behavior.

References

Angell, J. R. *Psychology*. New York: Henry Holt, 1904.

Birnbrauer, J. S., Bijou, S. W., and Wolf, M. Programmed instruction in the classroom. In L. P. Ullman and L. Krasner, (Eds.), *Case studies in behavioral modification*. New York: Holt, Rinehart and Winston, 1965. Pp. 358-363.

Blodgett, Harriet E., and Warfield, Grace J. *Understanding mentally retarded children*. New York: Appleton-Century-Croft, 1959.

Bott, H. Observation of play activities in a nursery school. *Genetic Psychology Monographs*, 1928, 4, 44-88.

Bridges, K. M. B. Occupational interests of three year old children. *Journal of Genetic Psychology*, 1927, 34, 415-423.

Cockrell, D. L. A study of the play of children of preschool age by an unobserved observer. *Genetic Psychology Monographs*, 1935, 17, 377-469.

Cromwell, R. L., Baumeister, A., and Hawkins, W. F. Research in activity level. In N. R. Ellis, (Ed.), *Handbook of mental deficiency*. New York: McGraw Hill, 1963. Pp. 632-663.

Cushing, H. M. A perseverative tendency in preschool children; a study in personality differences. *Archives of Psychology*, 1929, 108.

English, H. B., and English, Ava C. *A comprehensive dictionary of psychological and psychoanalytic terms*. New York: McGraw Hill, 1963.

Garton, Malinda D. *Teaching the educable mentally retarded*. Springfield, Ill.: Charles C Thomas, 1964.

Goldstein, H., and Seigle, Dorothy M. Characteristics of educable mentally handicapped children. In J. H. Rothstein (Ed.), *Mental retardation*. New York: Holt, Rinehart and Winston, 1961. Pp. 204-230.

Gutteridge, M. V. *The duration of attention in young children*. Australian Council of Educational Research, Melbourne University Educational Research Series, Number 41, Oxford University Press, 1935.

Herring, A., and Koch, H. L. A study of some factors influencing the interest span of preschool children. *Journal of Genetic Psychology*, 1930, 38, 249-279.

James, W. *The principles of psychology*. Volume 1. New York: Henry Holt, 1890.

Kerr, Nancy. Applications of behavioristic techniques and field theoretical concepts in somatopsychology. Unpublished doctoral dissertation, University of Houston, 1962.

Kuhlman, E. Experimental studies in mental deficiency. *American Journal of Psychology*, 1904, 15, 391-446.

Lewis, R. S., Strauss, A. A., and Lehtinen, L. E.

The other child. New York: Grune and Stratton, 1960.

Martin, G. L., and Powers, R. B. Social disruption of an operant response in retardates. Paper presented at American Association for the Advancement of Science, Flagstaff, Arizona, 1965.

Michael, J. L. The relevance of animal research. Paper presented at a symposium on language learning in the mentally retarded, University of Kansas, Lawrence, 1963.

Michael, J. L. Guidance and counseling as the control of behavior. In *Guidance in American Education: Backgrounds and Prospects.* Cambridge: Harvard Graduate School of Education, 1964.

Moyer, K. E., and von Haller Gilmer, B. Attention spans of children for experimentally designed toys. *Journal of Genetic Psychology,* 1955, **87,** 187-201.

Schacter, H. S. A method for measuring the sustained attention of preschool children. *Journal of Genetic Psychology,* 1933, **43,** 339-371.

Sidman, M. Operant techniques. In A. J. Bachrach (Ed.), *Experimental foundations of clinical psychology.* New York: Basic Books, 1962. Pp. 170-210.

Sloane, H., and Harper, L. J. Experimental control during an earthquake. *Journal of Experimental Analysis of Behavior,* 1965, **8,** 425-426.

Strauss, A. A., and Kephart, N. *Psychopathology and education of the brain-injured.* New York: Grune and Stratton, 1947.

Van Alstyne, D. *Play behavior and choice of play materials of preschool children.* Chicago: University of Chicago Press, 1932.

Weber, E. W. *Mentally retarded children and their education.* Springfield, Ill.: Charles C Thomas, 1963.

Zimmerman, Elaine H., and Zimmerman, J. The alteration of behavior in a special classroom situation. *Journal of Experimental Analysis of Behavior,* 1962, **5,** 59-60.

CHANGES IN RESPONSE FORCE DURING ACQUISITION AND EXTINCTION IN RETARDED CHILDREN [1]

THE phenomenon of increased response vigor following an extinction or response blocking operation is well known (Amsel, 1962). Operations which produce this effect have been viewed as frustrating, and the effect itself is held to be of importance to theories of social behavior, particularly in regard to the causes and expression of aggression in the child (Bandura & Walters, 1963). Although the variability of the force of response has been rather well investigated with normal human subjects and with rats, no attempts have been made to assess the stability of shifts in response-force distribution during extinction over repeated extinction sessions interpolated with reconditioning. Retarded children were felt to be potentially excellent subjects for this particular problem because of their noted characteristic of greater resistance to extinction than among normal children on similar tasks (Bijou & Oblinger, 1960). In other respects, however, they have been shown to perform very much like nor-

mals and animals in simple laboratory situations (Orlando & Bijou, 1960).

The purpose of this study was to provide data on the variability of force of response during repeated acquisition and extinction of an operant (bar pressing) in retarded children. Extinction-reconditioning sequences were employed in an attempt to assess the duration and permanence of the effect of extinction on response force distribution. Two such sequences, differing in the degree of similarity between acquisition and extinction conditions, allowed investigation of the stimuli presumed to control the force of response.

METHOD

Experimental Design

This study makes use of a single S, or individual analysis design of the type described by Sidman (1960). The responses of each S constitute the data of an entire experiment, and results are compared within Ss rather than among Ss. Three Ss were used to explore the intersubject generality. While the same basic experimental procedures were employed within each individual experiment, the number of sessions necessary to achieve

[1] This investigation was supported by NIMH Research Grants M–2232 and MH–12928. The author wishes to thank Dr. J. S. Birnbrauer for the use of the Rainier facilities, and Larry Hakala and Wayne Foley who assisted with the collection of the data.

stable responding varied from subject to subject.

Subjects

The Ss were three male, experimentally naive, retarded children drawn from the population of Rainier School, Buckley, Washington. S^1 was 11 years old at the time of the experiment. He had been diagnosed as cerebrally defective with a SB IQ of 43. S^2 was 13 years old, diagnosed as mongoloid, and had an estimated IQ of 50. S^3 was 14 years old, diagnosed as mongoloid, and had a SB IQ of 38.

Apparatus

Both experimental sequences employed the same apparatus and were conducted in the same experimental room within the Developmental Psychology Laboratory of the University of Washington at Rainier School.

The apparatus consisted of a vertical bar mounted in a wooden box, which in turn was fastened securely to a table within the room. The bar had a maximum downward excursion of six inches. Within the box an extension spring was attached to the rear of the bar in such a way that operation of the bar worked against the spring. Thus, downward excursion of the bar was correlated with a linear increase in response force. Four microswitches were arranged beneath the bar in such a way that downward excursion and force could be recorded in four intervals as shown in Table I. Hereafter, each interval will be designated by its number (1–4) only. Responses were recorded by interval on a 4-channel event recorder housed, together with the programming apparatus, in an adjacent control room.

Mounted on the wall above the bar was a red light which was used to inform the S when he was eligible to make a response to the bar. The reinforcement mechanism consisted of an automatically programmed uni-

TABLE I
RECORDING INTERVALS OF THE APPARATUS

Response Interval (Microswitch)	Approximate Excursion (Inches)	Approximate Force (Pounds)
1.	0.5–1.9	8.0–11.9
2.	2.0–3.9	12.0–15.9
3.	4.0–5.9	16.0–19.9
4.	6.0	20.0

versal feeder which, when operated, could be clearly heard by S. The feeder dispensed tokens into a tray mounted on the table beside the bar. These tokens were exchangeable for a variety of trinkets, candies, and pennies at the end of each session.

Procedure

Sequence I: During the first day of the experiment S was brought into the experimental room and shown the bar. The red light was turned on. S was then instructed that if he pressed the bar when the red light was on, he would get a token which he could trade for candy. He was further instructed that he was not to press the bar when the red light was off. No further instructions were given throughout the remainder of the experiment, except to one S, to whom the instruction not to press during the absence of the light was repeated during the second session.

All subjects were then given a minimum of ten 20-minute sessions in which they were reinforced for making a bar response in the 2nd interval. Responses in the 1st, 3rd, and 4th intervals were not reinforced. When the bar had been returned to the "rest" position, the red light was turned off and reinforcement was delivered. After a ten-second intertrial interval the red light reappeared.

Following acquisition to a stable baseline of force (excursion) emission, extinction was programmed in the following manner: the light was left on throughout the session (i.e., it did not go off after a 2nd interval response

110

as it had during acquisition); and the feeder was not operated. Extinction began in the middle of one session, continued throughout the entire next session, and terminated at the end of the first half of the third session. Following this period of extinction, Ss were reconditioned until a baseline approximating the original conditioning baseline had been obtained, then extinction was again programmed in the same manner. This sequence was continued until five complete extinction-reconditioning sequences had been run for two Ss, and three had been run for the third S.

Sequence II: After a lapse of approximately six weeks, the Ss were given a further series of reconditioning sessions until they achieved the stable baseline which had been obtained during Sequence I. Extinction was then programmed under the following conditions: the red light went off following a response but reappeared after the ten-second interval as it had in the conditioning procedure, and the empty feeder operated if the response had

been in the 2nd interval. This procedure was in effect for approximately 20 sessions per subject.

Sequence III: After two additional sessions of Sequence II procedure, the red light was turned out altogether, although the empty dispenser continued to operate after responses to the 2nd interval. This condition was in effect for three sessions.

RESULTS AND DISCUSSION

Sequence I: Figure 1 shows the percentage of responses for S^1 which were either more forceful (3rd interval) or less forceful (1st interval) than the 2nd interval responses reinforced during acquisition and reconditioning. Because few responses were made to the most forceful position (4th interval), these responses have been omitted from the figure. The principal results were as follows: (1) force of response became less variable as acquisition progressed; (2) during extinction the force of responding substantially in-

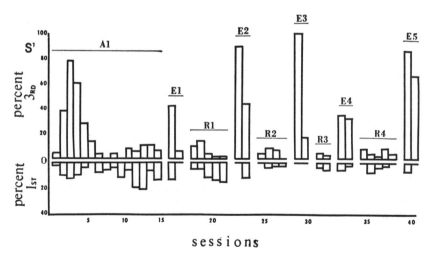

FIGURE 1. Sequence I: Percentage of 1st interval responses and 3rd interval responses during successive acquisition (A), extinction (E), and reconditioning (R) for one subject.

creased and did not diminish through the fifth extinction condition; (3) reacquisition produced a decrease in force of response and a return to the original baseline of variability; (4) greater response force was shown early in each extinction condition, and the effect decreased as extinction progressed.

Table II shows the percentage of more forceful responses (intervals 3 and 4) for each S. Inspection of the table shows that the response pattern exhibited by S^1 was essentially duplicated by S^2 and S^3. In each case, responding was more forceful during extinction than during either acquisition or reconditioning. That the increase in response force during extinction is a stable phenomenon is indicated by the high percentage of more forceful responses emitted by all subjects in

E4 and E5 in Table II. Although not shown in the table, the distribution of less forceful responses (1st interval) for S^2 and S^3 closely paralleled that of S^1 (see Figure 1).

Sequence II: This sequence was designed to reduce the stimulus differences between acquisition and extinction procedures. The red light (which might have acquired secondary reinforcing properties during acquisition) was now turned off following a 2nd interval response during extinction, as it had been during reinforcement conditions. Further, the empty dispenser was operated, thus adding another possible secondary reinforcing stimulus.

The results, shown in Table III, indicate that all Ss returned to a low level of force emission during reinforcement. This level was lower, and the response pattern somewhat less variable, than had been obtained at the end of acquisition in Sequence I. The result is similar to that found by Antonitis (1951) with rat Ss.

During the subsequent extinction sessions in Sequence II (representatives of which are shown in Table III), no increase in force of response comparable to that found in Sequence I extinction appeared. While all Ss showed the same general response pattern, the magnitude of the force increase was much smaller.

Sequence III: The data for this condition are also shown in Table III. When the red light was turned out altogether, responses again became more variable although few were made—a result in accordance with S's early instructions not to respond when the light was not present. These data are in essential agreement with those of Notterman (1959) who demonstrated an increase in force variability during extinction with rat Ss.

Rate data. Figure 2 shows the response rate for each S through each of the experimental sequences. During extinction sessions in Sequence I the response rates of S^1 and S^3 were observed to decline. Rate of response

TABLE II

Sequence I. Percentage of 3rd and 4th Interval Responses for the Last Five 10-Min. Intervals in Acquisition (A), the First Five 10-Min. Intervals in Each Extinction Condition (E1 through E5), and the Last Five 10-Min. Intervals of Each Reconditioning (R1 through R4) for Each S.

		S^1	S^2	S^3			S^1	S^2	S^3
	1.	18	0	18		1.	75	0	6
	2.	6	0	3		2.	98	98	0
A	3.	12	0	18	E3	3.	30	0	22
	4.	0	0	0		4.	0	66	0
	5.	3	0	0		5.	98	40	0
	1.	26	0	80		1.	0	12	3
	2.	66	36	.0		2.	0	0	0
E1	3.	22	0	32	R3	3.	0	6	0
	4.	50	20	15		4.	3	0	0
	5.	18	0	12		5.	0	3	0
	1.	6	0	0		1.	50	0	20
	2.	0	0	0		2.	24	98	0
R1	3.	0	0	3	E4	3.	0	98	33
	4.	0	0	0		4.	0	0	50
	5.	0	0	0		5.	30	50	0
	1.	10	12	0		1.	0	0	..
	2.	92	0	33		2.	6	0	..
E2	3.	96	32	36	R4	3.	6	0	..
	4.	98	0	33		4.	0	0	..
	5.	66	20	0		5.	0	0	..
	1.	10	0	0		1.	98	30	..
	2.	0	3	0		2.	60	98	..
R2	3.	0	0	0	E5	3.	50	94	..
	4.	0	0	0		4.	96	0	..
	5.	6	6	0		5.	50	96	..

TABLE III

SEQUENCE II AND III. PERCENTAGE OF 3RD AND 4TH INTERVAL RESPONSES FOR THE LAST FIVE 10-MIN. INTERVALS IN RECONDITIONING (R), THE FIRST FIVE 10-MIN. INTERVALS IN EXTINCTION (E1), THE LAST FIVE 10-MIN. INTERVALS IN EXTINCTION (E2), AND THE ENTIRE EXTINCTION (E) FOR SEQUENCE III, IN 10-MIN. INTERVALS FOR EACH SUBJECT.

		S^1	S^2	S^3			S^1	S^2	S^3
		Sequence II							
	1.	0	0	0		1.	0	0	0
	2.	0	0	0		2.	10	6	0
R	3.	0	0	0	E2	3.	10	20	0
	4.	0	0	0		4.	0	12	0
						Sequence III			
	1.	10	0	0		1.	0	0	0
	2.	0	10	0		2.	86	0	80
E1	3.	15	0	0	E	3.	98	0	50
	4.	0	0	0		4.	98	0	0
	5.	12	0	0		5.	0	0	0

during extinction declined more and more rapidly over subsequent extinction sessions for these Ss until fewer than 10 responses were emitted during the entire 4th extinction session for S^1 and S^3. No such decline in response rate was observed for S^2—his rate during the third extinction condition was as high as during the first, and neither differed significantly from rate during acquisition. It has already been noted, however, that the pattern of force emission for this subject did not differ generally from those of S^1 and S^3.

Discussion. During the extinction condition of Sequence II, no decline in rate was observed for any S. The failure of S^1 and S^2 to extinguish under these conditions as they did under the conditions of Sequence I may have been due in part to the secondary reinforcing aspects of the light termination and the dispenser noise. It may also have been due in part to the similarity (as viewed by S) of the reinforcement and extinction procedures. Further, because light termination may reasonably have become a discriminative stimulus for the termination of the response in the 2nd interval, 3rd interval responses would be less likely to occur. However, the brevity of the data in this sequence raises questions of reliability; further research will be necessary to clarify the finding.

It should be noted that while the magnitude of the observed shift toward more forceful responses in Sequence II was not great, the shift did occur to some extent. If force variability is taken to be a measure of S's perception of non-reinforcing conditions, then it is more sensitive than rate data in this particular instance. It is possible that response rate was under the control of an extraneous variable such as instructional set, while response force was under the control of the reinforcement variable. If future research were to further confirm this hypothesis, the theory that perseveration in the face of apparent non-reinforcement is due to the retardate's inability to discriminate non-reward from reward conditions would be seriously weakened.

The other principal data of the experiment, the observed shift in response distribution toward more forceful responding in extinction, is consonant with the findings of Amsel, and may be interpreted as a further example of the well known frustration-aggression effect. It is equally possible, however, that the result is dependent upon a transfer effect from extra-laboratory learning. Morris (1966), for example, demonstrated that when adult humans were differentially reinforced for either more or less forceful responding when extinction was programmed for one task, the response transferred to other dissimilar tasks. It is therefore not unreasonable to assume that previous extra-laboratory reinforcement for more aggressive responding in extinction conditions may have created a response set which in turn determined the experimental results. Future research might well be undertaken to determine whether retarded children can be taught to respond with less force in a non-reward condition.

Department of Psychology
Denison University
Granville, Ohio 43023

113

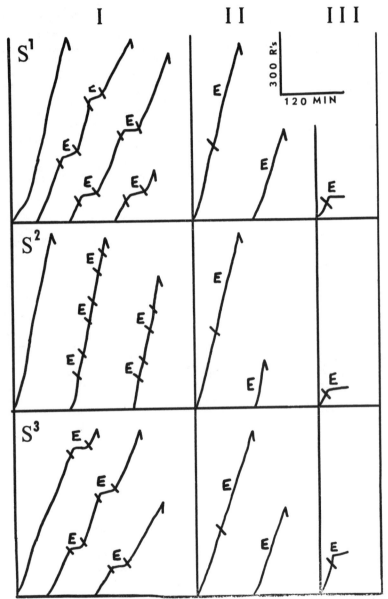

FIGURE 2. Hand drawn cumulative response curves for all Ss over Sequences I, II, and III regardless of response interval. Hatch marks indicate beginning and end of extinction conditions.

REFERENCES

Amsel, A. Frustrative nonreward in partial reinforcement and discrimination learning: some recent history and a theoretical extension. *Psychol. Rev.*, 1962, 69, 306–328.

Antonitis, J. J. Response variability in the white rat during conditioning, extinction, and re-conditioning. *J. exp. Psychol.*, 1951, 42, 273–281.

Bandura, A., & Walters, R. *Social learning and personality development.* New York: Holt, Rinehart, & Winston, 1963.

Bijou, S., & Oblinger, B. Responses of normal and retarded children as a function of the experimental situation. *Psychol. Reports,* 1960, 6, 447–454.

Lawson, R., & Marx, M. H. Frustration: theory and experiment. *Genet. Psychol. Monogr.*, 1958, 57, 393–464.

Morris, J. The effect of training on response force during operant extinction. *Psychol. Record.*, 1966, 16, 337–344.

Notterman, J. M. Force emission during bar pressing. *J. exp. Psychol.*, 1959, 58, 341–347.

Orlando, R. & Bijou, S. Single and multiple schedules of reinforcement in developmentally retarded children. *J. exp. anal. Behav.*, 1960, 3, 339–348.

Sidman, M. *Tactics of scientific research.* New York: Basic Books, 1960.

FRUSTRATIVE NONREWARD THEORY APPLIED TO
CHILDREN'S BEHAVIOR [1]

THOMAS J. RYAN   AND   PETER WATSON

In the present decade, frustration defined in terms of nonreward when reward is expected has been investigated in a variety of studies with children. The present paper reviews and evaluates the findings pertaining to frustrative nonreward and outlines possible directions of future research. It is hoped that others will develop a research interest in the type of problems presented since there are now a number of pressing questions to be answered but only a relatively small number of researchers in the area.

In the 1950s there were two trends of historical importance for the present review. The first was the growing concern for an improvement in both the quantity and quality of research in child psychology. It was proposed that child researchers adapt techniques found useful in other areas of psychology and engage in systematic laboratory studies of relatively simple aspects of children's behavior (Bijou, 1955; McCandless & Spiker, 1956; Terrell, 1958). The second trend involved a new stage in the development of frustration theory.[2] In the 1930s and 1940s frustration was dealt with as a unique behav-

ioral entity. In addition, frustration theory was highly influenced by the writings of Freud and by common-sense observations. The most evident trends in the 1950s were the attempts to integrate frustration within general behavior theory (Amsel, 1958; Brown & Farber, 1951) rather than to seek some unique model. Furthermore, rigorous experimentation played a larger role in the development of frustration theory. Amsel's (1958, 1962) theory of frustrative nonreward, originally designed to explain the behavior of hungry rats performing in runways under varying conditions of food reward, provides the basis from which much of the research to be reported was conducted.

The preponderance of research on frustrative nonreward has been restricted to the discrete-trial instrumental appetitional performance of rats. The theory has already received and will, no doubt, continue to receive extensive testing within its original boundary conditions. The present paper reviews data concerning the performance of humans in discrete-trial instrumental tasks. It focuses upon those manipulations and behaviors which have been specified by frustrative nonreward theory and also adopts the theory's interpretive framework. However, an unduly rigid adherence to the theory is to be avoided. It is recognized that composition laws, necessary to explain the relatively complex behavior under study, will eventually have to be added to the theory. Perhaps some entirely different theory structured more in terms of cognitive factors will have to be

[1] Preparation of this article was financed by National Research Council Grant No. APB-2, Ontario Mental Health Foundation Grant No. 79, and by the Ontario Department of Health through the Children's Psychiatric Research Institute, London, Canada. The authors are indebted to G. N. Cantor and M. E. Rashotte for their criticisms of a prepublication draft.

[2] Excellent reviews of frustration theory and research are provided by Lawson (1965), Lawson and Marx (1958), and Yates (1962).

developed as the complexity of the behavior studied expands.

Although the research to be reviewed has generally been conducted within a fairly standard set of conditions, no attempt is made at present to specify any new set of boundary conditions within which the theory can be applied. We wish, for the time being, to remain free to explore reaction to nonreward in situations where the rewards, tasks, subjects, and variables are different. Such an approach may lead to the danger of introducing too many ad hoc explanations in order to incorporate within the theory those data which did not exactly conform to expectations. Thus, the theory may take on an appearance of useless elasticity as it is stretched to "explain" everything. Such a danger can be lessened if these explanations are provided within the framework of a research design which can test them, and, just as important, by seeing to it that the research is conducted. If follow-up experiments do not support the ad hoc explanation then this would be the point where a boundary condition could be specified and/or the point at which one might attempt to engage in higher-level theorizing.

FRUSTRATIVE NONREWARD THEORY

Although reference to nonreinforcement as a frustration factor dates back to Spence's (1936) investigations of discrimination learning in the chimpanzee, frustrative nonreward theory was first formally presented by Amsel (1958) as an attempt to account for the partial reinforcement extinction effect (PREE), that is, faster extinction following continuous as compared with partial reinforcement in acquisition. Within a short time the theory was extended (Spence, 1960, Ch. 6) to explain the partial reinforcement acquisition effect (PRAE), that is, greater asymptotic performance for subjects receiving partial rather than continuous reinforcement. Further extensions have involved the application of frustrative nonreward theory to discrimination and prediscrimination learning phenomena (Amsel, 1962; Amsel & Ward, 1965) and to comparisons of partial reinforcement effects within and between subjects (Amsel, MacKinnon, Rashotte, & Surridge, 1964; Amsel, Rashotte, & MacKinnon, 1966).

The essential features of the theory are as follows. Once a hungry animal has completed several rewarded instrumental responses, the stimulus cues in the goal box become classically conditioned to and elicit fractional components of the goal response. Through stimulus generalization and higher-order conditioning, the anticipatory goal response, or reward expectancy, is elicited earlier and earlier in the response sequence. Following this development of reward expectancy, nonreward produces an aversive emotional state called "frustration," which contributes to drive level. The resulting increment in drive level temporarily augments the immediately following behavior, a phenomenon that Amsel (1958) has termed the frustration effect (FE). Experiments with rats performing in a double runway have shown that speed of running in the second alley is faster following nonreward as compared with speed following reward in the first alley (Amsel, 1958, 1962); the FE has also been shown in infrahuman organisms other than rats (Davenport & Thompson, 1965; Staddon & Innis, 1966).

Anticipatory frustration develops in a manner similar to the anticipatory goal response and provides an added motivational factor in the earlier portions of an instrumental response. When both types of anticipatory response have emerged, an organism experiences a temporary conflict since the response-produced stimuli accompanying the anticipatory goal and frustration responses elicit incompatible approach and avoidance tendencies, respectively. An expected consequence of this conflict would be an increase in variability or a decrease in response speed. However, the conflict is easily resolved by approaching the goal—if frustrated, the subject is at least removed from the aversive situation, and if rewarded, the response was worth the effort. Consequently, the frustration stimuli eventually become conditioned to the approach response. From this line of reasoning one is able to account for the eventually higher acquisition performance of a partially as compared with a continuously rewarded group. Research supporting this conclusion was summarized by Spence (1960, Ch. 6).

Another derivation from frustrative nonreward theory pertains to extinction. During partially rewarded acquisition, the goal-approach response has become conditioned to anticipatory frustration cues. In a subsequent extinction session, nonreward continues to elicit the approach response, and so extinction proceeds relatively slowly. For subjects given continuous reward during acquisition, nonreward in extinction elicits only an avoidance response so that extinction should proceed relatively quickly.

Thus, one theoretical notion possibly accounts for three behavioral phenomena, the FE, the PRAE, and the PREE. Recently, the similarity between the operations defining frustration and secondary reinforcement has been spelled out in a series of experiments (Longstreth, e.g., 1966b). It has been suggested that frustration may turn out to be the more useful of the two concepts, at least in explanations of data acquired in instrumental conditioning tasks with human subjects. The following section reviews studies with children which dealt with the FE and PRAE. In addition, some work concerned with differential conditioning and discrimination learning is included because of its relevance to frustrative nonreward theory. Data concerning the PREE is not presented in view of Lewis' (1960) relatively recent summary.

BASIC STUDIES WITH HUMANS

Frustration Effect

Studies of the FE are concerned with testing the notion that the frustration-produced increment in drive due to nonreward enhances the vigor of an immediately following response. Research on the FE with children was initiated by Penney (1960), using a double-lever (R_1 and R_2) analogue of the double runway. The subjects, kindergarten children, first pushed R_1 at the onset of a stimulus light and on rewarded trials a marble was ejected into a plastic tube goal. Next, a second stimulus light initiated the pulling of R_2, which always led to a marble reward at a second goal box. During the test phase, the FE was revealed on R_2 movement speeds for a high-habit, but not for a low-habit experimental group; groups were defined in terms of prior training. Penney, however, mentioned problems encountered by a frustration inter-

pretation of his data; furthermore, Ryan (1963) has argued that the results reflected *an apparent* FE involving mainly slower speeds following reward rather than faster speeds following nonreward. Ryan invoked a conflict hypothesis taking into account Penney's complicated training procedure to explain the appearance of this apparent FE.

In two subsequent unpublished studies (Penney & Ryan, 1960; Ryan, 1960) with kindergarten children the FE was not obtained. It is possible that failure to demonstrate the FE in these studies is related to the fact that trials were highly massed. An increase in drive due to nonreward had perhaps not dissipated during the short (20-second) intertrial intervals employed. Consequently, a subject may have been responding under a heightened drive level on rewarded as well as nonrewarded trials. If this vigorous responding approached physiological limits, it would be difficult to demonstrate the FE since still further increments in R_2 speeds following nonreward would be required. MacKinnon and Amsel (1964) have postulated a similar "ceiling effect" in rats, that is, the absolute size of the FE was greater for measures representing relatively weak performance.

One possible technique for preventing generally fast speeds from obscuring the FE would be to space trials so that frustration-produced drive could not carry over from trial to trial. Studies of the FE in rats have typically employed spaced trials, so this problem has not arisen. Practical considerations, such as classroom disruption, do not make the spaced-trial procedure readily amenable for investigations with children. Thus, in the next study (Ryan, 1965) the intertrial interval was increased to 45 seconds, during which subjects blew bubbles or assembled a simple five-piece puzzle. It was hoped that this procedure would have the same effect as a wider spacing, yet would also allow for a sufficient number of trials without unduly prolonging the total time spent out of the classroom. One group (Group 50) received 50% reinforcement for responses on R_1, and another (Group 100) received 100% reinforcement for R_1 responses. Each R_2 response was always rewarded for subjects in both groups. The analysis of R_2 staring speeds (response latency)

118

indicated some evidence for the FE: For Group 50, speeds following nonreward were initially slower but by the end of training were faster than speeds following reward. For Group 100, speeds on trials corresponding to Group 50's rewarded and nonrewarded trials did not show this pattern. Although these data were in line with expectations, this demonstration of the FE is, at best, a weak one. First of all, when separate analyses were performed at each trial block for Group 50, at no individual block did the difference between speeds following reward and nonreward reach significance; second, there was no similar finding on R_2 movement speeds (time taken to move the lever through a 15-inch excursion). One important additional finding was that response speed on R_2 was generally faster for Group 50 as compared with Group 100 regardless of the type of trial. Thus, when rewarded (R_1+) and nonrewarded (R_1-) trials were pooled, it was revealed that R_2 starting speeds were significantly faster for Group 50 than for Group 100. This finding was also evident on the R_2 movement speeds and in the two earlier unpublished investigations (Penney & Ryan, 1960; Ryan, 1960) which had failed to obtain the FE. The writers recently reanalyzed the data from Ryan (1965) in order to compare R_2 starting speeds for Group 50 and Group 100 when both groups were treated alike, that is, employing only the data for responses following reward. It was found that Group 50 was faster than Group 100 even on these rewarded trials, which suggests a perseveration of frustration from nonrewarded to rewarded trials. It seems, therefore, that in these studies a ceiling effect might have prevented the occurrence of much separation in speeds following reward and nonreward for Group 50.

In order to eliminate the possibility of a ceiling effect masking the effects of nonreinforcement, an investigation was conducted (Moffitt & Ryan, 1966) with a one-trial-a-day procedure over 20 days. A trial consisted of one R_1-R_2 sequence. Nursery school children were employed in this study, since frequent disruption in the classroom would not be of great concern for such subjects. Within each 5-day block, subjects in the frustration group (Group 40) received two rewards and three nonrewards for R_1 responses. A control group (Group 100) was rewarded for each response. Analyses of both R_2 starting and movement speeds revealed an FE in Group 40 of a magnitude greater than that found in any previous study with children. It may be concluded that spacing trials facilitated demonstration of the FE, presumably since a subject does not begin each trial with drive already at a high level. In support of this assertion is the finding that R_2 speeds for Group 40 were not generally faster than those for Group 100. More important is the fact that R_2 speeds for Groups 40 and 100 did not differ significantly on the rewarded trials. An investigation involving different degrees of spacing of trials would be a worthwhile endeavor.

In addition to the intertrial interval, interresponse interval (time between R_1 and R_2) should also affect the FE. Such is the case in studies of the FE with rats (MacKinnon & Amsel, 1964; Robinson & Clayton, 1963), monkeys (Davenport & Thompson, 1965), and pigeons (Staddon & Innis, 1966). Watson and Ryan (1966) conducted a double-lever investigation with 22 kindergarten subjects in an entirely within-subjects design. For all subjects, R_1 was rewarded on 50% of the trials and R_2 was always rewarded. Interresponse intervals were either 5, 10, or 20 seconds. Analyses of R_2 movement speeds showed that at the 5-second interval, speed following nonreward was significantly faster than speed following reward. For the other intervals, R_2 movement speed was not related to reward conditions at R_1. A similar pattern was evident on R_2 starting speeds. Demonstration of such a short-lived effect gives important procedural information for future investigations. In those investigations which have employed massed trials and a 10-second interresponse interval, either no FE or only a weak FE was evident at the 10-second interval (Penney & Ryan, 1960; Ryan, 1960, 1965; Watson & Ryan, 1966). The same was true for the low-habit experimental group in Penney's (1960) investigation. Yet, in the one-trial-a-day study (Moffitt & Ryan, 1966) a strong FE was shown with a 10-second interresponse interval. The emerging picture seems to suggest that under massed trials, when speed is relatively fast, the FE can be detected provided the measure of second-response performance is taken as soon as possible following nonreward, that is, when the subject is maximally aroused. Under widely spaced trials, when speed is relatively slow, the FE can be detected even when the interresponse interval is relatively long. There is now a need for a study jointly manipulating interresponse and intertrial intervals.

Partial Reinforcement Acquisition Effect

The relationship between response rate and reward schedule on a free-operant task has been subjected to a good deal of investigation with normal and retarded children (e.g., Bijou & Orlando, 1961; Long, 1963; Long, Hammack, May, & Campbell, 1958; Orlando & Bijou, 1960; Spradlin, Girardeau, & Corte, 1965). However, only recently have reward schedules received extensive experimental attention in relation to acquisition of a single instrumental response with discrete trials.

There are now several examples of comparable investigations with children. Bruning (1964) had 64 kindergarten children move a lever in order to win candy. Half of the subjects were rewarded on a random 50% schedule, while the remainder received 100% reinforcement. Ryan and Moffitt (1966) presented 36 preschool and 36 kindergarten subjects with 56 trials on a lever-pulling device. Half of each age group received a marble for each pull (100%); the other half was rewarded on a 50% schedule. The marbles were later traded for a toy. In both investigations movement speeds were significantly faster for partially as compared with continuously rewarded subjects. A comparable finding has been obtained by Pederson (1967) where the 50% reward group received a valueless marble (one which could not be traded for a toy) rather than no marble on each nonrewarded trial. All of these results are amenable to a frustration interpretation.

Several investigations have compared response speeds under various schedules of partial reward with those of a 100% group. Ryan (1966a) divided 54 preschool and 54 kindergarten children into six reinforcement groups (100, 83, 66, 50, 33, and 17%). The subjects were administered 54 trials; increasing speeds for the partial-reward groups relative to those for the continuously rewarded group were demonstrated. In addition, asymptotic speeds were shown to be an inverted U shaped function of percentage of reinforcement, with fastest responding produced by intermediate percentages of reinforcement. A second study (Ryan & Voorhoeve, 1966) employed 120 kindergarten subjects divided into six reinforcement groups which received 100, 70, 50, 30, 10, or 0% reinforcement, and the major aim was to explore the effects of reinforcement percentages below 33%. Unfortunately, the 0% group had to be excluded because of an apparent sampling bias. The results, however, were strikingly similar to those obtained by Ryan (1966a), and compare interestingly with the results of a similar experiment by Weinstock (1958; see also Spence, 1960, Ch. 6, p. 103) with rats.

Semler and Pederson (1966) have demonstrated the PRAE employing a within-subjects design. Forty first-grade children were presented with 20 trials on a lever-pulling apparatus to each of two stimulus lights, S_{100} and S_{50}. For S_{100}, all lever pulls were rewarded with a marble; for S_{50}, reward was on a random 50% schedule. Movement speed was faster to S_{50} as compared with S_{100}. The authors' interpretation of the data suggested that the difference in response speeds to the two stimuli could not be attributed to any general increase in motivation since each subject served as his own control. Consequently, anticipatory frustration must play an important role in contributing to this finding.

Differential Conditioning

Except for the investigation by Semler and Pederson (1966), the studies of the PRAE have provided no means of determining whether partial-reward superiority is due to primary frustration perseverating from one trial to the next or to conditioned frustration. Some specific evidence concerning the conditioning of frustration will now be reviewed.

Rieber and Johnson (1964) were concerned with determining whether kindergarten children could learn to anticipate reward conditions. Forty-eight subjects performed a lever-pulling task under one of two treatments. One group received an alternating partial-reward schedule, and separate discriminative stimuli (red or yellow light) were associated with reward and nonreward. For a continuous-reward group, the light colors alternated, but subjects were rewarded on each of 30 trials. Within a few trials, the partially rewarded subjects were responding faster on reinforced as compared with nonreinforced trials. Presumably, once subjects had learned the schedule, presentation of S− would elicit anticipatory frustration and hence produce slower speeds, whereas presentation of S+ would elicit only expectancy for reward and hence faster speeds. On reinforced trials, speeds of the partially and continuously rewarded groups did not differ significantly. The last point is interesting in relation to previous findings (e.g., Bruning, 1964; Ryan & Moffitt, 1966) which have shown that groups partially rewarded on a random schedule do respond faster than continuously rewarded groups. A seemingly useful study would investigate factorially the effects of alternating and random partial reward with discriminative or irrelevant stimuli. Presumably, fastest response speeds would be obtained under random partial reward where the color of stimulus lights is not related to the reward condition. Response speed of the four partially rewarded groups could also be compared with that of a continuously rewarded group.

Pederson (1966) has recently replicated and extended these findings. Three groups of first-grade children depressed a lever at the onset of one of two lights. For all subjects, half of the trials were initiated by a red CS and the other half by a green CS. The differential-conditioning group (Group DC) was rewarded for each response to one light (CS+), but never for responses to the other (CS−). In addition to replicating the finding that subjects in Group DC respond faster to CS+ as compared with CS−, it was also found that Group DC did not differ significantly in response speed from a group (Group P) which received 50% reward for responses in the presence of each light. Group P was faster than a continuous-reward group (Group C). Groups P and C were similar to the par-

tial- and continuous-reward groups included in studies (Bruning, 1964; Ryan & Moffitt, 1966) which have compared response speeds under partial and continuous reinforcement, with the sole exception that color of the stimulus light provided the addition of an irrelevant dimension.

In two related experiments (Longstreth, 1966b), one with 60 second- and third-grade children and one with 32 retardates, moving a joystick to terminate a light of one intensity (S+) was reinforced whereas responses to the other light (S−) were not. During training each light was presented separately 18 times. The results indicated that response speed and response amplitude were greater in the presence of S+ as compared with S−.

Longstreth has also conditioned reward expectancy to a previously neutral cue and noted the effect upon extinction. His main interest was to test contrasting predictions from frustration and secondary reinforcement theories regarding resistance to extinction. In one study (Longstreth, 1960), 32 second-grade children were required to hold a lever down until a receptacle filled with marbles; in a second study (Longstreth, 1966a), 40 kindergarten children turned a crank in order to win poker chips. For the experimental groups in both studies, a light was paired with each delivery of the marble or poker chip rewards. For control subjects, the light was presented but not paired with reward. The light was presented at certain times during extinction. Contrary to what would be predicted from secondary reinforcement theory, extinction occurred more quickly for the experimental group. Comparable results have also been obtained in a recent series of experiments (Longstreth, 1966b). Interpretation of these data suggests that subjects in the experimental groups had a greater expectancy for reward when the light was on than was the case for control subjects. Hence, nonreinforcement would be frustrating for these subjects and extinction would occur relatively quickly. It would have been interesting if a second experimental group had been included for whom the light had been only partially reinforced during acquisition. Presumably, these subjects could learn during acquisition to continue responding even though frustrated and, consequently, should be more resistant to extinction than groups for whom the light had been either continuously paired or never paired with reward. The inclusion of such a group is, of course, mainly of interest for frustration theory and not crucial for the original purpose of Longstreth's experiments.

Discrimination Learning

Actually, it was in relation to discrimination learning that original mention was made of nonreward as a frustrative factor (Spence, 1936). Presumably, giving extra nonreinforcements in pretraining can condition frustration to S−, so that in subsequent discrimination learning the subject tends to avoid choosing the negative stimulus. Because of the difference between the relative slopes of generalization gradients of approach and avoidance tendencies (Amsel, 1962), little of the avoidance tendency generalizes to S+. On the other hand, when extra rewards are given to S+ in pretraining, relatively more generalization of the approach tendency from S+ to S− in discrimination occurs. This results in slower discrimination for a group given extra rewards for S+ than for a group given extra nonrewards for S−.

So far as the present authors are aware, there are only three published studies with children in which the procedure involved giving additional nonreinforcement to the negative stimulus in order to determine whether this facilitates discrimination learning. Cantor and Spiker (1954) employed 48 preschool children in a task which required choosing one of two differently colored cars to be rolled down a track. Two groups were differentiated on the basis of whether they received one or two nonrewards to S− during each of eight blocks of forced-choice trials. Analysis of eight free-choice trials indicated that the extra nonrewards had facilitated learning. These results have been corroborated in recent studies with noninstitutionalized (Lobb, 1966) and institutionalized (Riese & Lobb, 1967) retardates. These studies have not only shown that giving extra nonreward to S− during pretraining facilitates subsequent discrimination learning, but also that pretraining involving nonreward of responses to S− is more beneficial than that involving reward

of responses for the positive stimulus. Lobb [3] has recently replicated this finding with normal subjects (CA = 2–4 years).

Extra nonreward during pretraining does not facilitate discrimination learning, however, if given indiscriminably. Stevenson and Pirojnikoff (1958) employed 48 children in a three-choice discrimination problem. This study differs from those cited above in that three groups of subjects received either 100, 50, or 0% reward in pretraining with reward and nonreward not given to S+ and S−, respectively, but to all stimuli. With this arrangement, discrimination learning was interfered with for the two groups given extra nonrewards relative to the 100% group and a fourth group given no pretraining at all. A subsequent study (Steigman & Stevenson, 1960) showed comparable interference with discrimination learning when extra nonrewards in pretraining were given to stimuli other than those employed in the discrimination task. Subjective observations suggested that subjects who had received high frequencies of nonreward revealed later behavior characterized as restless, perturbed, demoralized, and anxious (or, in terms of the present hypothesis, frustrated).

NONREWARD AND FAILURE

At an operational level, a distinction between nonreward and "failure" to attain some previously set goal is not too difficult to make. However, both types of events are similar in that there is an interference with goal-directed behavior and both are conceived to result in an emotional response of some sort. Hence, it is of interest to compare the results of those studies in which "failure" was manipulated with studies cited earlier concerning the effects of nonreward.

The following investigations, not originally designed as FE studies, are particularly relevant because a thwarting event occurred at the end of a first response and the effect upon a second response was noted. Haner and Brown (1955) instructed second-, third-, and fourth-grade children to fill a 36-hole marble board with marbles in order to win a prize. The thwarting event consisted of the experi-

[3] Personal communication, July 1966.

menter pulling a handle to release all of the marbles that the subject had placed. This occurred at varying distances from the goal (9, 18, 27, or 32 marbles placed). Coincident with each release, a buzzer sounded until terminated by the subject pushing a plunger. The nearer to the goal that the marbles were released, the greater was the pressure of plunger pushing. These results may be interpreted within frustrative nonreward theory by suggesting that expectancy for reward is directly related to nearness to the goal.

A somewhat different pattern of results was provided in a provocative investigation by Ford (1963). Fifth-grade boys were instructed to attempt to respond faster than average on a formboard task. For certain subjects, a buzzer sounded to indicate failure; the buzzer could be terminated by pushing a plunger. The findings revealed an increase in latency (slower speeds) and a decrease in amplitude of plunger pushing following failure as compared with success on the first task. These results, diametrically opposed to those presented in the FE section, do not represent an isolated finding. Endsley (1966) had second- and third-grade children perform two consecutive tasks. The first involved an attempt to raise a $\frac{1}{2}$-inch steel ball to the top of a 48-inch vertical wooden shaft without the ball falling. Experimenter-controlled failure was introduced at different distances from the goal. Immediately following success or failure on Task 1, a buzzer sounded and the subject performed Task 2—depression of a lever. Lever depression was significantly slower following failure as compared with success on Task 1. There was no relation between speed of lever depression and distance from the goal when failure occurred, nor did the amplitude measure result in any significant findings.

These demonstrations of increased latency of responding on a task following failure as compared with a task following success may be reconciled with the findings of those studies which have shown increases in speed following nonreward. First, the operations defining frustration, nonreward as opposed to social failure, may produce qualitatively different kinds of responses. Failure on Task 1, in addition to raising drive level, may elicit more interfering tendencies than is the case for nonreward. If habit strength of one or

more competing tendencies is stronger than habit strength of the Task 2 response, then an increase in drive after a frustrating event would result in a decrement in Task 2 performance. One implication of this notion is that further training on Task 2 could lead to a reversal of the findings of Endsley (1966) and Ford (1963). In those studies which found increases in response speed following nonreward (Moffitt & Ryan, 1966; Ryan, 1965; Watson & Ryan, 1966), subjects made a total of 40–48 lever responses, that is, 20–24 trials with each trial consisting of two lever-pulls, R_1 and R_2. When decreases in speed were found (Endsley, 1966; Ford, 1963) subjects had only made 8–16 lever responses. If habit strength for lever pressing were increased by additional training the contradictory findings might disappear. This interpretation is supported by a reanalysis of previous data (Ryan, 1966a; Ryan & Moffitt, 1966). In these experiments, subjects were administered a series of either partially or continuously reinforced test trials on a single-lever apparatus. Present interest centers on the effect of the first nonreward on starting speed, a measure similar to Ford's (1963) and Endsley's (1966) latency-of-responding measures. Some subjects received the first nonreward after four rewarded trials; for other subjects, the first five trials were all rewarded. Results of the analysis of changes in speed from the fifth to sixth trial for both groups indicated that introduction of non-reward caused a significant *decrement* ($p < .025$) in starting speed, relative to continued reward. These results suggest that for the first few nonrewards, a decrement following nonreinforcement is to be expected on a response-latency measure.

Ford (1963) has presented an additional consideration, involving subjects' cognitions of the situation, which might be useful in designing further investigations. He argued that a failure manipulation may be conceived of by the subject as either a "self-blame" or an "other-blame" situation. In the Haner and Brown (1955) study, it is possible that the subject blamed the experimenter for the release of marbles from the marble board, whereas in Ford's study the burden for succeeding was put entirely upon the child. Ford asserted that self-blame situations are more likely than other-blame situations to lead to interfering responses. This variable could be manipulated by differentiating groups in terms of instructional sets or in terms of some situational arrangement designed to maximize the probability that the subject will blame either himself or the experimenter following some thwarting event. Additional research is needed to compare the effects of nonreward under conditions which may be construed as self- or other-blame situations. One might also consider manipulation of self-other blame as an individual difference variable. The considerable literature on locus of control, intellectual achievement responsibility, and chance versus skill instructions, (see Butterfield, 1964; Crandall, Katovsky, & Crandall, 1965; Cromwell, 1963) could be useful in constructing hypotheses relating to this question.

SUBJECT VARIABLES

Extension of any theory from the animal to human level necessitates consideration of certain subject variables. In terms of a truly comprehensive theory, it would be inadequate, for example, to manipulate reward schedule only with kindergarten children, retarded children, females, or subjects of some particular personality type. Although such variables have not been of concern to the animal experimenters, it is possible that an experimental interest in such factors as developmental level will not be unfruitful.

Chronological Age

White (1965) has summarized a number of behavioral changes which occur in the 5–7 year age range, but ontogenetic level has so far received only minimal attention in investigations concerning the relationship of reward schedule and performance. If expectancy for success in a given situation is correlated with chronological age, then this variable will be of some import in investigations of frustrative nonreward with humans and perhaps even infrahumans. There is some evidence (Ryan & Moffitt, 1966) which suggests that fast response speeds for a partially (50%) rewarded group are slower to develop for preschool as compared with kindergarten subjects. Ryan (1966a), however, failed to obtain similar results when comparing preschool and kindergarten subjects under sev-

eral reward schedules. More substantial differences in performance may possibly appear if a greater age range exists between the developmental groups studied. In fact, an investigation comparing performance of various reward groups across a wide developmental scale (i.e., preschool to old age) would appear to be in order.

Data from other situations imply that expectancy for reinforcement may indeed vary with age. An interesting relationship between reward schedule and age (and also between reward schedule and intelligence) has been shown in a concept-attainment task (Osler & Shapiro, 1964). The subjects were 60 children at each of four age levels (6, 8, 10, and 14 years). Two stimuli, one consisting of two black circles $\frac{1}{4}$-inch in diameter and the other consisting of three black circles of the same size, were presented for a maximum of 150 trials. The subjects had to learn to choose the stimulus with the two black circles. Correct responses were rewarded with marbles which could be later traded for a toy. Criterion of learning was 10 consecutive correct responses plus verbalization of the rule for getting marbles. Analyses in terms of trials to criterion, number of reinforcements to criterion, and number of solvers showed that partial reinforcement was relatively more difficult the older and the more intelligent the subject. Weir (1962) employed two age groups (5–7 and 9–13 years) in a three-choice probability-learning task. The correct response received 50% reinforcement. Younger subjects were found to choose the correct or reinforced response more often than older subjects. Weir's interpretation was that older subjects enter a task expecting to solve it and attain a high percentage of reinforcement. Since rewards can only be gained on 50% of the trials at most, the older subjects employ variable behavior in an attempt to obtain more frequent reinforcement. The same interpretation may be applied to the results presented by Osler and Shapiro. Two studies (Stevenson & Weir, 1961; Weir, 1962) provide additional information on this question. Stevenson and Weir (1961) reanalyzed data for the first few trials from two previous studies on probability learning. The 380 subjects were divided into four age groups (3, 5, 7, and 9 years). There was a greater tendency for subjects at the older age levels to change their response following nonreinforcement as compared with the 3-year-olds. This finding is in line with the suggestion that nonreward is more frustrating for older subjects. In addition, this negative recency effect (the tendency not to repeat the immediately preceding response) also prevailed in the older subjects after reinforcement. This finding is neither consistent nor inconsistent with frustration theory, but important in preventing too premature an application of frustration theory in interpretations of the negative recency effect. It may well be, for example, that more adequate explanations of such behavior will be in terms of the different problem-solving strategies employed at different age levels, as Weir (1964) has suggested.

Mental Age

The higher expectancy for success in older children has a parallel when comparing normals with retardates. The notion that retardates have a low expectancy for success has been advanced by Cromwell (1963) and Stevenson and Zigler (1958). Stevenson and Zigler argued that maximizing behavior in a probability-learning task would be greater for subjects who did not expect a very high degree of success. In support of the hypothesis, they found that institutionalized feebleminded subjects maximized their choices in both a 33% and a 66% reward condition to a greater extent than normals. Similar findings were obtained when low expectancy was experimentally induced. Normal subjects pretrained under 33% reward maximized choices to a greater degree than normals pretrained with 100% reward. All subjects received 66% reward for correct responses during testing.

Gardner (1966) had retarded and normal subjects perform a card-sorting task. One aspect of this study entailed the introduction of a failure experience on an immediately preceding task. Comparisons of pre- and post-failure card sorting indicated that (a) more normal than retarded children increased their performance, and (b) although performance increased for both groups, there was a greater absolute magnitude of change for normals. These results are in line with Moffitt and Ryan's (1966) results in suggesting that the reaction to failure or nonreward is of a lower magnitude for retardates than normals. Moffitt and Ryan's (1966) spaced-trial study of the FE, discussed earlier, also included 20 retarded children in each of the two reward groups. Contrary to the case for normals, there was no suggestion of an FE in the retardates. In a follow-up study,[4] 12 retardates were run in each group under a massed-trial procedure (30-second intertrial interval) rather than spaced trials. Again, there was no evidence for an FE in the frustration group. The conclusion based upon these findings was that in the presence of a common thwarting event, retardates are less frustrated than normals, possibly because of a difference in reward expectancy between subjects in these two intellectual classifications.

Some data were recently collected [5] on the double-lever apparatus in order to determine whether pretraining designed to build up expectancy of reward would facilitate demonstration of the FE in retardates. The 78 subjects (M MA = 73.17 months; M CA = 145.97 months) were subdivided into high- and low-expectancy groups on the basis of the number of rewards won through four pretraining tasks. Following pretraining, the two expectancy groups were administered 36 additional trials on the double lever. The frustration group (Group 50) received 50% reward on R_1, whereas the control group (Group 100) received 100% reward on R_1. All subjects were always rewarded for R_2 responses. Both the interresponse (time between R_1 and R_2) and intertrial (time between R_2 and R_1) intervals were approximately 5 seconds. The extremely short intertrial interval is now known not to be optimal for demonstration of the FE (Ryan, 1966b). It had been anticipated that subjects receiving 50% reward on R_1 would show an FE on R_2 if they had experienced the high-expectancy pretraining. No FE was obtained for any group. On R_1 movement speed, however, speed under 50% reward increased over training relative to speed under continuous reward. This effect appeared to be like that for normal subjects (Ryan, 1965) except that it developed much less quickly in the retarded subjects. Note that in the present investigation, subjects per-

[4] These data were collected by Alan R. Moffitt.
[5] These data were collected by Douglas Jackson and Robert McEwan.

formed a total of 48 trials on the lever apparatus, whereas in Moffitt and Ryan's spaced and massed trial studies only 20 trials were administered. There is additional support for the notion that retardates are frustrated less than normals (Watson, Ryan, & McEwan, 1967). Reinforcement schedules of 0, 10, 30, 50, 70, and 100% were employed and, as in similar studies with normal children (Ryan, 1966a; Ryan & Voorhoeve, 1966), asymptotic lever-pulling speeds were an inverted U shaped function of reinforcement schedule. However, differences between response speeds for partially and continuously rewarded groups were not as great for retardates as for normals.

There are two important qualifications to the conclusion that following failure or nonreward, retardates increase performance to a lesser extent than normals. First, this may only pertain to certain operations defining failure. Butterfield and Zigler (1965) employed retarded (M MA = 87 months; M CA = 164 months) and normal (M MA = 89 months; M CA = 90 months) subjects on a three-choice size discrimination learning task. The subjects were divided into three groups on the basis of prediscrimination experience on two simple tasks—Success (four positive statements were made to the subject), Failure (four negative statements), and Control (no statements). The results indicated that failure (as well as success) equally faciliated subsequent performance of both normals and retardates. Furthermore, effects of frustration in retardates have been shown under different procedures. Lobb, Moffitt, and Gamlin (1966) employed 36 retardates (MA = 2–4.5 years) on the double-lever apparatus. The subjects received 72 trials at the rate of 6 per day; however, the analyses reported pertain only to the first trial of each day. This procedure had the advantage of employing spaced trials, at least for the purpose of data analyses, yet a large number of trials were administered within relatively few days. A very short (approximately 5 seconds) interresponse interval was employed. Instead of marbles, the rewards were 2-gram pieces of shortbread which were immediately consumed. The subjects were deprived of food from 12 to 16 hours prior to each experimental session. Subjects in the frustration group received 50%

reward for R_1 responses, while subjects in a control group were never rewarded on the first response; all subjects received 100% reward on R_2. An FE was demonstrated on R_2 starting speeds for the 50% group. These studies, in addition to Longstreth's (1966b) investigation, leave no doubt that under certain procedures retardates react vigorously following frustration.

There is a further qualification to the conclusion that retardates react less vigorously to frustration or failure as compared with normals. Although this finding is characteristic of certain group data (e.g., Gardner, 1966; Moffitt & Ryan, 1966), some retardates do show marked increases in performance following failure or frustration. This suggests the need for investigations relating certain personality variables other than intelligence to reaction to failure.

Personality Variables

The notion that individuals may differ in their behavior after a thwarting event has long been recognized. Rosenzweig (1934) has postulated three types of reaction to frustration, which differ in terms of whether elicited aggression is directed toward the self, toward others, or suppressed. Whether or not this particular formulation will prove to be useful in our type of situation remains to be seen. Empirical evidence suggests that reliable individual differences do in fact exist. In a classic study, Barker, Dembo, and Lewin (1941) noted that some children failed to demonstrate any decrease in constructiveness of play following frustration. More recently, Ryan and Moffitt (1966) found that of 36 subjects in a partially reinforced group which, on the average, responded significantly faster than a continuously reinforced group, only 16 subjects showed a significant improvement in performance as training progressed. Seventeen showed no change, while three decreased significantly.

Two sources of individual differences were investigated in the following studies. Bialer and Cromwell (1965) separated 32 retardates into a group of 18 "failure avoiders" and a group of 14 "success strivers" on the basis of their preference to repeat a previously failed or a previously successful task. Following failure on a subsequent card-sorting task, the

126

success strivers showed a greater increase in performance as compared with failure avoiders. A deduction follows from these results: Following failure or nonreward, normal subjects as well as success strivers show a greater increase in performance as compared with retarded subjects and failure avoiders, respectively. This would suggest a relationship between success striving and intellectual level. Bialer and Cromwell (1960, 1965) have shown, at least with educable retarded subjects, a direct relationship between success striving and mental age.

Semler (1965) has isolated another individual difference variable that bears implications for frustration theory. Thirty retardates were partially reinforced during acquisition and then extinguished on two instrumental motor responses. Persistence was defined in terms of total resistance to extinction on both tasks. On the basis of these scores, subjects were separated into high-, medium-, and low-persistence groups. A new task was then introduced which involved learning to choose a stimulus which was rewarded on a 50% basis as opposed to a second stimulus which was never rewarded. Learning was accomplished more quickly for subjects rated high in persistence. Persistence, or resistance to extinction, may be related to the ease with which frustration is conditioned in a particular subject. It is hoped that over the next few years the relationship of personality variables to reaction to nonreward will be given more than the cursory attention it has received to date.

SOCIAL FACTORS

The final topic to be considered concerns social influences on reaction to nonreward. The studies to be discussed deal with two questions: What are the effects of *vicarious* nonreward, that is, when one subject observes another receiving nonreward? And does partial reward lead to comparable effects when the reinforcer is social rather than some tangible object?

Vicarious Nonreward

An interesting investigation by Kobasigawa (1965) employed first-grade subjects who observed an adult perform on a modified Haner and Brown marble board. The child's task was to depress a plunger in order to turn off a buzzer at the end of a trial. On various trials, the adult experienced success, far failure, or failure near the goal. Near failure led to significantly greater amplitudes and faster speeds as compared with far failure or success, a finding highly consistent with that obtained by Haner and Brown (1955) when the child was actually performing rather than observing the first of the two responses.

In another study (Whiteley & Ryan, 1967), an attempt was made to produce the FE through vicarious nonreward. As in earlier studies of FE, two groups received either 100% reinforcement on both lever-responses (Group 100:100) or 50% on R_1 and 100% on R_2 (Group 50:100). Each group, however, consisted of *pairs* of kindergarten subjects— Child A performed only on R_1, while Child B performed only on R_2. Child B never directly experienced nonreinforcement, and any difference between Groups 50:100 and 100:100 on R_2 speeds would be expected to occur through Child B's vicarious experience of what happened to Child A. Each pair of subjects was instructed that unless a sufficient number of marbles was accumulated in the common goal box, neither child would win a prize. No FE was obtained, that is, Child B in Group 50:100 did not respond faster on R_2 following nonreward, as compared with reward, on R_1. However, an interesting and unexpected finding was obtained: On R_1 starting and movement speeds, Child A in Group 100:100 responded faster than Child A in Group 50:100; on R_2 starting speeds, Child B in Group 100:100 responded faster than Child B in Group 50:100. These findings are exactly the reverse of what is typically obtained in similar situations where a child performs individually (e.g., Ryan, 1965). Interpretations of these data, even speculative ones, should perhaps await further empirical information.

Partial Social Reward

It is of interest to determine whether partial reward for an instrumental response leads to faster performance as compared with continuous reward when social rewards (e.g., "Good") are employed. Previous studies with tangible rewards such as candy or marbles (Bruning, 1964; Pederson, 1967) have, of course, demonstrated asymptotic partial-reward superiority.

In one study (Ryan & Watson, 1966), kindergarten subjects were given either 33% or 100% social reward on a single lever-apparatus. Unlike previous investigations, the marble delivery mechanism was disconnected and the experimenter sat facing the subject. Response speeds of the partially rewarded group were faster than those of the continuously rewarded group.

A recent doctoral dissertation (Watson, 1967) attempted to assess the relative effects of nonattainment of either a social reward or a candy. Kindergarten children performed a series of lever-pulling trials for 50% or 100% reward; rewards were either candy or social ("Good"). Response speeds of the 50% group increased during training relative to those of the 100% group. However, type of reward did not interact significantly with reward schedule. A 10-minute social isolation condition preceding the experimental session for half the subjects had no effect upon performance.

CONCLUSIONS

The foregoing review of children's reactions to nonreward suggests several conclusions. First, nonreward leads to increased vigor of performance in certain instrumental tasks. Investigations of differential conditioning indicate that frustration may become conditioned to previously neutral stimuli. In discrimination learning, nonreward rather than reward may provide the more potent effect upon learning. Such data are in accord with data gathered from research with infrahuman organisms and demonstrate that frustrative nonreward theory can profitably be applied to human behavior, at least in simple situations.

Where the thwarting manipulation consists of a failure experience, decrements in performance have been demonstrated, at least under certain conditions. It is suggested, however, that more detailed comparisons of results obtained from investigations of nonreward and failure must await further research. Of special importance would be comparative investigations of the effects of nonreward and failure while holding constant such presumably important factors as amount of training and the direction of blame. For the meantime, the extent to which frustrative nonreward theory may lead to useful hypotheses concerning failure manipulations must remain tentative.

Reaction to nonreward has been shown to be dependent on several individual difference variables. Although studies of personality differences in relation to frustration are scanty enough to make generalization difficult, this area appears promising for future research. Differences between younger and older children, and normals and retardates, are somewhat better substantiated. Probably the most valid conclusion is that reward expectancy is related to both CA and MA. However, this does not necessarily imply that reaction to nonreward is directly related to CA and MA. In line with White's (1965) suggestion that cognitive rather than associative factors become more prepotent with corresponding increment in increasing age, it is possible that older subjects react to nonreward by engaging in various problem-solving strategies rather than simply increasing vigor of performance.

Nonattainment of social reward seems to affect performance in a manner equivalent to that of nonattainment of expected tangible rewards; thus, the conclusion seems warranted that frustrative nonreward theory may ultimately provide useful implications for extralaboratory behavior.

REFERENCES

AMSEL, A. The role of frustrative nonreward in noncontinuous reward situations. *Psychological Bulletin,* 1958, 55, 102–119.

AMSEL, A. Frustrative nonreward in partial reinforcement and discrimination learning: Some recent history and a theoretical extension. *Psychological Review,* 1962, 69, 306–328.

AMSEL, A., MacKINNON, J. R., RASHOTTE, M. E., & SURRIDGE, C. T. Partial reinforcement (acquisition) effects within subjects. *Journal of the Experimental Analysis of Behavior,* 1964, 7, 135–138.

AMSEL, A., RASHOTTE, M. E., & MacKINNON, J. R. Partial reinforcement effects within-subject and between-subjects. *Psychological Monographs,* 1966, 80(20, Whole No. 628).

AMSEL, A., & WARD, J. S. Frustration and persistence: Resistance to discrimination following prior experience with the discriminanda. *Psychological Monographs,* 1965, 79(4, Whole No. 597).

BARKER, R., DEMBO, T., & LEWIN, K. Frustration and regression: A study of young children. *Uni-*

versity of Iowa Studies in Child Welfare, 1941, 18, No. 1.

BIALER, I., & CROMWELL, R. L. Task repetition in mental defectives as a function of chronological and mental age. *American Journal of Mental Deficiency*, 1960, 65, 265–268.

BIALER, I., & CROMWELL, R. L. Failure as motivation with mentally retarded children. *American Journal of Mental Deficiency*, 1965, 69, 680–684.

BIJOU, S. W. A systematic approach to an experimental analysis of young children. *Child Development*, 1955, 26, 161–168.

BIJOU, S. W., & ORLANDO, R. Rapid development of multiple-schedule performance with retarded children. *Journal of the Experimental Analysis of Behavior*, 1961, 4, 7–16.

BROWN, J. S., & FARBER, I. E. Emotions conceptualized as intervening variables—With suggestions toward a theory of frustration. *Psychological Bulletin*, 1951, 48, 465–495.

BRUNING, J. L. The effects of magnitude of reward and percentage of reinforcement on a lever movement response. *Child Development*, 1964, 35, 281–285.

BUTTERFIELD, E. C. The interruption of tasks: Methodological, factual, and theoretical issues. *Psychological Bulletin*, 1964, 62, 309–322.

BUTTERFIELD, E. C., & ZIGLER, E. The effect of success and failure on the discrimination learning of normal and retarded children. *Journal of Abnormal Psychology*, 1965, 70, 25–31.

CANTOR, G. N., & SPIKER, C. C. Effects of nonreinforced trials on discrimination learning in preschool children. *Journal of Experimental Psychology*, 1954, 47, 256–258.

CRANDALL, V., KATOVSKY, W., & CRANDALL, V. Children's beliefs in their own control of reinforcements in intellectual-academic achievement situations. *Child Development*, 1965, 36, 91–109.

CROMWELL, R. L. A social learning approach to mental retardation. In N. R. Ellis (Ed.), *Handbook of mental retardation*. New York: McGraw-Hill, 1963. Pp. 41–91.

DAVENPORT, J. W., & THOMPSON, C. I. The Amsel frustration effect in monkeys. *Psychonomic Science*, 1965, 3, 481–482.

ENDSLEY, R. C. Effortfulness and blocking at different distances from the goal as determinants of response speed and amplitude. *Journal of Experimental Child Psychology*, 1966, 3, 18–30.

FORD, L. H., JR. Reaction to failure as a function of expectancy for success. *Journal of Abnormal and Social Psychology*, 1963, 67, 340–348.

GARDNER, W. I. Effects of failure on intellectually retarded and normal boys. *American Journal of Mental Deficiency*, 1966, 70, 899–902.

HANER, C. F., & BROWN, P. A. Clarification of the instigation to action concept in the frustration-aggression hypothesis. *Journal of Abnormal and Social Psychology*, 1955, 51, 204–206.

KOBASIGAWA, A. Observation of failure in another person as a determinant of amplitude and speed of a simple motor response. *Journal of Personality and Social Psychology*, 1965, 1, 626–630.

LAWSON, R. *Frustration. The development of a scientific concept.* New York: Macmillan, 1965.

LAWSON, R., & MARX, M. H. Frustration: Theory and experiment. *Genetic Psychology Monographs*, 1958, 57, 393–464.

LEWIS, D. J. Partial reinforcement: A selective review of the literature since 1950. *Psychological Bulletin*, 1960, 57, 1–28.

LOBB, H. Visual discrimination learning in imbecile children with nonreinforcement of irrelevant tendencies. *American Journal of Mental Deficiency*, 1966, 70, 753–762.

LOBB, H., MOFFITT, A., & GAMLIN, P. Frustration and adaptation in relation to discrimination learning ability of mentally defective children. *American Journal of Mental Deficiency*, 1966, 71, 256–265.

LONG, E. R. Chained and tandem scheduling in children. *Journal of the Experimental Analysis of Behavior*, 1963, 6, 459–472.

LONG, E. R., HAMMACK, J. T., MAY, F., & CAMPBELL, B. J. Intermittent reinforcement of operant behavior in children. *Journal of the Experimental Analysis of Behavior*, 1958, 1, 315–340.

LONGSTRETH, L. E. The relationship between expectations and frustration in children. *Child Development*, 1960, 31, 667–671.

LONGSTRETH, L. E. Frustration effects rather than Sr effects in children. *Psychonomic Science*, 1966, 4, 425–426. (a)

LONGSTRETH, L. E. Frustration and secondary reinforcement concepts as applied to human instrumental conditioning and extinction. *Psychological Monographs*, 1966, 80(11, Whole No. 619). (b)

MACKINNON, J. R., & AMSEL, A. Magnitude of the frustration effect as a function of degree of confinement and detention in the frustrating situation. *Journal of Experimental Psychology*, 1964, 67, 468–474.

McCANDLESS, B. R., & SPIKER, C. C. Experimental research in child psychology. *Child Development*, 1956, 27, 78–80.

MOFFITT, A. R., & RYAN, T. J. The frustration effect in normal and retarded children using a one-trial-a-day procedure. *University of Western Ontario Research Bulletin*, 1966, No. 15.

ORLANDO, R., & BIJOU, S. W. Single and multiple schedules of reinforcement in developmentally retarded children. *Journal of the Experimental Analysis of Behavior*, 1960, 4, 339–348.

OSLER, S. F., & SHAPIRO, S. L. Studies in concept attainment: IV. The role of partial reinforcement as a function of age and intelligence. *Child Development*, 1964, 35, 623–633.

PEDERSON, D. R. Stimulus preference and response speeds as related to predictability of nonreward. Unpublished doctoral dissertation, University of Iowa, 1966.

PEDERSON, D. R. Associative versus motivational interpretations of reward percentage effects on children's performance. *Psychonomic Science*, 1967, 8, 139–140.

PENNEY, R. K. The effects of nonreinforcement on response strength as a function of number of previous reinforcements. *Canadian Journal of Psychology*, 1960, **14**, 206–215.

PENNEY, R. K., & RYAN, T. J. The motivational effects of nonreward as a function of consistency of reward. Paper presented at the meeting of the Canadian Psychological Association, Kingston, June 1960.

RIEBER, M., & JOHNSON, B. M. The relative effects of alternating delayed reinforcement and alternating nonreinforcement on response speeds of children. *Journal of Experimental Child Psychology*, 1964, **1**, 174–181.

RIESE, R. R., & LOBB, H. Discrimination learning in retarded children: Nonreward vs. reward. *American Journal of Mental Deficiency*, 1967, **71**, 536–541.

ROBINSON, A. W., & CLAYTON, K. N. Effect of duration of confinement in a nonbaited goal box on the "apparent frustration effect." *Journal of Experimental Psychology*, 1963, **66**, 613–614.

ROSENZWEIG, S. Types of reactions to frustration: A heuristic classification. *Journal of Abnormal and Social Psychology*, 1934, **29**, 298–300.

RYAN, T. J. Motivational properties of nonreward. Unpublished master's thesis, McMaster University, 1960.

RYAN, T. J. The effects of nonreinforcement and incentive value on response speed. Unpublished doctoral dissertation, State University of Iowa, 1963.

RYAN, T. J. The effects of nonreinforcement and incentive value on response speed. *Child Development*, 1965, **36**, 1067–1081.

RYAN, T. J. Instrumental performance as related to several reward schedules and age. *Journal of Experimental Child Psychology*, 1966, **3**, 398–404. (a)

RYAN, T. J. Methodology in investigating the frustration effect with child Ss. In, Frustrative nonreward in animals and children. Symposium presented at the Canadian Psychological Association, Montreal, June 1966. (b)

RYAN, T. J., & MOFFITT, A. R. Response speed as a function of age, incentive value, and reinforcement schedule. *Child Development*, 1966, **37**, 103–113.

RYAN, T. J., & VOORHOEVE, A. C. A parametric investigation of reinforcement schedule and sex of S as related to acquisition and extinction of an instrumental response. *Journal of Experimental Child Psychology*, 1966, **4**, 189–197.

RYAN, T. J., & WATSON, P. Children's response speeds as a function of sex and verbal reinforcement schedule. *Psychonomic Science*, 1966, **6**, 271–272.

SEMLER, I. J. Selective learning in severely retarded children as a function of differential reaction to nonreward. *Child Development*, 1965, **36**, 143–152.

SEMLER, I. J., & PEDERSON, D. R. Children's reaction to nonreward: Partial versus continuous reinforcement using a within-Ss design. Paper presented at the meeting of the Midwestern Psychological Association, Chicago, May 1966.

SPENCE, K. W. The nature of discrimination learning in animals. *Psychological Review*, 1936, **43**, 427–449.

SPENCE, K. W. *Behavior theory and learning: Selected papers*. Englewood Cliffs, N. J.: Prentice-Hall, 1960.

SPRADLIN, J. E., GIRARDEAU, F. L., & CORTE, E. Fixed ratio and fixed interval behavior of severely and profoundly retarded subjects. *Journal of Experimental Child Psychology*, 1965, **2**, 340–353.

STADDON, J. E. R., & INNIS, N. K. An effect analogous to "frustration" on interval reinforcement schedules. *Psychonomic Science*, 1966, **4**, 287–288.

STEIGMAN, M. J., & STEVENSON, H. W. The effect of pretraining reinforcement schedules on children's learning. *Child Development*, 1960, **31**, 53–58.

STEVENSON, H. W., & PIROJNIKOFF, L. A. Discrimination learning as a function of pretraining reinforcement schedules. *Journal of Experimental Psychology*, 1958, **56**, 41–44.

STEVENSON, H. W., & WEIR, M. W. Developmental changes in the effects of reinforcement and nonreinforcement of a single response. *Child Development*, 1961, **32**, 1–5.

STEVENSON, H. W., & ZIGLER, E. F. Probability learning in children. *Journal of Experimental Psychology*, 1958, **56**, 185–192.

TERRELL, G., JR. The need for simplicity in research in child psychology. *Child Development*, 1958, **29**, 303–310.

WATSON, P. Effects of reward schedule, type of reward and isolation condition on children's lever-pulling performance. Unpublished doctoral dissertation, University of Western Ontario, 1967.

WATSON, P., & RYAN, T. J. Duration of the frustration effect in children. *Journal of Experimental Child Psychology*, 1966, **4**, 242–247.

WATSON, P., RYAN, T. J., & McEWAN, R. C. Response speed in retardates as a function of CA, MA, IQ and reinforcement schedule. *Psychonomic Science*, 1967, **8**, 61–62.

WEINSTOCK, S. Acquisition and extinction of a partially reinforced running response at a 24-hr. intertrial interval. *Journal of Experimental Psychology*, 1958, **56**, 151–158.

WEIR, M. W. Effects of age and instructions on children's probability learning. *Child Development*, 1962, **33**, 729–735.

WEIR, M. W. Developmental changes in problem solving strategies. *Psychological Review*, 1964, **71**, 473–490.

WHITE, S. H. Evidence for hierarchial arrangement of learning processes. In L. P. Lipsitt & C. C. Spiker (Eds.), *Advances in child behavior and development*. Vol. 2. New York: Academic Press, 1965. Pp. 187–220.

WHITELEY, J. H., & RYAN, T. J. The effects of direct and vicarious nonreward upon instrumental performance. *Psychonomic Science*, 1967, **7**, 351–352.

YATES, A. J. *Frustration and conflict*. New York: Wiley, 1962.

130

Reinstatement of an Operant Response by the Delivery of Reinforcement during Extinction[1]

JOSEPH E. SPRADLIN, DEAN L. FIXSEN, AND FREDERIC L. GIRARBEAU

Recently, Spradlin, Girardeau, and Hom (1966) compared the number of responses following noncontingent (free) delivery of reinforcement during extinction with the number of responses following a control period during which there was no stimulus change. The results clearly indicated that the free delivery of reinforcement in extinction reinstated behavior which had previously been maintained by contingent reinforcement. The present study was designed to replicate the reinstatement effect with non-verbal children using a nutrient reinforcer with an added control to determine if reinstatement could be established by the presentation of an abrupt novel stimulus.

METHOD

The subjects were 12 severely retarded children between 7 years, 4 months and 14 years, 11 months of age. None of the subjects could be tested with such standardized tests as the Revised Stanford Binet or the Wechsler Intelligence Scale for Children. Their social age equivalents on the Vineland ranged from 1 year, 4 months to 3 years. Their social quotients ranged from 14 to 40. None was classified by the aide in charge of

[1] This study was supported by NICHHD grant HD 00870.

his cottage as having functional speech. There were seven males and five females. The subjects had to meet the following criteria to be included in the reinstatement study: They had to eat M&Ms, cereal, mints, or marshmallows when they were offered to them; they had to be able to grasp and hold an object (pencil); they had to meet a stability criterion. The stability criterion consisted of four consecutive sessions of responding in which the response rate for any single session deviated from the mean of four sessions by no more than 20%. Four of the original 17 subjects, selected on the basis of the first two criteria, were eliminated because they did not reach the stability criterion. A fifth subject was discarded because of an error in experimental programing.

Apparatus and Experimental Room

The experimental room in which the S was placed contained a white formica-covered response panel with two recessed Grason-Stadler pushbutton response keys located approximately 64 inches apart with a reinforcement receptacle located midway between the two keys. Both keys were located approximately 32 inches above the floor. Below the response keys were two Lindsley manipulanda. For this experiment, both Lindsley manipulanda and the left response key were inoperable. The right response key was illuminated by a red light at all times, except when reinforcement was delivered. When reinforcement was delivered, the light behind the response key was extinguished, the house light was dimmed, and the receptacle lighted for 5 seconds. The novel stimulus was a 90 dB (SPL) complex noise produced by a Line Electric Company six-volt buzzer. Reinforcement programing and response recording was done automatically by standard programing and recording equipment housed in a room adjacent to the observation room. The distance of the programing and recording equipment from the experimental room, plus 80 dB SPL of white noise, eliminated any control which relay clicks might exert over the Ss' behavior.

Establishing Responding on the FR Schedule

Each child was trained through demonstration and shaping procedures to press the response key. Once the child was responding, the experimenter left the room and gradually increased the ratio until an FR-25 was reached. The rapidity of the increase in ratio varied between Ss according to their response rate. The S was then maintained on an FR-25 schedule until the stability criterion was reached. There were two exceptions to this procedure—S_1 and S_2 were maintained on an FR-50 schedule since both of these Ss were high-rate responders who showed satiation effects toward

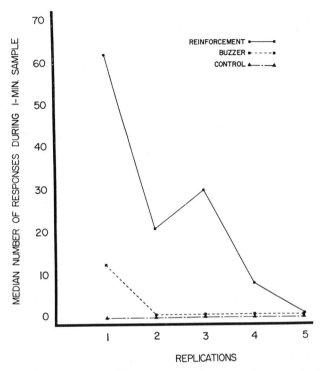

FIG. 1. Median responses during 1-minute period after the occurrence of reinforcement, the buzzer, or during the 1-minute control period.

the end of the session. During conditioning, all sessions were 15 minutes
long.

Extinction of the Response and Evaluation of the Reinstatement Properties of Reinforcement Versus a Novel Stimulus

Once the Ss met stability criterion, they were given a single extinction
session. During the extinction session, the equipment was programed so
that a 2-minute pause in responding resulted in the occurrence of reinforcement (plus correlated stimuli), a novel stimulus (5-second buzzer),
or a control period (no stimulus change was presented). A 1-minute
sample of responding was recorded immediately after the S met each
pause criterion. The presentation of reinforcement, novel stimulus, and
control period was replicated five times during the extinction period. The
sequence of presentation of the three events was the same during all five

replications for a given S. This resulted in six possible sequences of presentations of the three events. Two Ss received each sequence—thus completely counterbalancing sequence effects.

RESULTS

Eight of twelve Ss responded most during the 1-minute period following reinforcement; two Ss responded most after the buzzer; and two Ss responded most during the 1-minute control period. A Friedmann analysis of variance with ranked data was significant at the .05 level (Walker and Lev, 1953). When pairs of treatments were compared with the signed rank test for paired observations, the number of responses made during the 1-minute period following reinforcement was significantly greater than the number of responses made after either the buzzer or control. The number of responses made after the buzzer and during the control period did not differ significantly from each other. Figure 1 shows the median number of responses made during each of the five 1-minute periods for the three conditions. A Friedmann analysis of ranks for replications was also significant at the .05 level. This finding plus inspection of the data indicate that number of responses decreased with additional replications.

DISCUSSION

The present study, as well as previous studies, demonstrate that free reinforcement delivered during extinction results in the reinstatement of the acquired response above the level observed following either a control period or an abrupt auditory stimulus change (Spradlin et al., 1966; Campbell, Phillips, Fixsen, and Crumbaugh, 1968). These data lend further support to Jenkin's (1965) contention that reinforcement can develop discriminative properties during free operant training. According to this interpretation, during experimental training, a chain develops in which the S runs off a series of responses followed by the delivery of reinforcement. The S then stops responding, retrieves the reinforcement, and returns to responding again. After a series of such events, it is assumed that chaining occurs with the reinforcement serving as the S^D for resuming responding. Since reinforcement is followed only once by responding without reinforcement (onset of extinction), it is assumed that the S^D properties of reinforcement are only partially extinguished during traditional extinction. Thus, when free reinforcement is introduced during extinction, it immediately reinstates responding. The decrease in the reinstatement effect as a function of repeated presentations offers further support for this explanation.

134

SUMMARY

This study investigated the reinstatement of responding during extinction as a function of reinforcement versus a novel stimulus. The Ss used were nonverbal, severly retarded children. The Ss made significantly more responses during a 1-minute period following reinforcement than during either a 1-minute period following a novel stimulus or a 1-minute control period. Number of responses made after the novel stimulus and during the 1-minute control did not differ significantly.

REFERENCES

CAMPBELL, P. E., PHILLIPS, E. L., FIXSEN, D. L., AND CRUMBAUGH, C. Free operant response reinstatement during extinction and time-contingent (DRO) reward. *Psychological Reports,* 1968, **22,** 563–569.

JENKINS, H. M. Measurement of stimulus control during discriminative operant conditioning. *Psychological Bulletin,* 1965, **64,** 365–376.

SPRADLIN, J. E., GIRARDEAU, F. L., AND HOM, G. L. Stimulus properties of reinforcement during extinction of a free operant response. *Journal of Experimental Child Psychology,* 1966, **4,** 369–380.

WALKER, HELEN M., AND LEV, J. *Statistical inference.* New York: Holt, 1953.

Alternate Methods in Special Education

The dimensions of a
science of special education

Leonard S. Blackman

*T*HE many recent reviews and discussions of research into the product of and the process that is special education symbolizes at least the first step in the field's coming of age. The original motives for establishing segregated programs for the mentally retarded stemmed from a "relief" philosophy. Regular teachers and the normal children that they instructed were unable to tolerate the presence of the retarded child either because he was a "dragging anchor" academically or because of disruptive behavior. Since the benefits to be expected from special classes were at first designed to accrue to the normal child remaining in the regular class, it would have been, at best, superfluous to conduct research into the effectiveness of special classes for the mentally retarded.

Times change, however, and it was not long before special education attracted its own cadre of dedicated, knowledgeable professionals who saw their mission in a far more positive light. They believed that special classes and programs were for the purpose of providing the best possible education for children who would have been denied this privilege had they remained in the regular class. Research into the effectiveness of special education within this framework was, of course, manifestly logical.

The Special Class
Efficacy Studies

As the weight of research evidence began to accumulate, a new era of self-consciousness and introspection was introduced into special education. The reason for this self-consciousness was that the research data showed, rather consistently, that at least as far as academic achievement was concerned, educable mentally retarded children in regular classes were doing significantly better than those in special classes. Studies by Bennett (1932), Pertsch (1936), Elenbogen (1957), Cassidy and Stanton (1959), and Thurstone (1959) all confirmed the superior academic performance of retarded children in regular classes. Blatt (1958) found no significant differences in reading, arithmetic and language achievement between special class and regular class mentally retarded children.

Kirk (1964) reported that research into the value of special programs

138

for trainable children, in terms of the usual intellectual, educational, and social criteria, was equally disappointing. Generally negative results were obtained in studies of the stimulation value of programs for trainable youngsters conducted in Illinois, Michigan, New York, Texas and Tennessee.

In the wake of a numbing sense of disbelief in data which denigrated the academic achievement value of special education programs for the mentally retarded came a series of partially justifiable criticisms of these negative studies in terms of their inadequate design and sampling procedures. To help resolve the issue, Goldstein, Moss, and Jordan (1965) controlled for methodological inadequacies which had characterized previous investigations and conducted what was perhaps the most definitive study to date of the efficacy of special class training for the educable mentally retarded with respect to intellectual development, academic achievement, and social and personal development. They identified 126 children whose Stanford-Binet IQs were below 85 in three counties of central Illinois. The mean IQ of this sample was about 75 and mean chronological age was about 6.6 years. Roughly one-half of these children were placed randomly in special classes while the others remained in their regular classes.

The academic achievement data were analyzed in two ways: First, the total special class group was compared to the total regular class group; second, both groups were divided into high and low IQ categories and the special class highs were compared to the regular class highs while the special class lows were compared to the regular class lows.

At the conclusion of the four-year study, there were no differences between the total special class retardates and the total regular class retardates in either reading or arithmetic. It is of some interest that the regular class retardates were signifi-cantly superior in reading to the special class retardates after two years of the study, ostensibly because the special class group was exposed to an unnecessarily prolonged reading readiness program. When the data were analyzed in terms of high and low IQ groups, the low IQ special class retardates were found to be superior to the low IQ regular class retardates on a few of the language and reading subtests and in arithmetic achievement after the second, third, and fourth years of the study.

The authors of this study cling to the contention that partial support was afforded their hypothesis that the academic achievement of the mentally retarded will be enhanced by a special class placement. This contention is based primarily on the superior performance of the low IQ special class retardates relative to the low IQ regular class retardates on a few of the achievement variables. When the entire picture provided by this study is carefully evaluated, including the important total special class vs. total regular class comparisons and the failure of most achievement variables to yield significant differences even when the groups were divided, what emerges is the sobering generality that this methodologically sophisticated study of the efficacy of special classes for mentally retarded children blends into the long line of negative findings that have characterized this area of research for the past 30 years.

Psycho-Educational Characteristics of Learners and Tasks

By this time, it has become painfully clear to most workers in the field that when regular and special classes are compared, even when traditional efforts have been made to "clarify" curriculum objectives and "specify" approaches to instruction, the stimulus variable is still so complex and ill-defined that its relationship to the response variables of academic achievement and social adjustment is largely incomprehensible. This approach to educational research has been unproductive in terms of understanding specific teaching-learning processes in the special education of the mentally retarded. Kirk (1964) set the foundation for the general direction of needed research by stating that, "The present problem for research . . . is to identify more specifically the factors in the nature of the child and the variables in the nurture provided by the environment which effect change in the rate of growth, both positively and negatively."

This statement serves to introduce the basic premise of this paper that the effective modification of the classroom behavior of mentally retarded children depends on the development of a school-relevant taxonomy of their psycho-educational characteristics. The key words to be considered are "psycho-educational characteristics" and "school-relevant." By psycho-educational characteristics we mean: (1) an analysis of the retarded child's profile of abilities and deficits in a wide range of psychological processes such as perception, learning, cognition, retention, transfer, attention, discrimination, and language among others; and (2) a similar analysis of the child's profile in terms of his acquisition of educational skills, content and concepts appropriate to his level of development.

Knowledge of the learner's psychological and educational assets and liabilities is, of course, of general interest but has little educational utility independent of its relevancy to school; that is, a comparable understanding of the psycho-educational prerequisites for acquiring specific school tasks. A child whose psychological deficits are in the area of visual discrimination and retention is in no way educationally handicapped on those school tasks which do not require visual discrimination and retention skills. Obviously his deficits are handicapping in relation to the acquisition of those school tasks which do require these skills.

Up to this point, two overlapping

but nevertheless distinguishable *foci* of concern in the special education of the mentally retarded have been identified. One stresses the psycho-educational characteristics of the learner and the other the properties, in terms of psycho-educational requirements, of the school material to be learned. With the increasing confluence of data on the retarded learner and the necessary prerequisites for his school tasks,

The learner and that which is to be learned can then be matched on the basis of whether the former possesses the prerequisites for the latter. If not, remedial techniques geared toward upgrading the level of the skill appropriate to task mastery is indicated. This continual process of improving the learner and matching him with school materials as well as reshaping school materials so as to conform more precisely to the learner's skills becomes the pedagogical flywheel around which the special class program must be sensitively balanced . . . (Blackman, 1963, p. 382).

There has been a fair amount of research which has attempted to isolate specific learning and perceptual deficits in the mentally retarded. Deficits, relative to the performance of normal children, have been reported in verbal mediation (Reiber, 1964), short-term memory (Ellis, 1963), transfer (McIntyre & Dingman, 1963), incidental learning (Baumeister, 1963), cognition (Stedman, 1963), and discrimination (Spivack & Levine, 1962). In all fairness it should be pointed out that other investigators, working in the same variable fields but employing a variety of different experimental procedures and samples, have not confirmed these deficits. Much standardization of techniques and samples is required before definitive statements can be made concerning what levels or types of mentally retarded children manifest what deficits and under what conditions.

Although the evidence, albeit contradictory, is beginning to appear on the psycho-educational characteristics of the mentally retarded, little has been done, to date, in describing school tasks in terms of what psychological and educational "muscle" a child requires in order to approach that task with a reasonable probability of success. A good deal of research needs to be done before it is possible to specify the nature of tasks in terms comparable to the specification of the nature of the learner.

Instructional Systems

In analyzing this educational polarity—on the one hand, the learner and on the other hand, the task to be learned—there is the makings of an interesting but at the same time static system. To give the system movement and direction, it is essential to know more about those processes, steps, or strategies by which the learner is moved by the teacher and/or some technological extension of the teacher toward mastery of appropriate educational content. In brief, educators throughout the country are turning their attention to the development of carefully defined instructional systems designed to accomplish carefully considered and highly delineated educational objectives.

Gustafson and Komoski (1964), in an unpublished document, defined an instructional system as:

. . . a group of functionally related learning environments made up of humans, objects, devices, and symbols with which a learner interacts overtime in order to acquire designated behavioral capabilities and predispositions. A particular instructional system may contain many such environments, some extremely rigid, others highly flexible or permissive. The nature of each environmental component within a system depends upon the characteristics of the learner and the behavioral predispositions and capabilities to be fostered by the system.

They go on to explain that:

. . . the essential distinction. between an instructional system and any other type of educational or training environment is that the effects achieved by the former are predictable with a high degree of specificity. Each element of an instructional system is designed to foster a measurable outcome, and the system is redesigned or repaired whenever it fails to deliver the performance expected. Furthermore, because of the orderly manner in which the system is developed in the first place, it is possible to trace its failures to particular sources—if not infallibly then at least with minimal ambiguity. Thus a system can be proved not only by verifying that it does the job anticipated, but also by demonstrating that the deletion of certain components or subsystems leads to predictable decrements in over-all performance.

In building a teaching system, the instructional specialist in special education must decide, in specific and measurable terms, the behaviors that he would like to teach. The system that he develops must be limited and qualified by the parameters imposed by intellectual and other general forms of deficit encountered in mentally retarded children. He must have an analytical understanding of the abilities and disabilities of the particular group of retardates for whom the instructional system is being planned. He must have information concerning the psychological properties of school materials. He must be prepared to delineate clearly and meticulously the pedagogical steps and stages by which the learner is to achieve the desired terminal behaviors. He must have sufficient flexibility to permit modifications in the instructional sequence when the learners' behaviors so dictate. When appropriate, he may apply teaching machines and programmed instruction in other forms, films and TV when highly standardized and replicable learning environments are necessary.

As with less formalized approaches to instruction, the instructional system presupposes a certain uniformity of learning, perceptual, and cognitive processes in the learner. Thus, once an instructional system has been developed, it should be applicable, within tolerable limits, to a wide range of learners. There are individuals, however, who, because of the variety of etiological factors involved in mental retardation, neurological impairment, or emotional disturbance, or some combination of these, may exhibit learning characteristics so qualitatively deviant that instructional systems developed for broadly defined handicapped groups will be short circuited. Thus, the heterogeneity of learning handicaps within mental retardation or neurological impairment, for example, may preclude the development of appropriate instructional systems for a diagnostic category.

The somewhat troublesome point being made is that if instructional systems must be constructed so as to be sensitive to the particular pattern of learning abilities and disabilities manifested by the individual deviant learner, then the implication is that each child may require his own instructional system. Indeed, each child may require several instructional systems if some of the "transient" behavioral characteristics often exhibited in mental retardation or neurological impairment are to be accommodated.

The practical and economic implications of such a point of view are, at the moment, difficult to fathom. What does seem to be directly at stake, however, is whether the notion of instructional systems, translated freely from systems concepts in engineering, is a tenable one when the raw materials to be shaped oscillate as markedly as the deviant learner.

Illustrative of attempts to develop instructional systems for the mentally retarded without a clear awareness of the properties of the tasks to be taught or the particular deficits of the learners involved was a three-year study by Blackman and Capobianco (1965) designed to evaluate the effectiveness of self-instructional devices and programs in teaching primary reading and arithmetic skills to educable mentally retarded adolescents. Nineteen subjects in a teaching machine group receiving painstakingly developed programmed instruction in reading and arithmetic were compared, after one school year, with a comparable group learning the same material in a traditional classroom setting. An analysis of pre- and post-school-year achievement data revealed that both the machine and no-machine groups improved significantly over the school year in reading and arithmetic as measured by the Metropolitan Achievement Test, the Wide Range Achievement Test, and an achievement test designed to measure acquisition of the program materials themselves. There were no significant differences, however, between the improvement scores of the machine and no-machine groups on any of the achievement scales listed above with the exception of the nonstandardized arithmetic test of the program materials. On this test only, the gain scores of the machine group were significantly greater than those of the no-machine group. These essentially negative findings on the effectiveness of "teaching machine" instruction of academic tasks with the mentally retarded have been confirmed in studies by Merachnik and Quattlebaum (1963) and Sprague and Binder (1962), both in the area of arithmetic.

The objective in reporting these studies is not to undermine the value of instructional systems in this or any other form. On the contrary, the development of education as a science rather than an art form will be wholly dependent on concrete and measurable statements of educational objectives coupled with the highly specific delineation of instructional procedures leading toward those objectives. Rather, it is to emphasize the point that the instructional system is only one part of an educational troika which must include a clear understanding of the learner's psycho-educational characteristics and the task's psycho-educational requirements if progress is to be made.

To summarize, special education for the mentally retarded has been a relatively unsuccessful enterprise simply because there has been very little special about it. In training administrators and teachers, the broad and poorly understood curriculum objectives of personal, economic and social adjustment have been emphasized at the expense of understanding learning disabilities and developing specific instructional procedures. The gap between the broad principles espoused in the teachers' colleges and the day-to-day instructional needs of children has created a breed of teachers who are long on cliches and short on pedagogy.

It would appear that our objective in special education has been pragmatic and unambitious—that is, training mentally retarded children for well-adjusted mentally retarded adulthood. It is the contention of this article that the unique purpose of special education is to train retarded children to the highest possible levels of academic competence through the remediation of learning deficits and the development of the most efficient instructional systems for transmitting content.

The Teacher of the Future

Since the educational research reviewed in this paper has led to a series of rather abstract recommendations concerning the direction in which special education should move in the future, it might be enlightening to discuss practical applications by envisioning one teacher's day in the "Brave New World" of special education.

Miss X has a special class of primary, educable retarded children in a new school which enjoys the support of an up-to-date computer system. Before school began, all the children had been evaluated on a new series of instruments designed to measure the children's ability on all psychological processes deemed necessary for successful school performance at the primary level. Each child's scores on all of these process skills were stored in the computer.

Years of research had preceded the development of these instruments since before it was meaningful to determine which psychological skills to measure, it was first necessary to analyze all school tasks at the primary level to determine their composition in terms of the amount of each psychological skill necessary to master the tasks. Indeed, many validation studies had been done to confirm the hypothesis that children well matched with school tasks in terms of possessing the psycho-educational characteristics considered prerequisite to these tasks did significantly better than mismatched children or those who did not possess the appropriate prerequisites. It should be noted that the tasks and their psycho-educational prerequisites were also stored in the computer.

On a particular Thursday morning, Miss X started the school day with the Pledge of Allegiance and then decided that it was time to teach her children how to write the numeral "1." Miss X dialed the code number for this particular task into her desk telephone which was connected to the school computer. In a fraction of a second, the computer compared its stored information on the psychological process skills and the educational subskills required for learning how to write the numeral with psychological process and education subskill data available for each child. Almost before the dial had returned to its original position, Miss X saw the names of 10 children who possessed the necessary psycho-educational attributes printed on part of the television screen built into the top of her desk. Simultaneously, 10 of the classroom computer terminals were activated to present a program for teaching this task to children who presented all the necessary prerequisites. Each of the children was assigned to one of the terminals and began work.

Next to the list of "ready" children, were the names of five children who lacked one or more of the psycho-educational prerequisites of the task. The nature of the deficits was noted and the remaining five computer terminals were activated to present instructional systems geared solely to the amelioration of these deficits. The implication should be clear that methods will have to be described under two categories: (1) those methods designed to teach content to "intact" children; and (2) those methods specifically designed to ameliorate psycho-educational deficits entirely independent of formal school content.

Miss X now has her day and, in relation to some of the children, her weeks planned. Continual re-evaluations of the children will be required to determine if and when a particular deficit has been improved sufficiently to permit content instruction. Computer data will have to be kept up to date. It will be necessary, too, to develop instructional systems in the content areas for children whose deficits prove to be irreversible. Obviously, this system is simpler in description than in practice. Deficits may be complex, different in weight, and interactive in their effects upon learning particular school tasks. For example, a particular deficit may be remediable in the presence of another deficit but not remediable in the presence of a third. The problems are legion and will prove far more difficult in ultimate implementation than in current conception.

As one considers and studies the framework for special education proposed in this paper, there should be an almost immediate recognition that what has been described is not a system for special education only but a system for all education. All children suffer, to a greater or lesser extent, from school-relevant psychoeducational deficits. All children, at one time or another, require the remediation of deficits so that more effective learning might take place. And all professional educators, striving for maximum individualization of instruction because of the differences between children in intelligence, learning skills and information-acquiring stratagems, should find meaning and relevance in the proposed system.

If a small, professional bias can be forgiven, the proposed amalgamation of psychology, education and computer science in future classrooms of the "Brave New World" simply makes general education a special case of special education.

References

Baumeister, A. A Comparison of Normals and Retardates with Respect to Incidental and Intentional Learning. *American Journal of Mental Deficiency*, 1963, *68*, 404–408.

Bennett, A. *A Comparative Study of Subnormal Children in the Elementary Grades.* New York: Teachers College, Columbia University, Bureau of Publications, 1932.

Blackman, L. Research Needs in the Special Education of the Mentally Retarded. *Exceptional Children*, 1963, *29*, 377–383.

Blackman, L. & Capobianco, R. An Evaluation of Programmed Instruction with the Mentally Retarded Utilizing Teaching Machines. *American Journal of Mental Deficiency*, 1965, *70*, 262–269.

Blatt, B. The Physical, Personality, and Academic Status of Children Who are Mentally Retarded Attending Special Classes as Compared with Children Who are Mentally Retarded Attending Regular Classes. *American Journal of Mental Deficiency*, 1958, *62*, 810–818.

Cassidy, V. M. & Stanton, J. E. An Investigation of Factors Involved in the Educational Placement of Mentally Retarded Children: A Study of Differences Between Children in Special and Regular Classes in Ohio. (U.S.O.E. Cooperative Research Program, Project No. 043). Columbus: Ohio State University, 1959.

Elenbogen, M. L. A Comparative Study of Some Aspects of Academic and Social Adjustment of Two Groups of Mentally Retarded Children in Special Classes and in Regular Grades. *Dissertation Abstracts*, 1957, *17*, 2497.

Ellis, N. (Ed.). *Handbook of Mental Deficiency: Psychological Theory and Research.* New York: McGraw-Hill, 1963.

Goldstein, H., Moss, J. & Jordan, L. *The Efficacy of Special Class Training on the Development of Mentally Retarded Children.* U.S. Dept. of Health, Education, and Welfare, Office of Education, Cooperative Research Project No. 619. Urbana: Institute for Research on Exceptional Children, University of Illinois, 1965.

Gustafson, H. & Komoski, P. Application of Educational Technology to the Development of Instructional Systems. Research and development proposal, NDEA, 1964.

Kirk, S. Research in Education. In *Mental Retardation: A Review of Research,* H. Stevens and R. Heber (Eds.). **Chicago:** Univ. of Chicago Press, 1964.

McIntyre, R. & Dingham, H. **Mental Age vs. Learning Ability: An Investigation of Transfer of Training Between Hierarchical Levels.** *American Journal of Mental Deficiency,* **1963, *68,* 396–403.**

Merachnik, D. & Quattlebaum, B. Adaptation and Usage of Programmed Instruction in Arithmetic with Mentally Retarded. *Research Bulletin, New Jersey School Development Council,* **Rutgers** Univ., 1963, *8,* No. 2.

Pertsch, C. F. *A Comparative Study of the Progress of Subnormal Pupils in the Grades and in Special Classes.* New York: Teachers College, Columbia University, Bureau of Publications, 1936.

Rieber, M. Verbal Mediation in Normal and Retarded Children. *American Journal of Mental Deficiency,* 1964, *68,* 634–641.

Spivack, G. & Levine, M. A Note on Generality of Discrimination Deficiency in Life-long Brain Damage. *American Journal of Mental Deficiency,* 1962, *67,* 473–474.

Sprague, R. & Binder, A. Automated Arithmetic Instruction for the Retarded. Progress Report, PHS Grant M-5647 (A), 1962.

Stedman, D. Associative Clustering of Semantic Categories in Normal and Retarded Subjects. *American Journal of Mental Deficiency,* 1963, *67,* 700–704.

Thurstone, T. G. An Evaluation of Educating Mentally Handicapped Children in Special and in Regular Grades. (U.S.O.E. Cooperative Research Program, Project No. OE SAE-6452). Chapel Hill: Univ. of North Carolina, 1959.

An Interpretation of Effective Management and Discipline of the Mentally Retarded Child

by MARCENE POWELL

A retarded child presents for his parents a variety of complex problems. The child's physical needs and psychological requirements for security, firm discipline, and warmth may tend to be satisfied in a capricious fashion at best.[1] Some parents are incapable of dealing with the special needs that a retardate presents because they lack meaningful skills and instruction. Within the home, probably no single area continuously demands as much time as that of discipline or, to use its more generic label, behavioral management.[2]

Parental ability in the care and management of children is dependent upon the effectiveness of child-rearing techniques. Parents of the mental retardate must be assisted in developing useful techniques in a manner specifically adapted to the unique learning needs of these children.

DISCIPLINE—A DISCUSSION

Discipline is an attempt to educate a child to do what his parents desire, whether this means learning new social or self-help skills appropriate for a child his age or the relinquishment of less mature behavior, such as wetting the bed after training has been established, refusing to eat, throwing food, displaying temper tantrum behavior, or refusing to obey simple commands. Healthy discipline is an educational process. This means that what a child learns from his parents should help him to interact appropriately and productively with his surroundings throughout his life span. Yet discipline is subject to more confusion, controversy, and inconsistency and is related to more difficulties and problems than any other matter of child care. Is there any explanation for the failures of many parents to achieve success in disciplining their children? Why does the child continue "misbehaving" despite the fact that his parents have "tried everything"? Is there a set of disciplinary principles by which a child can be made to relinquish less mature behavior and acquire more desirable abilities?

Achieving Behavioral Control

In providing nurses with information that will prove useful to them in dealing with the home management problems of mentally retarded children, it is the author's contention that there are few significant differences in required management techniques between the ideally managed retarded child and the unimpaired child. Modern learning principles as interpreted by behavioral psychologists are known to be remarkably consistent from type to type and even from species to species. Similarly, the principles that govern learning in the retarded are basically the same as for the intellectually unimpaired. The chief differences in child management lie in the approach to teaching the retarded child. This consists of an acknowledgment of the child's slowness to learn, to discriminate, and to generalize learning experiences from one situation to another. Bijou states, "Behaviorists contend that conditions and behaviors observed in retarded development do not differ qualitatively, but only quantitatively from normal and accelerated development."[3]

Thus, in evaluating readiness to learn a given skill, we recognize that the retarded child may deviate from expected chronological norms. When he is ready to develop a new skill, he needs more repetition of the material being taught because of his low ability to assimilate, more immediate gratification because of his short attention span and inability to tolerate delays comfortably, and much patient, loving attention and appropriate approval for his attempts to please. Clearly, heavy demands are made on the time and attention of the parents of the retarded.

MODERN LEARNING THEORY AND DEVELOPMENTAL OPTIMIZATION

Child-rearing is not a technical term with precise significance. It refers generally to all the interactions between parents and their children. These interactions include parental behavior with respect to care-taking (eating, feeding, sleeping, cleaning, and protecting). What parents do is a reflection of their attitudes, values, interests, and beliefs. Such child-rearing practices all affect a child's behavior, and, whether by intention or not, change his potentialities for future action. To understand the implications of these defining statements about child-rearing, one must examine the apparent mechanisms by which parents and children influence one another. One is with respect to action and the other to learning.

It is the author's conclusion, based on scientific information available, that development of a mentally retarded child may be optimized within the context of his impairment, and that this optimization chiefly accrues from the effectiveness of the child-rearing techniques employed by his family. It has been a twentieth century fad for educators, psychologists, doctors, neighbors, and just about everyone else to tell mothers how to rear their children. The author does not wish to imply here that there is just one absolutely correct way. Quite to the contrary, the possibilities for variability of environmental experiences are nearly infinite. It is felt strongly, however, that there exists for each child a range of environmental reinforcement patterns which tend to optimize the rate and extent to which a child acquires the new behavior that his parents desire him to learn.

The following statements of some of the more important principles of learning as applied to child-rearing, together with the contrast of two particularly illustrative case studies, should aid the reader in forming some guidelines for practical evaluation of the effectiveness of parental attempts to change modes of behavior in their children. The stated principles are merely a sketch of operant learning theory. The examples cited do not cover all the ramifications of the theory.

For the interested reader, considerable literature is available on this subject (see References, and other articles in this symposium).

Learning Principles

1. All learning is a result of reinforcement. A reinforcer is defined as a stimulus event which influences behavior in a manner that promotes or inhibits its recurrence. Thus, reinforcers are seen to be either positive, promoting behavioral recurrence, or negative, inhibiting it. Stimuli with no effect on behavior are neutral, but they may have lost or may later acquire the ability to influence behavior. Indeed, development is highly dependent upon an organism's discriminating new reinforcement characteristics from previously neutral stimuli (as in development of speech) and relinquishing the reinforcement characteristics of old stimuli (as in thumb-sucking).

2. The power of a reinforcer to influence behavior is dependent on conditions which are, in practice, usually quite complex, because changes in environmental variables are seldom amenable to control outside the laboratory. Reinforcers may operate in conflict with one another, as when a child desires something he knows he will be punished for obtaining. In general, however:

a. Reinforcers, whether positive or negative, may be categorized as primary (intrinsic to the organism such as food, water, pain) and secondary (acquired or learned, for example affection, television, preference for ice cream over spinach).

b. The greater the promptness with which reinforcement is provided, the stronger its influence in controlling behavior. If too much time elapses, the behavior in question will not be reinforced at all.

c. Consistency of reinforcement affects the learning rate positively.

d. The strength of previously reinforced behavior is dependent upon the number of reinforcements in the past. The more often a behavior has produced positive reinforcement, the stronger it becomes.

e. The effect of a reinforcer on behavior at any given time it is offered depends upon:

(1) The cumulative strength it has acquired to influence behavior.

(2) The state of deprivation or satiation of the organism with respect to that reinforcer at that time.

f. Punishment can be defined as either provision of a negative reinforcer or removal of a positive reinforcer.[5]

One further point to be stressed concerning reinforcement is the importance of social interaction as a positive reinforcer for human behavior. Its effect is so powerful that it cannot be overemphasized, but its strength is still dependent upon the amount and context of past usage. The cases presented illustrate the different directions which social interactions may take in influencing behavior. If we may accept a reinforcement theory of learning, it becomes axiomatic that gross failure to achieve parental goals in child management indicates that inappropriate use has been made of reinforcers, or that reinforcement alone is insufficient to bring about desired behavior.

How can these scientific principles be interpreted and applied in analyzing parental effectiveness in behavioral control? Even if parents were to attempt to use them conscientiously in the rearing of their children, the results would still be dependent upon realistically oriented expectations and the kinds of methods selected for attempts to produce changes in behavior.

A COMPARATIVE ANALYSIS

As mentioned, a child's attainment of optimum development and

149

adjustment is interdependent with the nature of the interactions that take place between him and the principal figures in his environment. For this presentation, it was felt that the source of the subtle differences between successful and unsuccessful behavioral control could best be illustrated through an analysis of case studies showing the very different child-rearing techniques of two mothers of mentally retarded children. Both children, a boy and a girl, are moderately retarded, 5½ years of age, Caucasians from middle-class families, and both have younger siblings.

Material for the analysis was selected from data obtained by the author, who has recently been engaged in research that includes extensive interviewing of mothers of mentally retarded children. These interviews are structured to produce an overview of the child-rearing methods being used by these mothers with an emphasis upon their approach to discipline. The methodology consists of administering to the mother a standardized structured interview which is essentially patterned after a questionnaire designed by Sears et al. for investigating child-rearing techniques among mothers of intellectually unimpaired children.[4] Careful review of taped recordings of these interviews resulted in the selection of the two sets of highly contrasting responses.

I. TOILET TRAINING
(Both mothers reported having difficulty with their approach)

Robert

Training was commenced when the child starting walking, but "he has only stopped wetting the bed since he started school." If he were only wet, his mother at first left his trousers on for about ½ hour. If he had accidents, she generally ignored them and didn't scold much. When he was enrolled in a special school at 5 years of age, she told him, "Robert, you're a big boy now, going to school; you can't go to the bathroom in your bed any more." It worked very well. Once when he got to the bathroom a little too late, and soiled his trousers, he wept. His mother simply told him to start earlier the next time. In one isolated instance recently when he wet his bed, she asked him why and he told her he didn't awaken. She said no more about it because she remembered he'd consumed an excessive amount of fluid and felt it was her fault.

Mary

Training was not completed until she was 5½ years old. It was commenced at 18 months. The mother used suppositories which were not effective. "At that time we didn't know there was something wrong — well, we did, but didn't know what. I more or less stuck to the training in the spring or summer because it was warmer. When I first started, it was about every 10 or 15 minutes." Later when she had accidents she was shamed and called a "bad girl." To prevent bed wetting, she was taken to the bathroom before bedtime and awakened again later. Water intake was limited after 6:00 P.M.

150

Here we see a pattern establishing itself. It is plain that Robert's mother was realistically lenient in his toilet training while Mary's employed somewhat harsh methods at times and was not consistent in her application. In relating the measures she had tried, she expressed a great deal of frustration with her lack of success. Yet, when Robert's mother was afforded the opportunity to apply a social sanction, remission of soiling was nearly spontaneous while the social reinforcer of "shaming" had no apparent effect on Mary. Why has Robert discriminated social reinforcers where Mary has not?

II. Table Manners

Robert

He was usually fed on his own schedule. "If he wasn't hungry, then I'd try later when he was." He quickly developed his own predictable feeding schedule. When small, he didn't like meat. She didn't force it on him, but disguised it in other foods. The children now sit at their own separate table because the house is small and there's not enough room at the table with their parents. The mother, on this account, expects that their manners will be "not very good right now," but they are still expected to "sit, use their forks and spoons and eat properly." This includes Robert and even the baby. They may leave the table with permission for a good reason. "Actually we treat Robert pretty much like the other children." He's not permitted to interrupt adult conversation, but if it seems urgent she asks, "Is it important?" A six year old's table manners should be "pretty good, I think. Oh, they'll spill their milk or get restless, but I expect them to use their forks and spoons." She teaches Robert by "telling him and keeping right after him." He's scolded for spilling when he's playing, and made to wait for more, but if it's an accident, it's just cleaned up. Also he may be made to sit in a chair or face the wall for a short time. That "kills him." If he's good for several days she tells him "how nice the table looks and how proud I am." The mother is eager about plans for getting a new house

Mary

Her mother used to try to force her to eat, but now she doesn't "go too far with her" because she is "emotional." She eats with her hands, copying the baby, and they "just tell her" she's a big girl now and should use her fork. She's not allowed to leave the table during meals, or her plate is removed. This works well, but there was a previous period when she'd leave the table and come back. Now she "sits real good" while her parents are at the table, but when they leave, she gets up. She interrupts adult conversations—not that it's permitted, but, "If you don't look at her she keeps turning your head until you look at her, and as much as you try to ignore her or tell her to hush she won't until you answer her. Usually I'll try to hush her—and if I see I'm not getting anywhere—I'll answer her." She has learned to use a fork and napkin by watching her parents, and was praised for this. "Last night for the first time in I don't know how long, she cleaned up her plate—and she got quite a praising for it, but tonight it was the same old routine."

151

with a large dining area. She is concerned about improving table manners "but it's not fair to expect much
when we're not with them all the time."

Here we can see that both mothers have had some success with
methods of table manners training. What is significant is that where
punitiveness resulted in "emotional" behavior from Mary, Robert
quickly adapted himself to the rest of the family. In one instance, we
see high permissiveness paired with high usage of social reinforcers
which have become very effectively discriminated, while in the other
case it seems the child is being ignored except when she does something
undesirable. She must turn her parents' heads with her hands to get
their attention and they then finally respond to her insistence. Yet,
from other reports by this mother, the child's overall behavior at the
table is probably the best of any she exhibits. Why? Food is a powerful
reinforcer. The table ritual is probably one of the most highly structured
social interactions in which she may participate. There, Mary is imitating
her parents' behavior with their approval. One of the most evidently
effective reinforcement techniques which these parents have applied
appropriately is consistent food deprivation for leaving the table. In
the case of Robert, there is a pervasive impression that this mother is
quite effortlessly getting a great deal from her children. While highly
permissive, her limit setting is definite and consistent, and her expectations are always reasonable. The children are not pressured about
things that are too difficult for them, that they are not yet prepared to
learn.

III. GENERAL APPROACH TO DISCIPLINE

From the extensive additional material on both families, here are
presented a few excerpts related to discipline.

Sex and Modesty

Robert	Mary
Mother allowed limited freedom when they were small to satisfy curiosity, but "keeps right after them" about modesty. If he plays with himself it "bothers" her and she tries to divert him. She thinks he does it out of boredom, and doesn't press the subject. Sex play is not permitted because "they've seen each other and know they're different. I tell them that's just for them to see and not to show anyone else. There's no shame to it...."	She masturbates excessively. Mother says, "Honey, don't do this, it'll make you sore." The mother is *very* anxious about sex play. She does not scold but attempts extensively to change be-havior with verbal reasoning.

152

Neatness

Robert	*Mary*

He "folds his clothes and puts 'em away." "Of course, we keep right after them." Marking on walls or jumping on furniture isn't allowed. If it happens, he's scolded, or sits in a chair—he's kind of punished." Roughhousing is allowed unless it gets to the point where someone might get hurt.

Washing hands is an excuse to play in the water. "She dresses herself." "I'm very strict about writing on the walls." They taught her to print all their names and once she printed the proper occupant's name on each bedroom door. It was "cute," but she was scolded.

Respect for Property

Robert	*Mary*

Once he tore up a neighbor's yard with some other children. He was spanked, kept in his yard for a week, and made to do chores to help pay for the damage.

"Everything is hers." She'll share anything but toys. She has a tantrum if she's made to return toys she takes.

General Rules

Robert	*Mary*

He is governed by a very specific set of rules concerning where he may go and what he may touch. "They have their own things to play with." "If they want something, they can ask." He can play as far as the other side of the block, if she has met the people, but he may not cross the street by himself. He dries the dishes and cleans up messes he makes through carelessness. He needs constant reminders not to drag the dish towel on the floor.

Attempts are made to be quite restrictive, but "it's gotten to the point where she's running the whole household." She's allowed to do some jobs, and if mother is in a hurry and won't let her do them, she has a tantrum. "When I'm doing something and it involves her help, she's right there waiting." She's not permitted to leave the yard.

Immediacy of Obedience

Robert	*Mary*

He's always required to do what he's asked. "We feel they should obey when you speak to them—pay attention. They get a couple of warnings and that's it." "They are thanked when they finish a task."

"She gets a couple of warnings first to make her believe it. I'd be shocked if she did something right away."

153

Mother-Child Relationship

Robert

She enjoys him because he tries so hard to please her in improving his speech. She likes seeing him develop. He only makes her nervous following her about the kitchen because he might get burned. He likes to sit in a chair with her when she's watching TV and cuddle.

Mary

"She has tantrums from the time she gets up in the morning until she goes to bed at night — she'll bite herself or beat on herself." Discipline for her is the hardest thing to find.

Punishment

Robert

"He sits in a chair, and he gets corrected." He's not often spanked, but lately more than usual (three times in the past two weeks). His discipline equals that of the other children. If spanked, he shows no reaction at the time, but she has detected a later reaction. She is very sensitive to him. She always makes certain that he understands if she punishes him.

Mary

Any of four things: sitting on a chair, standing in a corner, going to her room, or a spanking. None does any good. If things go smoothly? "Gee, I don't know; I never paid any attention." She spanks her frequently. "I'm afraid you'll report us to the Humane Society." "I get so mad at her sometimes that I know if I touched her it would be terrible! I'm scared, really scared."

We see that the same general picture continues to emerge here as with toilet and table training. Robert's mother is permissive, but provides firm, consistent limits and makes available many positively reinforcing stimuli in the environment. She is warm and more sensitive to her children's needs than her own. She watches them closely, but without interfering with their activities unless there is danger. She permits whatever degree of dependency they need, so that they are ultimately independent. She has reasonable expectations and is satisfied with her role as a mother and with the development of her children. When this mother was interviewed she was remarkably spontaneous with her responses. There was no hesitancy or uncertainty because she knew exactly what her goals were as a parent and how she could best implement them. The amount of independence and security she has fostered in Robert, such as permitting him to go to the other side of the block by himself (he has his own reporting system), is very exceptional for a retarded child. His behavioral development is probably very close to optimum for his mental age.

Mary's mother by contrast is in desperate straits. Her failure to develop a reinforcement repertoire for Mary has resulted in a circular negative reinforcement pattern. What the child does is negative to the mother who then resorts to nearly exclusive negative means in her attempts to eliminate the undesirable behavior. When this child is playing quietly or behaving herself, she's ignored. Only Mary's negative behavior gets attention. The mother's caretaking activities, which otherwise might be reinforcers, are provided on an interval schedule which is unrelated to the child's behavior. Meals were the sole significant exceptions noted.

The power of social interaction as positive reinforcement has been noted previously. How is this working with Mary? Remember that she is ignored when she's good and that she demands "too much" of her mother's attention. Clearly she is in a state of deprivation of social reinforcers. What social reinforcement is available to this child? We remember that the mother resorts often to "explaining" things to the child, even when she is spanked. This is simply a child so socially deprived that she is often willing to be spanked merely to get her mother's attention for a moment.

REMEDIAL MEASURES

Can anything be done to correct a situation like this? Yes, but it is an involved problem. First, how can we approach the child? We see that her reinforcement pattern is inharmonious with desired changes in behavior. Also significant portions of it have become self-reinforcing. Note her self-stimulatory behavior, such as masturbation (which also produces a maternal response and is thus reinforced), playing in water, tantrums, and self-abuse. In her whole behavioral repertoire there is almost nothing worthy of positive reinforcement. Mary has not developed any desirable behavior because no appropriate reinforcers for it were available in her environment. We are faced with the task now of getting her attention and trying to find and build upon change worthy behavior almost from scratch. And yet, had this child had an optimum schedule of reinforcement, she should have developed at least as well as Robert.

Next, of course, we see that in order to change Mary's behavior we first have to change the attitudes of her parents. This means that their responses to Mary must be altered or nothing can be done. Suffice it to say that most parents certainly are not ineffective because they like it. They, too, are products of an inadequate reinforcement network. They too need help, counseling, education, and sometimes therapy.

NURSING IMPLICATIONS

Nurses have infrequently been able to define methods of behavioral control for retarded children, nor have they generally attempted to teach parents methods of shaping and manipulating behavior. It appears, however, that nurses will find themselves increasingly confronted with a need to provide parents with the best possible information to cope with behavioral problems. Progress in this area would appear to be highly dependent upon several key factors. These include the constant reappraisal of overall management methodology and its effectiveness, and an increased emphasis on behavioral control. Such an appraisal must be oriented toward the optimum development of the mentally retarded child.

When a child is suspected of being mentally retarded, the nurse needs to know many things about the child and his family that may bear on his condition and future care. The following areas are suggested as a framework for the nurse to use in making an assessment of the child and his family. Nursing efforts in giving services to parents of retarded children essentially consist of assisting the family to learn to assess the child's developmental level, or mental age, and to set their expectations, discipline, and training to the mental level.

Evidence of mental retardation, as expressed in the child's behavior, is the first thing to be noted. When such evidence has become clear, and when the nurse has taken appropriate action, various types of observation are called for.

When visiting the child in his natural environment, it is advisable to rely heavily on observed behavior in regard to the following:

Relationship with Family

1. How much attention does the child seem to want and get as a result?
2. How does the child communicate most effectively? Are his needs anticipated and indulged?
3. What appears to be the mother's attitude, i.e., punitive or rewarding, if she is busy and the child is attempting to get her attention.

Peer Group Relationships

1. How responsive is the child to tactile or verbal signs of affection?
2. Does the child notice other children, but remain self-centered in play?
3. Does he imitate another child's behavior?
4. With whom does the child generally play? What are the age levels, and how does he interact?
5. Can he share toys and food willingly?
6. Is he assertive if his toys are removed? Does he stand up for his own rights and is it encouraged?
7. Can he play cooperatively with a small group of children?

Sleeping Patterns

It is useful to gain information as to resistance during bedtime preparation and how it is handled by the parents. What methods are used if the child awakens during the night and cries when no distress is evident?

Dressing

How much is the child encouraged to dress himself? Do his clothes seem suitable or conducive to developing dressing skills? It is significant to note whether clothing has buttons, what size they are, and if they are located in the front or back.

A revealing factor is whether the mother finds it easier to dress the child just because of the time element.

Play

Does the child have free access to toys? Note whether play objects are out and if they have been used. If toys are out of reach or stacked neatly away it is a clue that the child doesn't have much opportunity to play. Is there a wide assortment? Do the toys appear stimulating, i.e., colorful, movable, and constructive? What is the child's attention span for a given toy?

It is significant to know whether the mother spends time playing with her child and how much.

Nutrition

An excellent time to visit the home, particularly for children who have not developed self-help skills in feeding, is during meal time. Does the child eat with family members? Is the mother encouraging independence in the feeding situation? What methods is she employing to teach her child to use utensils? Is hand to mouth coordination apparent? Does the child feed himself at the beginning or end of a meal? Is the child praised for attempts at self-feeding?

"Hypo" or "Hyper" Characteristics of General Behavior

Does the child sit and rock or move from one activity to another with rapidity or lethargy? Does the child ever resort to self-abusive behaviors such as biting or hitting himself, or engage in self-stimulatory behaviors such as masturbation? What is the frequency of temper tantrums? What appears to provoke them? What is their duration and intensity? What does the behavior seem to be gaining for the child? How do the parents respond to acting out?

Toileting

It is essential to have objective data about training techniques. Does the child exhibit discomfort when wet or soiled? This often can be picked up casually on a home visit. Clues can then be pointed out to the mother who may not be alert to signs of readiness.

In the approach to toilet training, when does the mother take her child to the bathroom and by what methods is she enticing him to the bathroom area? Does she remain during the time the child is seated? How long is the child left in the bathroom? Is he praised for success or punished for failures? Is the toilet training process gone about in a logical and systematic fashion? Some mothers might find it useful to keep a record of elimination over a period of a week or two and attempt training at more appropriate times rather than using an intuitive haphazard approach.

Discipline

How effective are the parents in setting limits and do they? How responsive is the child to the methods being used? Is the child consistently responsive to the word "no"? Are spankings preceded by scolding or warnings? Does the mother follow through with threats? Do her moods govern her disciplinary approaches? Does she use deprivation of privileges? Is the discipline associated immediately with the misbehavior? Is there a system of rewards employed for desirable behavior? Are parents in agreement with disciplinary techniques being employed?

Mothering Attendance

How much time does the mother actually spend during a given day either playing with or teaching her child something she wants him to learn? Does she pay attention to him when he is exhibiting desirable behavior or is she preoccupied with other activities and ignoring good behavior?

From this type of information the nurse can make a more accurate assessment of a child and thus assist a family to plan more effectively for the child's present and future needs.

SUMMARY

We have sought to present some workable scientific principles whereby a nurse may appraise child-rearing techniques within a framework of their effectiveness. The aim has been to provide a basis for sound decisions in parental counseling through the construction of a practical frame of reference from which the nurse-counselor may pragmatically develop her analytical skills. The goal is to optimize the development of mentally retarded children through positively fulfilling learning experiences which are mutually rewarding to the child and his parents.

The nurse has been guided through an interpretation of the theory of operant learning and an illustration of how it works in practice. It is hoped that, with this in mind, she will be able to lead less successful parents toward a meaningful reorientation of their methods, promote the facility for realistic assessment of their child, and enhance parental skills toward the achievement of optimal development for the child.

REFERENCES

1. Stevens, H. A., and Heber, Rick: Mental Retardation. Chicago, University of Chicago Press, 1964, p. 6.
2. Robinson, H. B., and Robinson, Nancy M.: The Mentally Retarded Child. New York, McGraw-Hill Book Co., 1965, p. 516.
3. Bijou, Sidney: Theory and research in mental (developmental) retardation. Psychol. Record, 13:95–110, 1963.
4. Sears, R. R., Maccoby, Eleanor E., and Levin, Harry: Patterns of Child Rearing. New York, Row, Paterson and Company, 1957, pp. 491–501.
5. Bijou, Sidney, and Baer, D. M.: Child Development. New York, Appleton-Century-Crofts, Inc., 1961, pp. 1–86.

Parent education in managing retarded children with behavior deficits and inappropriate behaviors

Leif Terdal
Joan Buell

*I*n January 1967 a behavioral program was initiated at the Crippled Children's Division of the University of Oregon Medical School as part of a medical-behavioral-educational pilot project in mental retardation. The behavioral aspect of the program is designed to train parents of retarded children in methods of:

1. accurately observing their child's behavior and their own behavior;
2. eliminating problem behaviors at home;
3. building up in their child appropriate behaviors in areas such as self-help, verbal communication, social interaction and emotional reactions to stress situations.

Additional aims are:

1. to determine whether any generalities can be valid as to types of problems and extent of deficiencies relative to parent repertoires in handling retarded children;
2. to train personnel of various disciplines in observational techniques and behavior therapy.

The present paper describes a program in which trainees were involved in all phases of operation, data analysis, and treatment planning and implementation.

Staff and Facility

At present the staff consists of psychologist, speech pathologist, social worker, public health nurse, occupational therapist, physical therapist, research assistant, and special achievement teacher—all either trained or receiving training in the use of operant techniques.

The facility includes an observation room, a playroom with a one-way window, two office rooms for interviewing parents, a physical therapy room, and an occupational therapy room. Observation is also done in the child's home.

Conceptual Framework

The child, to be accepted in this behavioral-educational phase of the program, must have first undergone an intensive multiple-disciplinary diagnostic program. Children previously diagnosed as retarded attend the medical diagnostic program in groups of ten for two hours each day for four weeks. During the four weeks, they are observed by a pediatric nurse and other staff as they engage in group activities structured by a special achievement teacher. They are taken from the observation room to undergo neurological, pediatric, orthopedic and dental diagnoses and treatment for any physical problems such as seizures, dental problems, nutritional problems, and visual and hearing problems. They are also evaluated by standard psychological, speech, occupational therapy and physical therapy evaluation procedures. At the end of this period the staff confers with parents to inform them of the findings and to make recommendations for the child's schooling and continuing medical and dental care. The goal is to assure that each child is functioning in an optimal health state. Selected children with the most severe behavioral deficits or the most markedly disruptive behaviors are seen in the behavioral phase of the program.

Types of Behavior Treated

Behaviors explored in the clinic include deficiencies in self-help skills such as dressing, grooming, feeding, toilet care, and deficiencies in speech and language such as vocalizing in jargon rather than in already acquired speech, echolalia, and low rate of speech. Inappropriate behaviors are varied but have included tantruming, hitting children, and even such extremes as putting eye glasses in garbage disposal units, smearing food on walls, etc.

In each case the therapists observe the child closely, pinpointing exact behaviors, the context in which they occur, the current social consequences, and the possible competing responses. Potency and variety of available reinforcers are assessed independently. The procedure is based on operant principles: Skinner (1938), Bijou and Baer (1961), Holland and Skinner (1961).

Enlisting Parents as Cooperative, Effective Therapists

The parents have come in with a plea for help. They find that they cannot handle their child in certain situations. Discipline may be a problem. Specifically, when they see that their child is lacking in many areas of performance, they become worried and seek help. Their child's be-

havioral problem and/or deficiencies may have either excluded the child from school programs or seriously interfered with the child's progress in school. For some families a major portion of activity and time is spent in attempts to cope with their child's behavior. They may even have curtailed normal social activities because of embarrassment over their child's behavior and their inability to cope with it.

The clinic requires parental participation since changes in the child's behavior are directly related to changes in parental management of the child. Improvement in the child's behavior will in turn reinforce the parents' attempt to try new approaches and responses to their child.

Interview and Observation

Parental participation in the program begins with the initial interview. They are encouraged to report to the staff their concern about their child and they are asked to report situations in which problem behaviors occur and to describe how they handle them. The first interview also provides an opportunity to explain to the parents the need for clinic and home observation of the child's behavior.

The parents' report of their child's behavior serves as one basis for the development of the parents' own observational skills; i.e., staff observation and their own observations later in the program can be compared with their initial report. Their verbal report does not serve as a basis for giving guidance on child care and management.

More specifically, when first seeking help, parents may be able to see quite clearly what their children are doing part of the time, but they do not have a clear over-all picture. They are generally so concerned about specific nuisance behaviors that they frequently fail to recognize significant gains in adaptive skills that are possible for their child. For instance, a child who at the age of four continues to be spoon-fed by his mother, may occasionally put some food in his mouth. The parent, *never having broken down the process of learning to eat* into small steps, does not see this as an approximation but only as a messy habit of an uncooperative child. Also, few parents recognize a relationship between the child's behavior and their response to it.

Clinic Observations

The setting event or context in which behavior problems occur can be replicated in a lab session, so that the child's behaviors can be observed as well as the parent's responses to the child. For example, a child may scream or cry when his mother gives him a command or fall on the floor and bang his head when asked a question; he may hit the parent, or knock over furniture as the parent reads alone, but not while the child plays with her. Or, he may poke another child who is receiving parental attention. These behaviors can be replicated by instructing the parent to give a command, ask a question, read to the child, play with the child, or read alone and not respond to the child, etc. In this way, observations can be made as to the specific context in which certain behaviors occur, as well as to the reinforcers that maintain those behaviors.

A lab session also provides an opportunity to evaluate the potency of parental attention as a reinforcer for the child. This is accomplished by observing the play behavior of a child and mother and recording data regarding frequency and/or duration of a particular response class. It could be time spent playing with a particular toy, time spent in one section of the room as opposed to another, etc. The mother is then instructed to respond to the child whenever a specified behavior occurs and to withhold responding when any other behavior occurs. The parent is also told that when she does respond she should try to encourage the child by joining him in his activity, commenting on what he is doing, and avoiding criticizing the child or giving him verbal directions. After about five minutes a reversal technique is employed in which the originally reinforced behavior is put on extinction (the mother is instructed not to respond to the child when the behavior appears), and a different play behavior receives attention from the mother.

In this way it becomes clear whether the parent's attention is reinforcing to a child; i.e., whether, when the parent attended verbally or by smile or touch to one behavior, this behavior continued or increased in frequency. In most cases a mother's talking to a child while he is doing a puzzle, for instance, is enough to insure that he will stay with the puzzle. If he shifts and she does not, he will, if her attention is reinforcing, return to the puzzle. In some cases this is not true. A child's responses may be reinforced by termination of the mother's attention. In one case when the mother followed instructions and expressed interest to the child, her child hit her, used abusive language, and at other times simply left what he was doing and went to something else. This information was put together with: (a) the fact that in group activities when a teacher had said, "My, you're doing a good job," the same child hit her and went into a tantrum, and (b) the fact that during home observations both the father and mother, while the child was slumped over, tears on his face, refusing to eat, used such sarcasm as, "Well, look at that handsome boy we've got. Isn't he fine, mother?" The conclusion was that verbalization from adults, which to most children would be reinforcing, was to this child aversive.

In another case, the mother and father stated that their child knew how to walk for three months before he would walk in their presence. (Friends and relatives informed them that the child walked but would stop whenever his parents entered). They also indicated that if their child vocalized something which sounded like a word, he would not repeat it if either parent expressed an interest. In a separate lab session both parents were instructed (individually) to join their child while he was engaged in an ongoing activity (playing with a toy telephone) and to show interest and respond to him. The child's response in each case was to stop playing, suck his thumb and stare into space. In these cases giving the parents advice, without taking into account that their parental attention was aversive to the child, would have been expected to worsen the situation.

In the majority of cases, parental attention is a strong reinforcer, and the lab session serves to demonstrate to the parents the effects of positive reinforcement for a desired behavior and withholding positive reinforcement for an undesired behavior.

Home Observations

Although time consuming, home observations provide an invaluable source of information about environmental factors that relate to a child and his behavioral problems. Home observations are based on interview information about what situations seem to be most troublesome for the family in dealing with the problem child. The time before, during, and after dinner frequently is relevant for a wide range of behavioral problems.

To prepare for home observations, parents are told that the staff wants to observe their child in situations which are as natural as possible, with all members of the family behaving toward the child as they normally do.

During a home observation, the observer takes either a running record of exact verbalizations and actions or, in a later visit, a count of certain behaviors. In each case he is recording not impressions and vague descriptions but actual occurrences: verbalizations, movements from room to room, screams, hits, laughs, hugs, directions, requests, statements, etc. and in exact temporal sequence. During the time that he is recording, he in no way interacts with the parents or the child, nor does he conduct any interview during the home observation.

The observer has asked to be completely ignored. If, at first, the child approaches him he may say, "I'm working now," and from then on he makes no response whatever. After a few minutes the child ignores him also. The parents frequently report that "this is just about the way it always is." Two or three different observers return with very similar data from separate visits.

Evaluation of Data, Treatment Plan

The observations provide highly specific information which gives a context in which to view the child's problem. For example, one child who reportedly never did as he was told was observed to have received 35 commands during a 20-minute play session. When the child ignored commands and went on playing, the mother dropped her request and continued playing with him. When the child began following through on a command, the mother turned away from the child. In this way she was actually putting "following commands" on extinction. Another child who yelled frequently was found to be ignored when he spoke in a normal voice and responded to when he yelled. A third child, whose mother complained, "He will not sit still when I read to him," was observed as his mother "read" to him. The mother gave her child a series of questions about words that were too difficult for him and then severely criticized him for his incorrect answers. When his squirms escalated to jumping in the air and shrieking, he was told, "O.K. I won't read to you anymore." Apparently "reading" had become highly aversive to him and he had learned ways to terminate it.

Children with serious delays with self-help skills were typically confronted with situations in which parents criticized the child as he was attempting to dress or feed himself, and, when the child gave up, the parents dressed or fed the child. One nine-year-old mildly retarded child was spoon-fed by his mother; a four-year-old was not allowed to touch food even at meal time and thus never went through the finger-feeding and spoon-feeding stages.

Speech and language difficulties were similarly analyzed. A child who seldom initiated speech but who echoed was observed at three home sessions. Over half of his utterances were echoed back to him; *e.g.,* when he said, "I want a truck," rather than bringing him a toy, his mother replied, "You want a truck." A four-year-old girl, who in speech evaluations showed no recognizable speech, and who had a pattern of bizarre hand movements, was observed in her home. She was an only child. She had no toys. Both mother and father mimicked her hand movements and smiled when she imitated. In three one-to-two-hour sessions, not one utterance made by either parent to the child was recognizable as a word by either of two observers. Without a series of home observations, the therapists would not have known how strongly the child's environment supported the behavior deficits.

By the time three to four clinic and home observations have been completed, the parents have observed the effect of their attention on the behavior of their child, and have discussed these observations with therapists. It is at this stage, as all the small parts are put together into a whole, that the parents can help choose what problem they want to work on first, to what extent they want to include siblings in the treatment plan, and whether they want to start with clinic sessions or whether they want to start at home.

When the parent decides to work on a certain problem behavior or to try to build in a needed behavior, the first question to be answered must be "What behavior on the part of the parent will we help him

change in order to alter a behavior in the child?" Whether or not the parents will withhold attention, contingent on a problem behavior, and give it only contingent on behaviors that are incompatible with the problem behavior, depends on whether we have found the parents' attention to be a reinforcer for this child.

In cases where parental attention is a strong reinforcer, teaching the parent to withhold attention contingent on a problem behavior is only part of the solution. In some cases the mother has found it difficult to give warm loving attention when the child is doing well. The patterns of response which involve "leaving him alone when he's not getting into trouble," are so strong that it has taken several sessions to teach the mother to respond to the child as he is behaving appropriately. Occasionally a therapist has taken the child into the playroom and worked on shaping a small behavior using social reinforcers, while the mother and another therapist watch and discuss what is going on. As the mother sees the therapist at work, she is encouraged to try different ways of motivating her child. It is as she uses these patterns and as they begin to show results, and only then, that she begins to find the child himself more reinforcing to her, and begins to find more confidence in working on problems and building in new behaviors. It is at this point that the parent can usually begin to see small approximations toward other useful, desirable behaviors to which she could respond in her child.

The situation is more difficult in cases where parental attention is not a reinforcer. For one thing, when parental attention is not reinforcing to a child, the pattern of parent-child interaction will be unusual because many behaviors of the parent will have been extinguished by a lack of response on the part of the child. Play between parent and child will be absent, and the parents will generally interact by punishing a child and attempting to suppress an ongoing behavior. When the child is not actively causing a disturbance, the parents will not intervene. In these cases the parents must first be taught to use potent extrinsic reinforcers and to pair them with a class of verbal and gestural responses on their part that can eventually be used as reinforcers. They must also be taught when to reinforce approximations toward useful behaviors in areas of grooming, dressing, feeding, playing, and talking.

Types of Treatment Sessions

Clinic

In beginning treatment, the most successful method has been to give the mother a chance to try out suggestions while in the clinic. She and the child play together in the playroom under observation, and she practices, for example, reading to a child while he is sitting still next to her and not attending to him while he wiggles around or leaves her to go and play with something else in the room. This gives her experience in making her attention contingent on a desired behavior. As soon as she has accomplished a marked change in the child's rate of sitting and listening, she can discuss with staff the methods she used and the ways to use them at home. A following session then might be on a more marked problem behavior such as whining, tantruming when given a direction, or distracting the mother from a task at hand.

Home

Concurrent with clinic sessions, the staff has conducted home treatment sessions. The therapist, having helped the family decide what problem to work on, goes to the home and observes them as they put the changes into effect. These visits are much like the early observations except that now, with definite behavioral contingencies planned, discussions will hinge on the ways in which the parents are succeeding

and on elements that deserve further consideration or possible change.

In Hawkins, Peterson, Schweid, and Bijou (1966) and Allen and Harris (in press) detailed studies, an individual set of parents was trained to work on a problem behavior at home. The program under discussion here was developed to assist a large number of parents, each dealing with a retarded child.

It is obvious that parents constitute a large portion of a child's social environment and that they have control over a variety of potent reinforcers. Behaviors which are followed either inadvertently or intentionally by one or more of these reinforcers will increase in frequency whether they are adaptive or disruptive. Teaching parents to observe carefully and to respond at times when adaptive behaviors appear in their child's repertoire will increase the child's chances of learning a significant number of skills. Only when a child has been observed interacting with his family can specific help be given. Following the isolation and treatment of one or more specific problems, the parents can begin to apply their skills in other areas of the child's behavior.

As we learn more about the repertoires of parents who have retarded children, though each case still must be treated as an individual instance, some broad patterns may appear. Systematic study of common pitfalls should aid in planning that will help parents avoid these typical problems.

References

Allen, K. Eileen, and Harris, Florence. "Elimination of a Child's Excessive Scratching by Training The Mother in Reinforcement Procedures." *Behavior Research and Therapy.* In press.

Bijou, S. W., and Baer, D. M. *Child Development: Volume One, A Systematic and Empirical Theory.* New York: Appleton-Century-Crofts, Inc. 1961.

Hawkins, Robert P., Peterson, Robert F., Schweid, Edda, and Bijou, Sidney W. "Behavior Therapy in the Home: Amelioration of problem parent-child relations with the parent in a therapeutic role." *Journal of Experimental Child*

Psychology, 1966, *4 (1)* 99–107.

Holland, J. G., and Skinner, B. F. *The Analysis of Behavior*. New York: McGraw-Hill. 1961.

Skinner, B. F. *The Behavior of Organisms*. New York: Appleton-Century-Crofts, Inc. 1938.

Special Education - The Case of Deafness

Hearing Standards— Fact or Fiction?

Howard P. House, MD

THE NEED for education, and for the skilled personnel that education creates, has never been greater than it is today. Many individuals seeking educational opportunities or applying for employment are rejected on the basis of unrealistic physical standards.

The purpose of this presentation is to review some of these unrealistic standards as they pertain to hearing, standards that prevent one from pursuing his educational interests or obtaining employment in his particular skill.

Unrealistic School Placement Hearing Standards

My interest in this subject developed after many years of sharing the disappointment of parents of hearing handicapped children when their hopes for the child's future ended in despair due to unrealistic school placement hearing standards.

Children with impaired hearing are assigned to various school programs by school administrators or placement personnel. The assignments are based on the child's audiogram rather than the child's ability to function in his environment. Consequently, many children are transferred to a different educational environment and their entire future is altered by this decision.

Too often a child who is pronounced "profoundly deaf" on the basis of his audiogram may function well with a hearing aid in a school program for the hard of hearing.

The Walter E. Heck Memorial Lecture, read before the Section on Laryngology, Otology, and Rhinology, during the 117th annual convention of the American Medical Association, San Francisco, June 17, 1968.

From the Otologic Medical Group, Los Angeles.

Reprint requests to 2122 W Third St, Los Angeles 90057.

Likewise, the so-called "hard-of-hearing" child may be assigned to an integrated hard-of-hearing program, who could function as an essentially normal-hearing child by making adequate use of his residual hearing with a hearing aid.

I shall review four such instances.

EXAMPLE 1.—The first audiogram (Fig 1, *top left*) is that of a 9-year-old child who has a sensorineural impairment due to maternal rubella. A hearing aid had been worn since the age of 2. He entered grade school at 6 years of age and functioned well for three years, receiving grades of A and B with a scattering of C's. In spite of this performance, the parents were told the child had been classified as profoundly deaf and, therefore, must attend a school for the deaf. After one semester in the school for the deaf, the child lost all interest and motivation in the educational process and his language and speech deteriorated considerably.

This child was classified as profoundly deaf on the basis of the audiogram. The use of his residual hearing with hearing aids, however, places him in the category of the "hard-of-hearing" rather than the "profoundly deaf." After considerable difficulty this boy was returned to an integrated hard-of-hearing program and is again performing well in this environment.

EXAMPLE 2.—This second child would normally be classified as profoundly deaf, based on the audiogram (Fig 1, *top right*). Her hearing loss was diagnosed before 2 years of age and a hearing aid obtained immediately. A twin brother helped stimulate a constant flow of communication. The parents worked diligently with her in auditory and speech reading before she was 3 years of age. At 9 years, she was given binaural hearing aids and was able to obtain a sound field speech reception threshold (SRT) of 43 db.

This child has graduated from a large suburban high school with better than average grades for her high school career. Fortunately, she was not placed in a deaf school on the basis of her audiogram.

EXAMPLE 3.—The next audiogram (Fig 1, *bottom left*) is that of a young man of 16 who was first evaluated at age 10. A diagnosis of a sensorineural impairment of congenital origin was established. Since age 3, he had worn a monaural aid. At age 10, binaural instruments were recommended and his hearing level shifted from a 53 db sound field to a 25 db sound field, with a 74% discrimination score.

The boy was enrolled in a program for the hard-of-hearing in an integrated school system

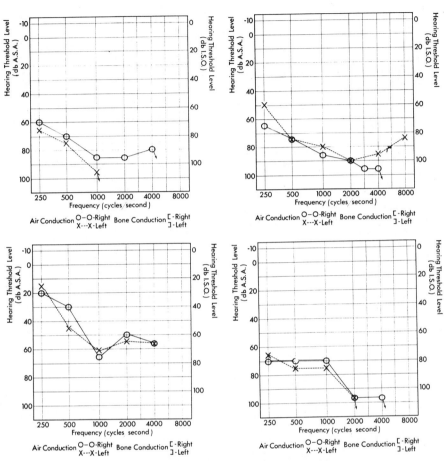

Fig 1.—**Top left,** Audiogram of a 9-year-old boy with sensorineural impairment due to maternal rubella (example 1). Right ear: SRT = 85 db; left ear: no discrimination. **Top right,** Audiogram of a child classified as profoundly deaf (example 2). SRT = 90 db bilaterally. **Bottom left,** Audiogram showing congenital sensorineural impairment (example 3). Right ear: SRT = 50 db; PB = 64%; left ear: SRT = 52 db; PB = 68%. **Bottom right,** Audiogram of a severely hard-of-hearing girl (example 4). Right ear: SRT = 83 db; PB = 60%; left ear: SRT = 95 db; PB = 36%.

where he did very well. After two years, the parents were told the boy was deaf and must be sent to a school for the deaf. They were informed that his hearing tests clearly indicated that he did not belong in a hard-of-hearing program.

For one year this boy was assigned to a school for the deaf; during this time he lost motivation and his reading level and speech deteriorated considerably. After this one year, he returned to the previous hard-of-hearing integrated school program and graduated from high school with a B average.

This boy represents a case classified as profoundly deaf who is functioning essentially as a normal youngster with the use of binaural aids. This is another example of a youth whose entire future would have been greatly altered had he been required to remain in the school for the deaf.

EXAMPLE 4.—The final example (Fig 1, *bottom right*) concerns a severely hard-of-hearing 12-year-old girl. This young lady was enrolled in an elementary school with a special class for the deaf and hard-of-hearing children. She was first examined at the Otologic Medical Group at the age of 4, at which time she had been wearing a hearing aid on the right ear for approximately one year. A second hearing aid was added to be worn on the left ear. The girl was not seen for another eight years. When she returned at the age of 12, speech thresholds were established at 83 db on the right ear and 95 db on the left ear, with a sound field of 90 db. The discrimination score was 60% on the right ear and 36% on the left ear.

The parents of this young lady reported she was now in a school with all hearing children, was progressing normally from one grade to the next, and obtaining better than average grades in all of her school subjects.

Comment

These four examples point out the need for us to look at the child and the way he functions in his environment, rather than looking solely at the audiogram and classifying the youngster as hard-of-hearing or profoundly deaf. The ability of the individual to function as a person, using his intellect, his visual acuity, and his residual hearing with hearing aids is of paramount importance. Some children can utilize their residual hearing and function as a hard-of-hearing individual in spite of a "deaf" type audiogram. Other children may function as essentially normal hearing individuals in spite of a "hard-of-hearing" type audiogram.

The future of these children lies in the intelligence of those responsible for their placement. What a tragedy it would have been if these four children had been confined to a school for the deaf for their educational experience. Unfortunately, many similarly handicapped children are doomed to this destiny. This must not continue!

Unrealistic Vocational Hearing Standards

I see many examples in which a high school or a college student interested in a career in teaching, nursing, or other professions has been discouraged in pursuing this interest because of a mild or moderate hearing impairment. Two examples will be cited.

EXAMPLE 5.—This audiogram (Fig 2, *left*) is that of a young lady who has a congenital unilateral sensorineural hearing impairment. She became aware of this at 10 years of age when it was discovered accidentally through a routine school hearing test.

After completion of high school, this girl worked as a nursing aide and decided on a nursing career. She enrolled in a junior college program for nurse's training, at which time a hearing test was performed and the unilateral impairment confirmed.

With one year remaining in her training period, this young lady left school to work for one year to obtain funds for her continued education. On reentering the college program another hearing test was performed, following which she was told she could not continue in

Fig 2.—**Left**, Audiogram showing congenital unilateral sensorineural impairment (example 5). Right ear: SRT = 15 db; PB = 92%; left ear: SRT = 50 db; PB = 92%. **Right**, Nonprogressive sensorineural impairment (example 6).

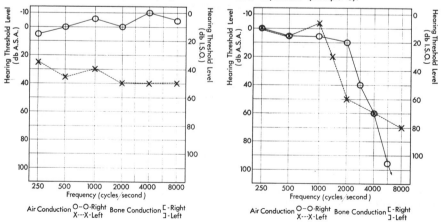

her nursing education because of her hearing impairment.

We are making every effort to reinstate this girl in her training program, even to the extent of assuring the school and the girl that we will employ her when she completes her nursing education. To date we have not been successful.

Incidentally, Dr. Walter Heck, whom we are honoring on this occasion, with his unilateral hearing loss could not have been a nurse on the basis of the unrealistic standard imposed on the aforementioned young lady.

EXAMPLE 6.—The second example (Fig 2, *right*) is that of a young man who has a nonprogressive congenital sensorineural impairment. This man entered and completed satisfactorily a four-year college program, fulfilling the curriculum requirements for a teacher. Following graduation he was denied his teaching credential by the Los Angeles Board of Education because of his hearing impairment. This occurred in spite of normal hearing in the right ear in the three speech frequencies with excellent discrimination.

It is possible to cite many other similar cases. Little or no consideration may be given to whether the hearing impairment is remediable by medical or surgical therapy, or whether it can be benefitted by the use of a hearing aid. Little attention is given to the nature of the hearing loss, whether it is of a static or progressive type. Essentially no effort is made to determine the individual's adaptability, intellect, or utilization of his residual hearing.

Unrealistic Hearing Standards for Employment

The President of this great country can be elected to serve four years as a public servant and yet not have a mandatory, thorough physical examination. By contrast, a maintenance man, also employed as a public servant, may be rejected on the basis of unrealistic physical standards encountered during the course of a mandatory physical examination.

The time has arrived for the establishment of realistic guidelines for physical standards in each occupation and in each job rating of that occupation. In this way, our manpower shortage in vital areas will be reduced; the number of unemployed rejected due to hearing standards will be decreased and individual initiative, enterprise, and productivity will ensue. This is a momentous challenge, but one with tremendous rewards.

Current Hearing Standards

The testing methods and the hearing standards for employment in some common occupations are shown in the Table.

The standard for test criteria and employment in Boston is as follows:

Municipal Boston Transit Authority.— Any employees that work on or around moving vehicles (including porters, laborers, operators, yard masters, truck drivers, etc) must have hearing sensitivity no worse than 20 db, 500 to 3,000 Hertz units, without a hearing aid. The requirement further states that the men must be able to hear spoken voice with each ear no less than 20 feet away. A nurse administers the tests.

Hearing Requirements*

Occupation			Pure Tone	Speech	Retest
Los Angeles schools			40% loss binaural 26% loss better ear	No	No
Firemen			25 db maximum loss 15 db better ear	No	Annual
Yellow Cab			Whisper test at 20 feet		
Teamsters			Whisper test at 20 feet		
Civil Service			Ability to hear conversational voice with or without aid. Some positions stricter.		
US Forces	Officers		15 db @ 500, 1,000, 2,000	Live voice	Annual
	Enlisted		Average 20 db		2 Years
TWA	Ground		Conversational hearing		
	Pilots		25 db each ear @ 500, 1,000, 2,000	No	Annual
American Airlines	Ground	Flight	20 db each ear @ 500, 1,000, 2,000	No	Annual
Student nurse				Live voice	No

*Test methods and hearing requirements of common occupations. Note the wide variation. In general, no consideration is given for the use of a hearing aid.

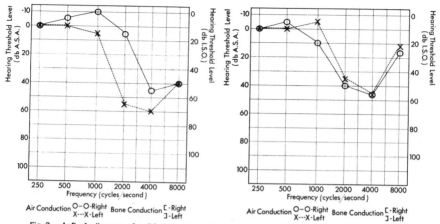

Fig 3.—**Left,** Audiogram of a 54-year-old veterinarian dismissed because he could not meet driving requirements (example 7). **Right,** Audiogram of a medical case worker discharged because of nonprogressive congenital bilateral sensorineural impairment (example 8).

Requirements are dictated by the State Department of Public Utilities.

School Bus Drivers.—The State Registry of Motor Vehicles controls these standards. These men, as well as those that drive trucks interstate, must be able to hear whispered voice at ten feet or have "10/20 hearing in the better ear" without a hearing aid. Licenses to drive cars and trucks are issued to the deaf. There is at present no chauffeur's license in Massachusetts.

Civil Service.—Policemen, firemen, correction officers, Board of Vehicle examiners, watchmen, drawbridge tenders, lock and draw operators, and alcoholic beverage investigators must be able to hear whispered voice at 20 feet in each ear without a hearing aid or device. An applicant will be rejected if he has a missing external ear or acute or chronic otitis media. All applicants for other positions will be rejected if auditory acuity is insufficient for proper job performance. Hearing devices are acceptable.

Two patients recently evaluated at the Otologic Medical Group will illustrate clearly the effects of unrealistic hearing standards in various occupations. Note that both were dismissed from their jobs because of an inability to meet hearing standards necessary to drive a county-owned automobile, an activity purely incidental to their primary jobs.

EXAMPLE 7.—This 54-year-old veterinarian had been employed by the County of Los

Angeles for 12 years. The audiogram (Fig 3, *left*) was obtained during a routine physical examination. Since his hearing did not meet the standards demanded by the County of Los Angeles to drive a county automobile, he was dismissed by the county, in spite of the drastic need for veterinarians' services. Fortunately, we were able to reverse this dismissal.

EXAMPLE 8.—A medical case worker employed by the County of Los Angeles was discharged on the basis of her hearing test (Fig 3, *right*). Note that her hearing is within normal limits in both ears through 1,000 cycles per second (cps), but recedes sharply in the high frequencies. The SRT is 25 db for each ear, with excellent discrimination for speech.

This individual's hearing loss was first discovered as a result of a routine school audiogram, taken at the age of 12 years. She had not been aware of the hearing loss prior to that time. Her only problem in communication at the present time is that she occasionally misses telephone or door bells.

The diagnosis of a nonprogressive congenital bilateral sensorineural hearing impairment was established. Dismissal from employment was the same as the veterinarian's in that she did not meet the required standards for driving a county automobile.

There is no evidence, to my knowledge, that justifies a hearing standard for the driving of an automobile. There are some 50,000 licensed deaf drivers in the county and the driving record of this group indicates 54% fewer moving violations than in the nondeaf group.

172

Hearing standards for employment in the County of Los Angeles were as follows: "An uncorrected hearing acuity using the frequencies 500 through 4,000 Hz must show no more than an average of a 20 db loss nor more than a peak of 35 db loss at one or more of these frequencies." Inquiry failed to reveal any direct source for these hearing standards. It seems these standards were established on the advice of "some committee." These standards have now been liberalized and made more realistic by adding the following sentence: "Significant variations from these standards will be evaluated on an individual basis." A panel of interested otologists in Los Angeles County has been established for the purpose of evaluating persons with significant variations from these standards.

Occupational Opportunities for the Profoundly Deaf

We have spoken primarily about mild and moderate hearing impairments in relation to occupational opportunities. What about the occupational opportunities available to those with a profound hearing impairment, those who might be considered deaf?

Many opportunities are available for both the training and employment of individuals who have profound or total deafness. These opportunities occur in all areas of occupation that do not require direct communication. The Bureau of Vocational Rehabilitation makes training and placement available in occupations that are particularly well adapted for the profoundly or totally deaf individual. Private enterprises such as the Goodwill Industries and others are also engaged in this fine work.

A large aircraft concern recently began a pilot program and employed 20 totally deaf individuals. A normal hearing supervisor was given training in manual communication. This maneuver allowed these 20 deaf persons to be instructed by and communicate with this supervisor.

These persons have been found to be extremely competent, their productivity is superb, and their absenteeism rate is nil except for bona fide illness. Fortunately, more and more corporations are following this format.

As more hard-of-hearing and profoundly deaf individuals are employed, statistical information will become available regarding accident rates, production figures, etc, for hearing impaired workers. This statistical information is essential if hard-of-hearing and profoundly deaf persons are to be readily accepted by industrial physicians, safety engineers, and insurance carriers. Only by this means will government and industry be willing to employ the hard-of-hearing and the profoundly deaf.

Conclusions

This presentation has pointed out the need for otologists to accept the challenge of leadership for the welfare of the hard-of-hearing and the profoundly deaf.

This challenge begins in the correcting of the malplacement of hearing handicapped children in our educational facilities. Proper placement must be based on the adaptability of the child to function in his environment, rather than on the basis of a pure tone audiogram. Let us look more at the ability of the child to function as a person through the use of his residual hearing and his intellect.

This challenge continues by correcting the many unrealistic hearing standards based on the pure tone audiogram that prevent young people from being accepted in advanced educational programs. Every effort must be made to reverse the many unrealistic standards that now prevent advanced educational opportunities.

This challenge extends to encouraging industrial leaders to accept the hard-of-hearing and the profoundly deaf for training and employment in their enterprises.

The Conservation of Hearing Committee of the American Academy of Ophthalmology and Otolaryngology, of which I am chairman, has established working groups that are now reviewing these problems. We hope to be able to establish more realistic guidelines in this area. In the meantime, let us rate the hearing handicapped on individual ability rather than on the basis of unrealistic and nonflexible standards.

Let us, the otologists of the country, accept this challenge and provide the necessary leadership to get this momentous task accomplished!

PICTURE-SOUND ASSOCIATION IN
DEAF CHILDREN

DONALD G. DOEHRING

The ability of children with hearing disorders to identify meaningful nonverbal sounds has not been extensively studied, probably because of the overwhelming importance of verbal sounds for both normal children and those with hearing impairments. That nonverbal auditory perception may operate as something other than a process basic to verbal audition is suggested by Myklebust's comments that "a certain number of young children have disturbances of auditory perception without symbolic language disorders" and that "the child with an auditory perceptual disturbance, but without aphasia, can comprehend the meaning of words when the total auditory world has been appropriately simplified and structured" (Myklebust, 1954, p. 157). Likewise, in one of the few studies concerned with the auditory perceptual abilities of children (Beard, 1965), nonverbal auditory tests were found to have very high loadings on a factor described as "recognition and recall of *Gestalten.*" This suggests that there may be a specific ability or class of abilities associated with auditory nonverbal perception.

In the study reported here the ability of children to recognize common sounds was assessed by using an instructional program in which the child was required to associate sounds and pictures. The purpose was to obtain systematic information regarding nonverbal auditory perception in deaf children.

174

Subjects

The picture-sound program was given to 26 children, aged four to ten, from the Montreal Oral School for the Deaf. Their average hearing loss for 500, 1000, and 2000 Hz in the better ear ranged from 60 dB to beyond 110 dB (ISO). All but three of the children were rated by teachers as average or above average in intelligence.

The program was also administered to 38 children with normal hearing, including two children, aged four and five years, from a special nursery class associated with the Montreal Oral School for the Deaf, 16 four- to six-year-old children from the Montreal Day Nursery, and 20 children ranging in age from 7 to 15 years from a summer program for children with learning disorders conducted by the Learning Center, Montreal Children's Hospital at the Westmount School in Montreal. Both of the hearing children from the Montreal Oral School and all but three of those from the day nursery were rated by teachers as average or above average in intelligence. The IQ scores of the children with learning disorders, all but three of whom had been given the Wechsler Intelligence Scale for Children, ranged from 64 to 125.

Equipment

A Uher Universal 5000 tape recorder with Sharpe HA-8 earphones was used to present the sounds. Pictures were presented by means of a Davis Scientific Instruments Model PP-152 Projector Programmer, which includes a modified Kodak Carousel Projector Model 550. The pictures were back-projected on a 6″ × 9″ viewing area in a specially constructed viewing response device. The viewing area contained six windows 2½″ square, arranged in two rows of three. The windows were mounted in such a way that pressure upon any part of a window would close a set of electrical contacts. A one-half inch blue panel light, used for the signaling of incorrect responses, was mounted just above the center of the viewing area.

The three lower windows were used for the projection of multiple-choice picture stimuli. The correct window for a given trial—the window containing the picture which matched the sound—was coded by means of holes punched in the cardboard slide mount, which activated a photo-electric control circuit in the projector programmer. The sequence of events produced by a correct or an incorrect window-pressing response was controlled by DigiBits solid-state programming modules with associated pulse-shaping input components and reed relay output controls. Both the presentation of a new slide following a correct response and the repetition of a sound following an error or failure to respond were initiated by an inaudible pulse on the recording tape near the end of each sound. These pulses were recorded and played back through a Uher Dia.-Pilot.

Materials

The 12 sounds and associated pictures used for programmed instruction were taken from the "Sights and Sounds" auditory training program developed by Saleh (1965). These included the following sounds and pictures, all taken from a filmstrip-record sequence entitled "On the Farm": rooster, horse, duck, cow, dog, thunder, hen and chicks, kittens, frog, school bus horn, bumble bees, and train. The sounds were dubbed from a master tape supplied by Saleh. All sounds were recorded at approximately the same overall level, as indicated by the VU meter of the tape recorder. The pictures to be used as multiple-choice stimuli were photographed three at a time from 3″ × 4″ colored pictures supplied with the "Sights and Sounds" program. The photographs were taken in such a way that they could be projected on the three lower windows of the viewing-response device.

A number of color cartoon sequences were also photographed, one frame at a time, in such a way that each cartoon frame could be projected on the middle upper window. These pictures, which were used as reinforcement for correct responses, were obtained from comic books. Sequences involving largely panto-mimed action were purposely selected in order to maintain the interest of non-reading subjects.

A 1000 Hz test tone, one minute in duration, was recorded before the beginning of each series of sounds. The level of this tone was adjusted to 30 dB below the approximate overall level of the sounds, as indicated by the VU meter of the tape recorder. Setting the volume control of the tape recorder at the threshold of audibility for this tone served as a crude means of equating the sensation level at which tones were presented to subjects with varying degrees of hearing loss. Sufficient amplification was available through the tape recorder that a threshold level could be obtained in this manner even for subjects with profound hearing impairment.

Sequence of Trials

Four series of 36 trials each were prepared. Each sound occurred three times in each series, with the order of sounds randomized in blocks of 12 trials, wherein each sound was presented once. For the three pictures presented in conjunction with each sound, the two incorrect choices were varied from trial to trial, as were the horizontal positions of correct and incorrect pictures. Each stimulus slide was followed by a reinforcement slide, with the reinforcement slides arranged in the original sequence of the comic strip.

Procedure

All training was carried out in a quiet, distraction-free room. The subject was seated before the viewing-response device, the earphones were fitted, and the level of sound presentation was determined by adjustment of the 1000 Hz re-corded tone to the subject's auditory threshold. Several demonstration trials

METHOD

were given; during each trial the child was instructed to find the picture which corresponded to the sound, and the consequences of correct responses and errors were illustrated. Then the actual programmed instruction was begun. The experimenter remained seated behind and to one side of the subject throughout, and intervened with further instructions whenever necessary.

The subject's task on each trial was simply to press the window containing a picture which corresponded to the sound that had been presented through earphones. Each trial was 12 seconds in duration, and the length of the sounds ranged from 7 to 8 seconds. If the subject failed to respond or responded too late, the tape was automatically rewound and the same sound repeated. If an incorrect window was pushed during presentation of a sound, the blue light turned on to indicate an error, the tape was rewound after completion of the sound, and the same sound was repeated. Pushing the correct window during presentation of a sound turned off the sound and produced an immediate slide change to a reinforcement picture. Then, at the time when the sound would have been completed had it remained on, the reinforcement slide changed to a stimulus slide and the next sound was presented.

Once begun, an entire series of 36 trials could be completed in 10 minutes or less without intervention of the experimenter. However, there was provision for the experimenter to interrupt the program sequence by a manual switch. This procedure was sometimes used during the early training of younger children for whom additional instruction was required.

For the majority of children an entire series of 36 trials was completed in one session, and two or three sessions per week were given until the learning criterion was reached. The four test series were alternated from session to session, with the entire sequence repeated where more than four sessions were required. For several of the younger children it was necessary to present some or all of the training material in half-sessions of 18 trials each.

Training was terminated when the learning criterion was achieved, if a child became unavailable for further training, at the child's own request, or when it became obvious that the child could not achieve the learning criterion within a reasonable number of sessions.

Criterion of Learning

Each of the 12 sounds was presented three times during a session of 36 trials. The criterion of learning was no more than three errors in a complete session, with no more than one error for any given sound. This criterion allowed for a small number of errors due to distraction or carelessness.

RESULTS

Deaf Children

Of the 26 deaf children with whom training was initiated, 19 reached the criterion of learning. Table 1 shows the number of sounds correctly identified on all three of the trials given for each sound during the first session, the number of sessions required by the 19 children who reached the learning criterion, and the number completed by the seven children who did not reach the criterion. Also shown are age, sex, hearing loss, an estimate of aided hearing ability, and an estimate of intelligence. The judgment of aided hearing ability

TABLE 1. Individual results for deaf children.

Subject	Age	Sex	Hearing Loss (dB)	Aided Hearing Ability	Intelligence	Sounds Correct 1st Session	Sessions to Learning Criterion
	Children who reached the learning criterion (N = 19)						
1	5- 3	F	85	1°	C°°	4	9
2	5- 7	F	95	2	B	7	3
3	5-10	M	105	3	B	3	8
4	5-11	F	95	4	A	2	9
5	7- 3	M	90	1	A	5	4
6	7-10	F	100	3	A	4	6
7	8- 0	M	110+	5	A	3	6
8	8- 4	F	100	2	B	10	1
9	8-10	M	70	2	B	10	1
10	8-11	M	110+	5	A	4	6
11	9- 0	M	95	4	B	8	5
12	9- 2	M	95	2	B	6	4
13	9- 4	F	100	3	B	3	4
14	9- 9	F	90	2	B	6	6
15	9- 9	M	85	2	B	7	2
16	9- 9	F	100	3	B	2	6
17	9-10	F	95	4	A	10	2
18	10- 1	M	110+	5	B	0	11
19	10- 4	M	110+	5	A	5	4
	Children who did not reach the learning criterion (N = 7)						
20	4- 8	M	60	1	A	5	(7)†
21	5- 0	M	80	3	B	0	(7)
22	5- 2	F	90	3	B	4	(14)
23	5- 6	M	90	5	B	0	(4)
24	7-11	F	110+	5	C	0	(6)
25	9- 7	F	110+	4	C	4	(7)
26	9- 7	M	110+	4	A	1	(7)

°Rating of aided hearing ability: 1 = good, 3 = average, 5 = poor.
°°Rating of intelligence: A = above average, B = average, C = below average.
†For the children who did not reach criterion, the number of sessions completed is given.

was obtained from the principal of the school, and the judgment of intelligence—as indicated by classroom performance—was obtained from the child's teacher. All judgments were made without knowledge of the child's performance on the training task.

The number of sounds correctly identified on all three trials during the first session ranged from 0 to 10, indicating considerable variability among the deaf children in the number of sounds they were able to identify at the beginning of training. Subjects 8, 9, and 17 were able to identify almost all of the sounds, whereas one of the children who learned and three who did not reach the learn-

TABLE 2. Relationship between number of sounds correct on the first session and number of sessions to learning criterion for the 19 deaf children who reached the learning criterion.

Number of Sounds Correct First Session	Number of Subjects	Mean Sessions to Learning Criterion
0- 2	3	8.67
3- 5	8	5.87
6- 8	5	4.00
9-12	3	1.33

ing criterion were unable to identify even one sound with complete accuracy on the first session.

There was a strong relationship between the number of sounds correct on the first session and the number of sessions required to reach the learning criterion, as shown in Table 2. In general, the more sounds identified on the first session, the fewer sessions were required for achievement of the learning criterion. It can also be seen from Table 1 that the children who did not reach criterion tended to know fewer sounds on the first session than the children who reached criterion.

TABLE 3. Relationship between the number of sessions required to reach the learning criterion and age, hearing loss, aided hearing ability, and intelligence for the 19 deaf children who reached the learning criterion.

Attributes of Subjects	Number of Subjects	Mean Sessions to Learning Criterion
Age		
5	4	7.25
7 and 8	6	4.00
9 and 10	9	4.89
Hearing Loss (dB)		
70-90	5	4.40
95-105	10	4.80
110 & above	4	6.75
Aided Hearing		
Good (1 & 2)	8	3.75
Average (3)	4	6.00
Poor (4 & 5)	7	6.14
Intelligence		
Above average	7	5.29
Average	11	4.64
Below average	1	9.00

The relationship of learning rate to age, hearing loss, rating of aided hearing ability, and rated intelligence is shown in Table 3. Older children, children with less profound hearing loss, children with better aided hearing, and children with higher intelligence might be expected to learn the task more quickly, and to a certain extent they did. The youngest children tended to require more sessions, but there was a slight reversal of this trend among the older children; children with the most profound hearing loss tended to require the most sessions, with a smaller difference between children in the two categories of less-severe hearing loss; and children with good aided hearing tended to require the fewest sessions, with a much smaller difference between subjects rated as average and poor. However, with the exception of the one child rated as below average in intelligence (who was also the youngest deaf child to reach the learning criterion), there was a slight reversal of the expected relationship between rated intelligence and number of sessions to reach criterion. A more rigorous assessment of these relationships was prevented by unavoidable imbalances of group composition, such as the tendency for the older children to have more profound hearing loss, a factor which undoubtedly obscured the relationship of age and hearing loss to learning. In a larger group of deaf children, more adequately equated with regard to these characteristics, the predicted relationships of age, hearing loss, and aided hearing ability to the acquisition of picture-sound associations might be much more obvious. The relationship between rated intelligence and picture-sound association appears questionable, and will undoubtedly vary according to the exact procedure used to estimate intelligence.

Distributions of the incorrect responses to individual sounds by the 19 deaf children who reached the learning criterion are shown in Table 4, where the data are presented in the form of a confusion matrix. The fewest errors were made to the sound of a dog barking, and the most to the sounds of a rooster, bees, and thunder. Errors for the remaining sounds were evenly scattered between these extremes. Incorrect picture responses—that is, the pictures designated in incorrect responses to sounds—showed some correspondence to the sound errors. The picture of a dog was selected incorrectly the least number of times, and pictures of a train, bees, and thunder the greatest number of times. There were only a few instances of consistent confusion involving a particular picture and a particular sound, and in such instances the reversed condition of sound-picture confusion did not necessarily occur. The picture of a train was incorrectly associated with the sound of thunder 24 times, but the sound of a train was incorrectly associated with the picture for thunder (dark clouds and rain) only five times. Likewise, the picture of bees and the sound of a duck were associated incorrectly 20 times, but the sound of bees and the picture of a duck only four times. The data of Table 4 do not indicate that any particular sounds were extremely difficult for the deaf children, nor that any pairs of sounds were consistently confused.

Of the children who did not learn, Subject 20, who knew five sounds on Session 1, had not begun to learn the picture-sound associations for rooster, frog, and duck when training was discontinued; Subject 22 had learned only five sounds after 14 sessions; and Subjects 23 and 24 were still responding to all sounds with chance accuracy when discontinued. The remaining three children all seemed well on the way to reaching the learning criterion when it was necessary to discontinue training. Thus, only about 15% of the group of deaf children encountered serious difficulty in learning the picture-sound associations. The four children who had the greatest difficulty (Subjects 20, 22, 23, and 24) tended to be young, but showed no marked tendency toward

180

TABLE 4. Confusion matrix for all errors made by the 19 deaf children who reached the learning criterion.

Sound	Incorrect Picture Response												Total Errors Per Sound
	Dog	Rooster	Cow	Bus	Train	Bees	Kitten	Thunder	Frog	Duck	Hen	Horse	
Dog	—	4	0	3	1	0	2	2	0	1	2	1	16
Rooster	5	—	9	4	7	5	7	12	8	7	12	13	89
Cow	2	6	—	9	6	4	5	3	8	5	3	5	56
Bus horn	2	2	11	—	3	2	5	1	0	0	1	5	32
Train	0	3	11	6	—	9	2	6	3	2	3	4	49
Bees	1	7	7	11	17	—	8	10	4	4	7	11	87
Kittens	2	5	3	2	4	10	—	6	4	6	2	3	47
Thunder	0	9	4	11	24	11	0	—	6	2	7	9	83
Frog	6	6	5	2	3	7	2	12	—	13	8	5	69
Duck	1	8	2	6	3	20	4	5	17	—	3	5	74
Hen	10	9	2	4	0	4	1	6	3	9	—	5	53
Horse	1	2	6	3	5	5	9	12	2	9	9	—	63
Total Incorrect Picture Responses	30	61	60	61	73	77	45	75	55	58	57	66	

profound hearing loss, poor aided hearing, or low intelligence in comparison with the children who learned.

Children with Learning Disorders

There were no children younger than 7 years old among the 20 children with learning disorders. The majority had IQ's within the normal range. All had a learning problem which could presumably be associated with auditory and visual perceptual disorders, and for eight children there was specific mention in the case notes of problems in auditory perception, auditory memory, auditory discrimination, or auditory attention span.

All but two of the children with learning disorders achieved the learning criterion on the first session. Of the two children who did not, one made only two errors on the first session, but to the same sound, and then made no errors on the second session. The remaining child, a 7-year-old with an IQ in the normal range and no problems explicitly associated with audition, made nine errors on Session 1 and responded incorrectly to all three presentations of thunder on Session 2 before reaching the criterion of learning on Session 3.

The results for children with learning disorders demonstrated that the picture-sound associations are familiar to normal-hearing children of age 7 and above, including children with learning problems associated with auditory perception.

Normal-Hearing Day Nursery Children

The individual results for the normal-hearing children from the day nursery are shown in Table 5. Of the 18 children with whom training was initiated, 13 reached the criterion of learning. As compared with the 19 deaf children who learned the task, the day nursery children tended to respond correctly to more sounds on the first session (median of eight sounds for day nursery subjects and five for deaf subjects) and to reach the learning criterion in fewer sessions (median of two sessions for day nursery subjects and five sessions for deaf subjects). Although there was a slight trend toward better performance with increasing age, the four-year-olds learned the task almost as rapidly as the six-year-olds. Of the five children who did not reach the learning criterion, subjects 14 and 15 did not wish to continue after the second session, and subjects 16 and 18 had almost reached the learning criterion when it was necessary to discontinue testing after five sessions. Subject 17, classified as mildly retarded, was discontinued after part of a session because he was unable to understand the task.

A confusion matrix for the errors made by the 13 day nursery children who learned the task is shown in Table 6. The total errors per sound were distributed in a somewhat similar manner to those of deaf children, with the fewest errors to the sounds of the dog and the horse, and the most errors to the sound of the rooster, thunder, and duck. The distribution of incorrect picture re-

TABLE 5. Individual results for normal-hearing day nursery children.

Subject	Age	Sex	Intelligence	Sounds Correct First Session	Sessions to Learning Criterion
	Children who reached the learning criterion (N = 13)				
1	4- 5	F	B°	7	2
2	4- 6	M	B	5	2
3	4- 8	F	B	5	3
4	4- 9	F	B	7	5
5	4-11	F	C	4	4
6	5- 3	M	A	10	1
7	5- 3	M	A	10	2
8	5- 5	F	B	8	2
9	6- 1	F	B	5	6
10	6- 5	F	A	11	1
11	6- 5	M	A	8	2
12	6- 5	F	B	8	2
13	6- 5	F	B	9	3
	Children who did not reach the learning criterion (N = 5)				
14	4- 3	F	C	4	(2)°°
15	4-10	M	A	7	(2)
16	5- 0	M	B	1	(5)
17	5- 2	M	C	0	(1)
18	5- 3	F	B	4	(5)

°Rating of intelligence: A = above average, B = average, C = below average.
°°For the children who did not reach the criterion, total number of sessions is given.

sponses differed from that of deaf children, with the picture of a kitten selected incorrectly least often and the picture of a hen most often. The picture-sound confusions were well scattered. Interestingly enough, however, the most common confusion—the picture of a train with the sound of thunder—was also the most common confusion for the deaf children.

The younger children with normal hearing were not as proficient in their initial knowledge of picture-sound associations as the older hearing children (learning disorder group), but tended to reach the learning criterion in fewer sessions than the deaf children.

DISCUSSION

The results of this study suggest that the majority of deaf children can learn to identify meaningful nonverbal sounds when the sounds are presented in the context of a simple auditory-visual association task. Most of the deaf children responded correctly to at least a few of the sounds at the beginning of training, probably because of the emphasis upon auditory training in their educational program (Ling, 1964). This joint indication of sound-recognition ability suggests that the perceptual functioning of the deaf child could be enhanced by the development of meaningful auditory associations to objects and events in his visual environment.

Individual differences among deaf children in the amount of training necessary for the acquisition of picture-sound associations bore some relation to age,

TABLE 6. Confusion matrix for all errors made by the 13 normal-hearing day nursery children who reached the criterion of learning.

Sound	Incorrect Picture Response												Total Errors Per Sound
	Dog	Rooster	Cow	Bus	Train	Bees	Kitten	Thunder	Frog	Duck	Hen	Horse	
Dog	—	0	0	0	0	0	0	0	0	0	1	0	1
Rooster	1	—	1	0	2	2	1	4	4	4	9	0	28
Cow	0	0	—	1	0	0	0	0	1	1	1	0	4
Bus horn	0	1	1	—	0	3	0	0	1	1	0	3	10
Train	0	0	1	1	—	0	0	3	0	0	1	1	7
Bees	1	0	1	2	1	—	1	0	0	1	1	1	9
Kittens	0	0	0	0	0	2	—	0	0	1	0	1	4
Thunder	2	0	2	2	10	3	0	—	1	3	3	2	28
Frog	2	3	1	0	2	2	0	0	—	1	5	0	16
Duck	0	1	0	3	4	3	1	1	6	—	4	1	24
Hen	6	1	2	2	0	0	0	1	3	4	—	0	19
Horse	0	0	0	0	0	1	0	0	0	0	0	—	1
Total Incorrect Picture Responses	12	6	9	11	19	16	3	9	16	16	25	9	

hearing loss, and aided hearing ability, but not to teacher ratings of intelligence. A more thorough assessment of auditory nonverbal learning in relation to age, hearing status, and experiential variables, and also in relation to the learning of auditory verbal skills and other nonverbal skills, should provide further information regarding the potential use of various kinds of auditory input for the training of profoundly deaf children. Additional information must also be obtained regarding the development of auditory nonverbal perception in children with normal hearing, since our present knowledge in this regard is not sufficient for an adequate comparison with the perceptual learning of deaf children.

Programmed instruction was used in this study as a systematic and objective method of determining initial knowledge of sounds and the capacity for further learning of picture-sound associations. Although there was no direct comparison with a nonprogrammed training method, some inferences regarding the usefulness of programmed instruction for perceptual training can be drawn from a comparison with data obtained by Saleh (1965).

Saleh assessed the effectiveness of his "Sights and Sounds" auditory training materials by presenting the filmstrip-record story "On the Farm" to 10 deaf children in daily sessions over a 10-week period. The children were between 6-8 and 8-0 in age, with hearing loss between 65 and 85 dB and IQ between 69 and 91. The story contained the 12 picture-sound associations used in the present study, and the children were tested for knowledge of the 12 associations at the beginning and the end of the 10-week training period. The number of associations correctly identified at the end of the first week (5 sessions) ranged from 2 to 7 with a mean of 4.3, and the number correct at the end of the tenth week (50 sessions) ranged from 4 to 10 with a mean of 7.5. Although the two samples cannot be directly compared because of differences in relevant variables, it is quite obvious from the results in Table 1 that the deaf children in the present study progressed much more rapidly in the acquisition of picture-sound associations under programmed instruction.

It appears, then, that systematic programmed instruction may be a very efficient means of teaching specific auditory-visual associations. For a more precise estimate of the relative efficiency of programmed instruction, however, it would be necessary to carry out a formal comparison of alternative instructional procedures. The need for careful comparative studies is indicated by the results obtained by Swets et al. (1962), who investigated the use of programmed instruction in teaching adult subjects to identify meaningless sounds, and concluded that programmed instruction may be no more effective than conventional teaching procedures for auditory perceptual learning.

The 12 sounds used in the present study can probably be classified as relatively simple for the normal listener, since the majority of the hearing children of age seven and above were able to identify the sounds correctly on the first session. Most of the younger hearing children required two or more sessions to reach the learning criterion, but for children of this age the identification of the pictures and the mechanics of the instructional procedure might have added to the difficulty posed by the sounds themselves. Further and more elaborate investigations of sound-recognition in young children are needed. In any case, the performance of the older children with learning disorders suggests that the perception of common nonverbal sounds is not markedly impaired in normal-hearing children classified as having relatively subtle perceptual deficits.

No attempt was made to determine the acoustical characteristics of the 12 sounds, or to relate the spectral properties of the sounds to the audiograms of the deaf children. However, the results amply demonstrated that the majority of deaf children, even those with very severe hearing loss, were able to discriminate among the sounds to the extent of learning the required sound-picture associations. Furthermore, the analyses of picture-sound confusions did not reveal any pairs or triads of sounds which tended to be indistinguishable to the deaf children, and certain confusions which did occur frequently in deaf children were also relatively frequent in the younger hearing children. It seems quite reasonable to expect, therefore, that deaf children can usefully distinguish among common environmental sounds when these sounds are sufficiently amplified.

In arriving at conclusions about auditory perceptual abilities it is necessary to consider the nature of the learning task. In the present study the subject learned to associate a restricted set of visual and auditory stimuli. This could be classified as the associative learning of relatively simple discriminations. To demonstrate the kind of learning that would be characterized as perceptual, it would be necessary for the subject to identify a variety of somewhat different sounds as belonging to a single perceptual category, such as "barking dog," and it would also be necessary to increase the total set of different sound percepts to be learned. Thus, the further study of auditory nonverbal perception in deaf children would require considerable elaboration of the auditory stimuli used in programmed instruction.

This study represented an initial attempt to assess the auditory nonverbal abilities of deaf children. The necessity of further investigation in a number of directions has been pointed out. Several important implications of such research have been suggested. The acquisition of percepts having both auditory and visual attributes should enhance the perceptual development of deaf children, and any knowledge regarding auditory nonverbal ability could be usefully related to the study of auditory verbal perception in deaf children. Finally, the method of systematic programmed instruction in nonverbal picture-sound association could be extended to related skills such as the association of pictures and spoken words for further analysis of the acquisition of basic habits by deaf children.

This research was supported by Public Health Research Grant 604-7-507 from the Canadian Department of National Health and Welfare. All training was done by Judith Rabin. Beverly Sanders and Nina Mayerovitch assisted in the development of instrumentation and procedures. The writer is greatly indebted to Harold Saleh, South Connecticut State College, for the use of pictures and sounds from his "Sights and Sounds" program; to Zada Robinson, Montreal Day Nursery, Sam Rabinovitch, McGill University, Daniel Ling, McGill University, and the staff of the Montreal Oral School for the Deaf for their cooperation with the training project; and to Ling and K. K. Charan for advice concerning methods and instrumentation.

REFERENCES

BEARD, R. M., The structure of perception: a factorial study. *Brit. J. educ. Psychol.*, **35**, 210-222 (1965).

LING, D., An auditory approach to the education of deaf children. *Audecibel*, 13, 96-101 (1964).

MYKLEBUST, H. R., *Auditory Disorders in Children*. New York: Grune and Stratton (1954).

SALEH, H., Sights and sounds: an auditory training program for young deaf children. *Amer. Ann. Deaf*, 110, 528-534 (1965).

SWETS, J. A., MILLMAN, SUSAN H., FLETCHER, W. E., and GREEN, D. M., Learning to identify nonverbal sounds: an application of a computer as a teaching machine. *J. acoust. Soc. Amer.*, 34, 928-935 (1962).

HEARING AIDS AND
CHILDREN IN ELEMENTARY SCHOOLS

John H. Gaeth

Evan Lounsbury

This report presents the information gathered during the initial observation in a longitudinal study to evaluate a group of children and their hearing aids.

There have been very few formal studies of the child in elementary school who wears a hearing aid. We were able to find only one dealing directly with the subject. Rushford and Lowell (1960) sent questionnaires to 5,000 families who had been enrolled

188

in the John Tracy Clinic Correspondence Course. A total of 1,515 families had completed and returned the questionnaire by the time their report was written. The summarizing data give useful information about hard-of-hearing children, but many of the facts are difficult to interpret. For instance, approximately 44% of the parents reported that their child's reaction to his first hearing aid was good or satisfactory. Rushford and Lowell did not interpret this figure, and no meaningful interpretation seems possible.

This report is based on the evaluation of 134 children from the public and parochial schools in the Detroit metropolitan area. One or both of the parents of 120 children were interviewed in the Hearing Clinic at the time of their child's appointment.

PROCEDURE

The information was obtained in three ways: an interview with the parent(s), tests with and without the hearing aid, and measurements of the acoustic characteristics of the hearing aid.

A form was used in the interview with the parents in order to obtain uniform information. Questions were asked about the age of the hearing aid, the extensiveness and number of repairs, the family-dealer relationship, the life of the batteries, earmold or feedback problems, how much the hearing aid was used, and the child's progress in school.

During the first observation of the children, the controls on their hearing aids were taped to fix them temporarily in the "as worn" setting. After pure-tone thresholds at 500, 1,000, and 2,000 Hz were obtained for both ears, aided and unaided speech thresholds and speech discrimination scores were measured for the ear in which the hearing aid was worn. Speech thresholds were established using spondaic words, but a speech awareness threshold and a threshold for common questions were also established.

The acoustic characteristics of the hearing aid were measured on a Bruel & Kjaer apparatus designed for these purposes. Measurements were taken at the "as worn" setting and at full volume. These measurements included a frequency response curve, a curve of the second harmonics, the measurement of power output and acoustic gain, and the percentage of total distortion. For these measurements an input signal of 72 dB re 0: 0.0002 dyne/cm^2 was utilized. In addition, recorded speech was passed through the system in such a way that a simultaneous recording could be made of this speech through the auxiliary microphone in the hearing aid box and through the hearing aid itself using a two-track tape recorder. Thus, it was possible to compare the speech as picked up by a high fidelity microphone near the hearing aid with the speech as it sounded after amplification by the hearing aid.

Of the 120 children whose parents brought them, 64 (53.3%) were boys and 56 (46.7%) were girls. The average of the hearing losses for the better ear at 500, 1,000, and 2,000 Hz were used as the criterion for the severity of the involvement. Of the children, 28% had thresholds from 20 to 35 dB, 44% from 36 to 50 dB, 14% from 51 to 65 dB, and 14% 66 dB or greater. A wide variety of socioeconomic conditions were represented, but the sample may have been biased because somewhat more families from the semiskilled, the laboring, and the unemployed categories were included than one would expect by random sampling.

The age of the children varied from 3 to 18 years; they were enrolled in grades from preschool through twelfth grade, plus 12% in special classes and 14% in classes for the hard of hearing. Eighty-three per cent of the children had been fitted with a hearing aid by one of the two major hearing clinics in Detroit. The remaining 17% wore aids bought on the recommendation of an otologist, teacher, hearing aid dealer, or friend.

Information Obtained from the Interview

The average age of the 120 hearing aids was 2.86 years. Thirty per cent of the hearing aids were less than two years old, 33% were two or three years old, and 37% were four years old or older. Ten per cent of the children had worn their present hearing aid for more than five years. It was reported that 31% of the hearing aids never needed repair, 32% needed one repair, 17% two repairs, and 14% more than two. The information was too uncertain to be useful in 6% of the children. Unless the repair involved the replacement of a receiver or a receiver cord, most of the parents were unable to describe the nature of the repair.

With regard to battery life and use,

in 7% of the hearing aids, the battery lasted for up to three days, 9% for four to six days, 38% one to two weeks, 8% three to four weeks, 13% a little over a month, 11% two months or over, and 14% had no idea how long the batteries lasted. Twelve (9%) of the parents reported that the hearing aid batteries lasted 12 months or more. Eighteen per cent of the children were reported to carry a spare battery, and another 6% kept a spare battery at school.

Three questions were asked about the earmold: the fit, the amount and degree of feedback, and the number of earmolds purchased. Since two of the children were wearing bone-conduction receivers, these data are based on 118 cases. Seventy-five per cent of the parents reported that the earmold was fitted properly, 15% thought it did not fit properly, and 10% had no idea what the question was about. Only 60% of the parents reported no feedback problems, and, even though only 15% reported that the earmold did not fit properly, a total of 30% reported feedback. Again, there were 10% who did not know.

There were some unexpected results from the question about what proportion of the time the children wore the hearing aids and in what situations. One parent reported that the child wore the hearing aid at home but never in school, and 10% reported that their children never wore their hearing aids at all. The remaining 90% wore the instrument in school, and 55% of this group also wore it at home. Thirty-two per cent of the children wore their hearing aids at all times: school, home, and play.

Each parent was asked what behavioral differences he noted when his

190

child obtained his first hearing aid and what behavioral differences he noted now in his child with and without his hearing aid. Forty-nine per cent reported that it made some or a big difference in the child's life, but the other 51% were uncertain. We thought that the answer to this question would concern the child's progress in school, and at first the parents were asked general questions about school. A total of 15% reported excellent progress, 47% reported good progress, and 22% reported satisfactory progress. Thus, 84% of the parents reported that school progress was at least satisfactory. However, when specific questions were asked about grade placement, conflicting results were uncovered. Thirty of the children could not be judged on the basis of academic progress because they were in preschool or kindergarten classes, rooms for the hard of hearing, or ungraded special education classes. Of the remaining 90 children, 50% had failed one or more grades.

Clinical and Physical Evaluation of the Hearing Aid

Although detailed tests were carried out with the Bruel & Kjaer equipment on many of the hearing aids, many of those data are meaningless because so many of the instruments had defective components.

If we were to define an adequate hearing aid as one worn by the child when he came for his clinic appointment, with the volume control set at less than "full," and with all parts present and functioning, then 31% of the total of 134 children had adequate

hearing aids. If the requirements are liberalized and the facts overlooked that the child did not wear the hearing aid when he came to the clinic, that live batteries had to be installed as necessary, and that the hearing aid was worn at full volume, then 55% of the hearing aids could be considered adequate. The remaining 45% had feedback problems, defective controls, cracked receivers, distorting or noisy amplifiers, or other defects.

Forty-two (31%) of the children came to the clinic with hearing aids functioning properly. Two other children were wearing their hearing aids at full volume, but the severity of their losses seemed to justify it. Thus, 44 children appeared to be doing well with their hearing aids. However, whether the gain was adequate to overcome, at least in part, the child's hearing loss was another question. Gain was considered adequate when the aided threshold was within 20 dB of normal or when there was a gain of at least 40 dB over the unaided speech threshold as measured by selected spondaic words. Of the 44 children studied, 48% met the criterion of adequate gain and 52% did not.

Only 16% of a total of 134 children met our original requirements of adequate hearing aid use. By a very lenient definition, no more than 50% of the children were getting any benefit at all from their hearing aids.

Although the subject of binaural versus monaural hearing aids was not part of the investigation, seven children in the project were wearing binaural fittings. Of these, five were functioning properly and four met the criterion of adequate gain. Certainly this group is too small to permit any definitive conclusions, but the fact remains that although these children represented only 5% of the children wearing hearing aids, they accounted for 19% of the 21 children whose hearing aids were adequate.

DISCUSSION

The study revealed that the parents in the sample knew very little about a hearing aid and its care. Although a frequent complaint was that hearing aids were expensive to maintain, the parents knew little or nothing about what the repair bills were for, or what they had to do with the performance of the hearing aid. The information from the parents about battery usage and life was probably not accurate. Probably the parents were simply uninformed. Follow-up study revealed that teachers occasionally buy batteries out of petty cash or their own pockets and give them to the children at school. This could account for the reports that batteries lasted from four months to a year.

The parents also knew little about the earmold. Even under persistent questioning, many of them did not relate acoustic feedback to an improperly fitting earmold. Several parents admitted that the child's hearing aid frequently had feedback, but that they solved the problem by asking the child to turn down the gain. The evidence was clear that for at least 10% of the children the volume setting was based on the functioning of the hearing aid itself. For eight children the procedure for setting the gain was to turn it down until the feedback stopped. One child had a defective receiver that produced gross distortion when the volume control was turned past the one-third point; the hearing aid was worn just below one-third.

The relationship between the reported functioning of the hearing aid and the reported progress of the child in school, and the results of measuring the aid's performance and evaluating the child's actual progress, are not in good agreement either. Forty per cent of the parents thought the hearing aid made a big difference in the child's life, and another 10% thought it made some difference. Yet our data suggest that not more than 16 to 30% of the hearing aids were functioning properly. Likewise, 62% of the parents reported that their children were making good or excellent progress in school, and 22%, for a possible total of 84%, said that they were making satisfactory progress. Yet about one-third, based on the total sample and not just the graded children, had failed at least one grade. One cannot help but wonder whether the ups and downs of "accepting the hearing loss," "abandoning the search for a cure," and "managing the purchase of a hearing aid" do not cause the parent to adopt an unnecessarily low level of expectancy about the child's achievement.

Routine orientation programs for parents are needed. In spite of the probable claims of local audiologists and hearing aid dealers to the contrary, the parents repeatedly reported that no one had told them how to care for the earmold or judge its adequacy, how to help the child adjust the gain or determine whether the aid was working

192

properly, or what to watch for in its ultimate breakdown. Actually, the parents said that the audiologist had told them which hearing aid to buy and the hearing aid dealers how to pay for it and put it on. The fact that these reports are in contrast to the information that was given to them is really irrelevant. The information was not given at the right time or often enough. Clinical centers and hearing aid dealers share the responsibility.

Secondly, the school systems need programs more clearly geared for the hard-of-hearing child. They undoubtedly must share some of the responsibility for these dismal facts. It has been our impression that the hard-of-hearing child has been too much ignored in research studies and in special programs throughout the country. In one study (Gaeth, 1960) it was found that children with losses not exceeding 30 dB were deficient in auditory learning, and in a study by Goetzinger et al. (1964), the language achievement of children with mild losses was found to be below normal. We believe that special programs should be developed for hard-of-hearing children. While they need not be separate from clinical speech programs, they are really not a part of these programs either.

Finally, perhaps too little attention has been paid to the environment in which the aid is worn. Watson (1964) discusses the problems of discrimination in noisy classrooms with poor acoustics where the teacher is a considerable distance from the microphone. The conditions could be so bad that the child develops little concern for whether his hearing aid works adequately or not.

SUMMARY

A total of 134 hard-of-hearing children, most of them in regular public and parochial elementary school classes, were interviewed and tested as the initial step in a longitudinal study. The results were derived from the initial contact and are a summary of the interview with the child and the parents, the results obtained from clinical tests of the child's unaided and aided hearing levels, and measures of the physical characteristics of the hearing aids.

The interview indicated that the parents were poorly informed about all aspects of hearing aids and hearing aid usage. They were uncertain about the life of the battery used in the hearing aid, knew little or nothing about the types of repairs that had been made on the hearing aids, and they did not know how to judge when a hearing aid or earmold was working adequately. For instance, there was lack of agreement between the number of instances in which the earmold was reported as adequate and the number of cases reporting feedback problems. There is evidence that some parents urged the child to turn the hearing aid down below feedback level without regard to the amount of gain provided by such a setting.

When fairly stringent requirements on the mechanical conditions of the aid and the gain obtained from it were applied, only about 16% of the children were wearing hearing aids that could be considered adequate. By the most lenient type of standards, no more than 50% were getting adequate hearing.

Apparently, our present program is deficient in counsel and guidance with the parents and in thorough training with the child and his new hearing aid.

ACKNOWLEDGMENT

The assistance of the Hearing Conservation Section, Division of Maternal and Child Health, Michigan Department of Health and the U.S. Children's Bureau is gratefully acknowledged.

REFERENCES

GAETH, J. H., Verbal learning among children with reduced hearing acuity. Final Report, Cooperative Research Project #289, Office of Ed., HEW (1960).

GOETZINGER, C. P., HARRISON, C., and BAER, C. J., Small perceptive hearing loss: Its effect on school-age children. *Volta Rev.*, 66, 124-131 (1964).

RUSHFORD, GEORGINA, and LOWELL, E. L., Use of hearing aids by young children. *J. Speech Hearing Res.*, 3, 354-360 (1960).

WATSON, T. J. The use of hearing aids by hearing impaired children in ordinary schools. *Volta Rev.*, 66, 741-744 (1964).

SOME POSSIBLE EFFECTS OF THE DELAY OF EARLY TREATMENT OF DEAFNESS

LOIS L. ELLIOTT *and* VIRGINIA B. ARMBRUSTER

This report is the third of a series which describes a population of young hearing-impaired children. A previous publication analyzed audiometric and psychometric scores for all children enrolled in Central Institute for the Deaf during the academic year 1964-65 (Elliott, 1967). A second report described procedures and results of a questionnaire study which was concerned with the early experiences of these same children (Armbruster, 1966). Here, results of the questionnaire study are summarized and considered in relation to audiometric scores and academic progress which were the concern of the first report.

THE QUESTIONNAIRE

The questionnaire was planned to elicit information from parents about family background, the child's birth and development, and early experiences related to diagnosis, use of hearing aids, parent-child interactions, and educational guidance. Because the procedure was considered as a possible pilot study for a larger investigation, a range of topics was explored and several question formats were used (e.g., free response, multiple choice, rating scales). Information identifying the respondent was elicited on the first page which was removed before responses were coded and analyzed. Other records were not utilized; thus, information obtained from parents of the older children applied to events which had occurred as much as ten years earlier while a much shorter time had elapsed for parents of the younger children.

Questions about family background included items about parents' educations, occupations, and marital status; number of siblings and the child's place in the family in relation to the ages of brothers and sisters; incidence of speech and hearing problems among parents and relatives; and the number of adults living in the home in addition to the parents.

Questions about birth and postnatal development included items to determine the age of the parents when the child was born; the conditions at birth, as well as special care during the neonatal period; the age of sitting and walking for the first time; reasons for as well as number and length of hospitalizations after the neonatal period; observations about problems of coordination, balance, vision, and chronic illness.

Separate pages were provided for questions about the discovery of a hearing problem and efforts to find diagnosis and correction. Here, parents were asked to report the child's age when they first suspected something was wrong, and what they suspected. They were asked to tell the reasons for the visits to various examiners, the examiners' professions, the tests each examiner used, the information and recommendations received from each examiner.

In exploring the child's early education we asked the age when he attended each school or clinic, the kind of school, hours of instruction per week, and the reasons for withdrawal. Parents also were asked if they had moved to be near a special school.

Questions about the use of hearing aids included: how old was the child when he wore an aid for the first time, who suggested its use, how it was selected, what kinds of aids were used, what were the parents' opinions of the value of the aids?

One section of the questionnaire was planned to elicit opinions about the child's language behavior as well as his general behavior. This parent-child interaction was explored at three different age levels from birth through 71 months. Questions were asked about the parents' early level of confidence that the child could be taught to read, write, and communicate with spoken language. They were also asked to evaluate the effect of the child's early education on his later accomplishment. Finally, they were asked to report their expectations for the child relative to social, educational, and occupational levels of achievement.

THE SAMPLE

Questionnaires were mailed to the homes of all 177 children enrolled at CID during 1964-1965. Also included were a letter from the principal explaining the purpose of a questionnaire and a stamped return envelope. A follow-up letter was sent to those who had not returned the completed questionnaire at the end of two weeks.

For analysis, the children were divided into seven groups on the basis of their ages and the division of the school in which they were taught (Table 1). Criteria for placement in one of the divisions of CID include age, hearing level,

196

response to teaching, and academic achievement. Groups 2, 4, and 6 contained children from the Division for the Deaf (D), who may be characterized as exhibiting primarily one handicap—that of severe hearing impairment. Groups 3, 5, and 7 contained children from the Division of Speech Pathology (SpP), who also exhibit severe hearing impairment apparently complicated by other

TABLE 1. Grouping of children by school division and by age.

Group No.	Division	Number	Age Range (years-months)
1	Partially Deaf	17	4-4 to 8-8
2	Deaf	41	3-9 to 8-11
3	Speech Pathology	23	6-1 to 8-11
4	Deaf	18	9-1 to 11-6
5	Speech Pathology	31	9-0 to 11-11
6	Deaf	31	12-0 to 16-2
7	Speech Pathology	16	12-3 to 15-8

language or learning problems. Although Speech Pathology children score only slightly lower than the Deaf on intelligence tests (performance scales), their average rate of academic progress has been considerably slower. Group 1 contained children from the Division for the Partially Deaf (PD), whose mean Speech Frequency Average (250 and 500 Hz, better ear, first audiogram) was 15 dB less severe than for children in the Division for the Deaf. Figure 1 displays median, 25th, and 75th percentile audiograms for all groups. Groups 1, 2, and 3 were the youngest children while 6 and 7 were the oldest. If a child had ever been placed in the Division of Speech Pathology, he was treated in that classification for this set of analyses even though he might later have been transferred to another division of the school. For this reason, the group assignments of three children differ from those of the first study. The hearing levels for all except two of these 177 children are now believed to have stayed approximately the same since birth. We believe the two exceptions experienced hearing impairment prior to the age of two.

The acknowledged policy of CID is to place children in a school for the normally hearing as soon as they are judged capable of the transition. Consequently, the oldest children are those whose handicap and rate of progress have prevented them from completing an early transfer to a school for hearing children.

Treatment of Responses

Questionnaire responses were tabulated directly whenever specific response alternatives had been provided or were coded according to a set of criteria. Many parents omitted questions, causing the N to vary between items. Differences between groups for individual questionnaire items were tested with chi-

197

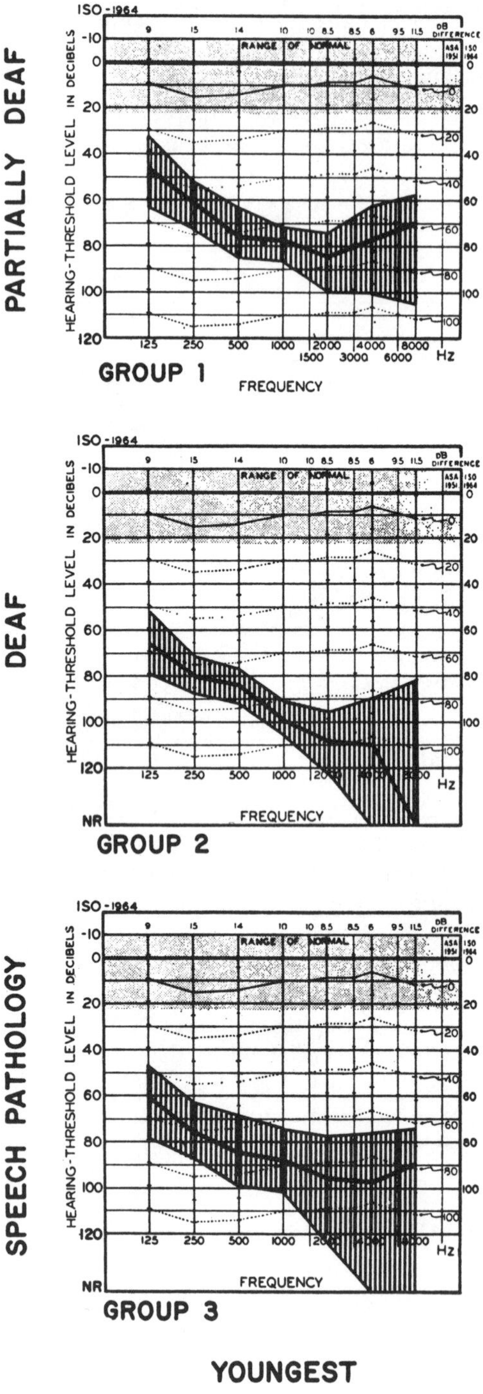

FIGURE 1. Group audiograms showing median (heavy line) and range from 25th to 75th percentiles (shaded area).

198

RECENT AIR CONDUCTION AUDIOGRAMS

GROUP MEDIAN
AND
INTERQUARTILE RANGE

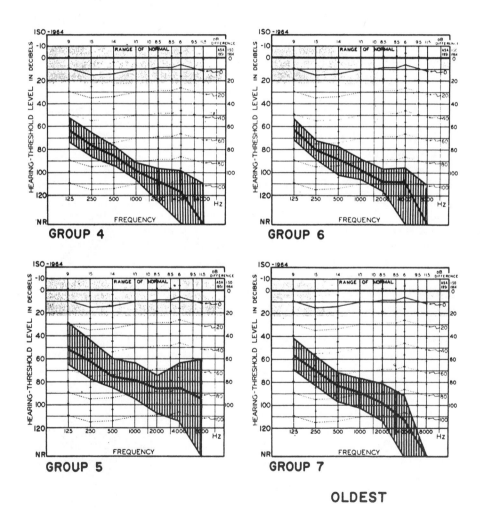

GROUP 4

GROUP 6

GROUP 5

GROUP 7

OLDEST

square procedures. (A more complete description of procedures and results is found in Armbruster, 1966.)

Parents of 158 children (89%) returned the questionnaire. There were no differences in the proportion returned from the three divisions of the school nor from the three age groups.

For most of the topics covered by the questionnaire there was remarkable agreement across groups. Children in the three divisions did not differ in their family history, prenatal or postnatal problems, nor in their developmental history. Children in all groups were reported to have made early attempts to communicate by chattering, producing sounds, etc. A large majority of parents of both Deaf and Speech Pathology children suspected that their child had a special problem before he was two years of age and, in almost every instance, it was reported that the mother was the first to notice the problem. Eighty percent of both Deaf and Speech Pathology parents reported they had suspected a hearing problem before they took their child to the first examiner. Parents of all groups reported receiving a variety of opinions, particularly during the visit to the first examiner; 31% reported being told "nothing is wrong" and 27% were told "the child is too young to test." Only 18% were told by the first examiner that their child had a hearing problem.

Certain other topics elicited very different responses from parents of Deaf and Speech Pathology children. Table 2 summarizes results for the total Deaf and Speech Pathology divisions and for the older children of the two divisions. Because some Deaf children in group 2 were considerably younger than Speech Pathology children in group 3, there was a possibility that this age discrepancy might influence comparisons which were based on the age at which specific events had occurred among the children. By eliminating the youngest groups from analysis, the age range for the two divisions is equated. Table 2 shows that differences observed between the total divisions generally occur also for the subset of older children.

Major differences between the two divisions concerned the ages at which hearing impairment was identified and at which educational procedures were begun. Although parents of both divisions suspected a hearing problem and visited the first examiner at about the same age, Speech Pathology children were taken to a greater number of examiners or examining centers ($p < 0.001$) than the Deaf.[1] Examiners of Speech Pathology children more often suggested the possibility of a central nervous system dysfunction ($p < 0.001$). Speech Pathology children were finally diagnosed as hearing-impaired at a later age than the Deaf ($p < 0.001$). Parents of Speech Pathology children first received

---

[1]The terms, "Deaf," "Speech Pathology," and "Partially Deaf," when used in the report, refer to organizational divisions within the CID School and are not directly descriptive of children themselves. For example, the first report concluded that on the basis of hearing level alone it would often be impossible to determine the divisional placement of a child.

TABLE 2. Tabulated questionnaire results for the total Division for the Deaf and the total Division of Speech Pathology as well as for the older groups within each division.

Question	Total			Older		
	Deaf 2, 4, 6	Speech Pathology 3, 5, 7	p	Deaf 4, 6	Speech Pathology 5, 7	p
Number of separate visits to examiners						
1-5	63	37		36	26	
6 or more	12	21	0.001	4	13	0.05
Numbers of different diagnoses						
1	71	19		36	12	
2 or more	6	34	0.001	4	24	0.001
Diagnosed as "aphasic" or as having a nervous system dysfunction						
No	79	12		41	9	
Yes	3	48	0.001	2	31	0.001
Age at which hearing impairment was diagnosed						
0-35 months	70	29		33	18	
≥36 months	12	31	0.001	10	22	0.01
Age when first wore hearing aid						
0-36 months	53	18		22	11	
≥37 months	28	39	0.001	20	27	0.10
Age of first educational guidance						
0-30 months	54	24		28	15	
≥31 months	26	35	0.01	13	24	0.02
Age when first attended special school						
0-54 months	55	25		28	12	
≥55 months	10	27	0.001	6	22	0.001
Number of siblings						
0-1	38	18		20	14	
≥2	44	42	0.10	23	26	0.50
Has both older and younger siblings						
Yes	13	20		6	13	
No	69	40	0.05	37	27	0.10
Parents' confidence (before child was 6 years old) that child could be taught						
Always confident	41	17		24	11	
Sometimes doubtful	40	41	0.02	18	29	0.05
Parents' aspirations for child's education						
College graduation seems possible	65	31		30	17	
Do not expect college graduation	17	29	0.001	13	23	0.05

some form of educational guidance when their children were older than the Deaf children ($p < 0.01$) and Speech Pathology children began full time attendance at a special school at a later age than the Deaf children ($p < 0.001$). (All probability values stated here pertain to comparisons between the total Deaf and Speech Pathology Divisions.) Thus, even though the process of clinical evaluation was initiated at about the same age for both Speech Pathology and Deaf children, the severe hearing impairment of the Speech Pathology children was not diagnosed and educational and sound-amplification procedures were not instituted until a later age.

Although questions concerning parent-child interactions did not elicit differences between the groups, one aspect of the home environment revealed differences. Children in the Speech Pathology division tended to have a greater number of siblings and to occupy a middle-child position. The youngest groups (D_2, SpP_3) showed these same trends but the difference in age ranges complicates interpretation.

The data indicate that some changes have occurred with time. Among the older Speech Pathology children, 55% had not been diagnosed as hearing-impaired until after they were three years old while that percentage dropped to 45% among the youngest Speech Pathology group. First educational guidance was received after 31 months by 62% of the older Speech Pathology group but by only 55% of the youngest Speech Pathology group. Only 35% of the older Speech Pathology children had been enrolled in a special school by the age of 4½ years, while 72% of the youngest group had been enrolled by this age. Nevertheless, a larger percentage of the Partially Deaf (80%) and of young Deaf children (90%) had been enrolled in a special school by this same age of 4½ years. It is true that the trend has been toward earlier detection of hearing impairment among children in both divisions. Nevertheless, children who have been recently placed in the Division of Speech Pathology (because they showed evidence of language or learning problems superimposed on their hearing impairment) continue to have histories of late identification of their hearing impairment and late initiation of appropriate educational procedures.

A final section of the questionnaire concerned parents' current aspirations for their children and their early confidence in the child's learning to read, write, and communicate with spoken language. Parents of Deaf children were more confident than parents of Speech Pathology children ($p < 0.02$). This difference between divisions was significant among the older children ($p < 0.05$) but not as pronounced among the younger ones ($p < 0.30$). Although this question about confidence explicitly referred to the time preceding the child's sixth birthday, responses may have reflected parents' reactions to events occurring over a number of years. More parents of children in the Division for the Deaf than in the Speech Pathology Division felt it would be possible for their child to complete a college education ($p < 0.001$). While this difference was observed among the subset of older children ($p < 0.05$), it did not occur among the youngest children.

EARLY EXPERIENCES RELATED TO
HEARING LEVELS

The relation between hearing level and certain of these early experiences was examined by separately categorizing Deaf, Partially Deaf, and Speech Pathology Divisions into two groups on the basis of their Speech Frequency Average in the better ear at 500, 1,000, and 2,000 Hz. Within each division, children whose Speech Frequency Average was better than the division median are designated "hearing + " (H+); those with Speech Frequency Average poorer than the division median are called "hearing −" (H−). The first audiogram on record at CID was used for this purpose. Deaf children younger than six were removed from this part of the analysis in order to equalize age ranges for the Deaf and Speech Pathology Divisions. Although the Partially Deaf division is small, it also was split into two groups to permit comparisons based on hearing level. Unlike the H+ and H− groups in the Deaf and Speech Pathology divisions which contain only children over six years of age, the H+ and H− Partially Deaf groups contain children as young as four. Thus, comparisons between divisions may, in part, reflect change over time of diagnostic and therapeutic procedures. Median Speech Frequency Average (re ISO-1964 standard) and the number of children for each group are shown in Table 3.

TABLE 3. Median speech frequency averages for Hearing + and Hearing − groups in the three school divisions.

	Deaf*		Speech Pathology		Partially Deaf	
	SFA**	N	SFA**	N	SFA**	N
Hearing +	91.5	40	75.0	31	75.0	9
Hearing −	109.0	42	97.0	29	87.0	7

*Very young children have been eliminated from the Division for the Deaf so that age range equals that for the Division of Speech Pathology.
**Speech Frequency Average (re ISO-1964 Standard) at 500, 1,000, and 2,000 Hz, better ear.

For each of these resulting groups, responses for specific questionnaire items were compiled in frequency distributions which were then converted into cumulative percent distributions. Figures 2 through 5 depict the percentage of children who have had certain experiences prior to the ages on the horizontal axis. Separate cumulative percent curves are plotted for the H+ and for the H− children in each of the three divisions of the school. (A parallel analysis based on the average response at 250 and 500 Hz in the better ear produced almost identical results and is not reported separately.)

Figure 2 shows that both H+ and H− Speech Pathology groups had a greater number of visits to examiners than the Deaf groups (that is, both Speech Pathology group curves lie to the right of the curves for both Deaf groups). H+ Deaf children appear to have been taken to fewer examiners

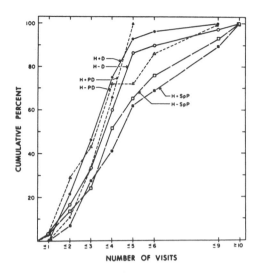

Figure 2. Cumulative percent distributions of number of visits to examiners for hearing + (filled symbols) and hearing − (unfilled symbols) groups from the Deaf (D: circles), Speech Pathology (SpP: squares), and Partially Deaf (PD: triangles) Divisions. Median Speech Frequency Average for each group is shown in Table 2. Age range is equal for the Deaf and Speech Pathology Divisions; the Partially Deaf Division includes some younger children.

than H− Deaf children. Differences between H+ and H− Speech Pathology groups are not large, but suggest that H+ Speech Pathology children were taken to more examiners than were H− Speech Pathology children. Questionnaire responses showed that within the Division of Speech Pathology a greater number of H+ children (62%) were evaluated by examiners as "aphasic" or

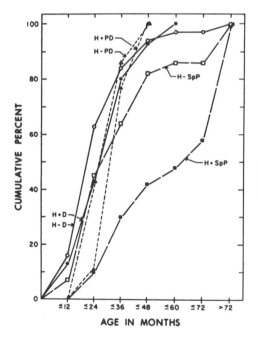

Figure 3. Cumulative percent distributions showing age by which hearing impairment was determined. Same groups as in Figure 2.

204

as having a central nervous system disorder than was true for the H— Speech Pathology children (42%). (Only three Deaf children had been classified as "aphasic"; two were H+ Deaf children while one was in the H— Deaf group.)

Figure 3 shows that H— Deaf children were diagnosed as having hearing impairments at a slightly earlier age than the H+ Deaf children. The H— Speech Pathology children were diagnosed slightly later than both Deaf groups, while the H+ Speech Pathology children were diagnosed as having hearing impairments at a much later age. The H+ Partially Deaf children, whose median Speech Frequency Average, like that of the H+ Speech Pathology groups, was 75 dB (re ISO-1964 standards), were diagnosed as hearing-impaired at a very young age.

Both H+ and H— Deaf children began to wear hearing aids at approximately the same age (Figure 4). The H— Speech Pathology children first wore

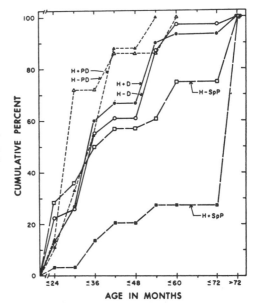

FIGURE 4. Cumulative percent distributions of age by which hearing aid was first worn. Same groups as in Figure 2.

aids at a somewhat later age than either Deaf group, but the H+ Speech Pathology children were first fitted with aids at a very much later time. For example, over half of the children in both Deaf groups and in the H— Speech Pathology group wore hearing aids by the time they were four, but 62% of the H+ Speech Pathology group were not fitted with aids until they were six or older. As might be expected on the basis of their early identification, both Partially Deaf groups were fitted with aids at an early age; over half of the H— Partially Deaf had been fitted by the age of 30 months while half of the H+ Partially Deaf group had been fitted by 36 months.

Educational guidance and special school enrollment are depicted in Figures 5 and 6. Although the H— Speech Pathology children received some type of

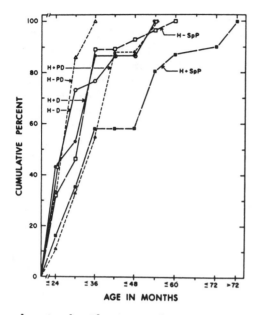

FIGURE 5. Cumulative percent distributions of age by which some type educational guidance was first received. Same groups as in Figure 2.

educational guidance as early as did both deaf groups, the H+ Speech Pathology children did not receive guidance until later (Figure 5). Since the H− Speech Pathology group received some form of educational guidance at an early age, it is difficult to explain on the basis of these data why they were not

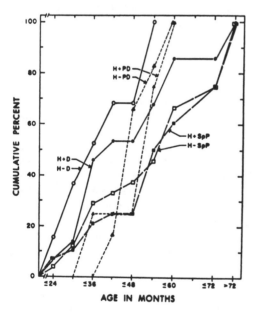

FIGURE 6. Cumulative percent distributions of age by which child was first enrolled in a special school for the hearing-impaired. Same groups as in Figure 2.

enrolled in a full-time special school until so much later (Figure 6). Earliest school enrollment occurred for the H− Deaf children, followed by the H+ Deaf group, and then by both Speech Pathology groups.

These figures show that within the Division for the Deaf, hearing level does not appear to influence early experiences strongly. Deaf children with poorer Speech Frequency Averages visited a slightly greater number of examiners and were enrolled in a special school at an earlier age, but other differences were not marked. However, the age at which hearing impairment among Speech Pathology children was detected and the ages at which aids were first worn and educational procedures were started all showed considerable relation to hearing level and, in general, occurred at a later age than for the Deaf children. It should be remembered that although one group of Speech Pathology children is called "Hearing+," their impairment is still severe and of a degree which necessitates special schooling.[2] Differences between experiences of Speech Pathology and Deaf children cannot be attributed exclusively to absolute differences in hearing level since the H+ Partially Deaf children, whose median hearing level equalled that of the H+ Speech Pathology group, were identified, wore hearing aids, received guidance, and were enrolled in a special school at as early an age as children in the Deaf division.

DISCUSSION

Results may be summarized as showing that the major differences in early experiences between a group of severely hearing-impaired children and another group, also severely hearing-impaired and with additional learning problems, indicated that the latter group were identified as hearing-impaired, started to wear aids, and began an educational program at a later age. The difference in hearing levels between Deaf and Speech Pathology divisions was not of sufficient magnitude to explain the great discrepancies in the ages at which hearing aids were first worn and school enrollment occurred. The question of why the hearing handicap of these Speech Pathology children was not detected earlier is not answerable by these data. There has been some tendency to believe that responsiveness to loud sounds, chattering, and intoned but unintelligible utterances by young children indicate that they can "actually hear" (Davis and Silverman, p. 448). The earlier study (Elliott, 1967) reported that nearly all CID children respond audiometrically at frequencies up to and including 1,000 Hz, and that 88% respond at 2.000 Hz. Questionnaire results indicated that children in all groups attempted to communicate with vocal sounds (Armbruster, 1966). Of course, the child with a hearing level of 75 dB in the low frequencies will be able to hear certain loud, nearby sounds and

---

[2]Silverman has recently reemphasized that children with a 60-80 dB (approximately 70-90 dB re ISO 1964 standard) hearing level in the speech frequencies require special education procedures in order to develop communication skills (S. R. Silverman, "Rehabilitation for Irreversible Deafness," *J. Am. Med. Assoc.*, June 6, 1966, **196**, 843-886.)

will respond to them. However, he will be unable to hear less intense or more distant sounds which are characteristic of most speech sounds. This child may try to imitate sounds because of his low-frequency hearing capacity but his chatter is likely to be unintelligible because of his severe hearing impairment. It may have been that examiners of some of the Speech Pathology children felt that "deafness" implied total unresponsiveness to sound and that any ability to perceive or imitate sound indicated that the child "was not deaf but could hear." Some examiners, who presumably did not regard deafness as a continuum (Hirsh, 1966) and who detected certain responsiveness to sound, suggested "aphasia" or "central nervous system disorder" as the probable diagnosis for the child's problem. Such labeling often resulted in delayed detection of the hearing impairment, and consequently delayed schooling and the use of hearing aids.

This study does not address itself to the question of whether there is an inherent, "real" difference among the children assigned to the Division for Speech Pathology which would continue to prevail and induce slower academic progress even if they had been identified as hearing-impaired at an early age and had begun their education early. Previous neurological examinations have not succeeded in pinpointing reliable differences between the two types of children (Goldstein, Landau, and Kleffner, 1958). While search for such a difference would seem to imply a hypothesized impairment in neurological functioning which is not the result of experience, recent neurological theory suggests that learning and experience induce change in neurological structure and function (Hebb, 1949). Interestingly, the placement of a child in the Division of Speech Pathology has usually occurred after (and as a result of) unsatisfactory performance in other learning situations which usually were initiated at a late age. One arrives at the untestable hypothesis that, had these Speech Pathology children received the same early treatment as the Deaf group, differences in the academic skills and learning of the two groups would, at least, have been much smaller.

These statements should not be interpreted as an open mandate for applying sound amplification to any young child who, at any particular age, has not attained parental or community expectations of speech and language. While educational procedures in themselves would probably not be harmful to a child with normal hearing, excessive sound amplification from an improperly or inadvisably selected aid could be damaging. Instead, this is a plea for suitable and adequate audiologic testing of every young child who presents any suspicion of impaired communicative ability. Newer procedures of play audiometry, averaged evoked cortical responses, etc., (Davis, 1965) permit more accurate assessment of auditory capacity. Pediatricians and even otologists not skillfully practiced in audiologic testing of young children should refer the patient to an appropriate center for such testing. Certainly it is preferable to maintain parental anxieties for the period of time necessary to complete an adequate evaluation rather than to attempt to reassure parents by informing

208

them "nothing is wrong," "all your child needs is a brother or sister," or "your child is too young to test, so don't worry." If hearing impairment is detected, appropriate educational procedures and suitable sound amplification should be initiated.

Among hearing-impaired children it is inevitable that differences should exist in style of learning—just as among children with normal hearing. Occasionally a child may not progress as rapidly as one might expect on the basis of his abilities. This slower rate of progress is to be viewed as occurring in a particular set of circumstances. Some features of the situation may be unchangeable (i.e., for a hearing-impaired child who did not wear an aid until age six, the lost years without auditory stimulation are irretrievable). However, other features of the situation may be modifiable and these include teaching procedures. A child's failure to learn in response to any one procedure should first signal the need for exploring other teaching approaches. It should not serve as sufficient basis for attributing the failure to some unspecified "central impairment."

Today many educational institutions for the deaf also offer special classes and training for the young hearing-impaired child who has some residual hearing. When such a program is started at an early age, many children may be able to achieve effective language and speech skills and, after a period of time, transfer to a school for normal children. Programs of this type were not generally in existence as recently as ten years ago. It may be that the late educational start of Speech Pathology children reflects both lack of understanding of their hearing handicap on the part of examiners and the previous scarcity of educational facilities for children with residual auditory potential.

Study of other species indicates that depriving a healthy, young, normal organism of sensory stimulation for periods of time as short as three to six months may introduce abberations in physiologic functioning which are never completely overcome (Wiesel and Hubel, 1965). While one should like to have information from a larger population of hearing-impaired children with balanced age ranges and representing other educational institutions, these data are interpreted as supporting the hypothesis that hearing-impaired children who are not identified at an early age and who are not provided sound amplification nor placed in an appropriate educational setting may experience a special type of sensory deprivation, the effects of which are only partly reversible. After the hearing-impaired Speech Pathology children of this study were identified and enrolled in school they received much individual teaching and attention. But, it appears that for many the stimulation offered in very small classes and the efforts of conscientious and able parents were inadequate to completely counter the effects of this early deprivation. McNeill (1966) has suggested that certain stages of development are most conducive to language learning and that attempts to establish learning at a later time may meet with diminished success. While all hearing-impaired children, even under the best circumstances, are challenged by the task of developing communicative skills, the inadequate stimulation that results from delaying educational procedures and amplification may produce an overwhelming learning handicap.[3,4]

The authors wish to thank the parents of CID children who so conscientiously completed the lengthy questionnaire. Mary Grable assisted with many technical details of this study.

This research was supported, in part, by Public Health Service Research Grant NB 03856 from the National Institute of Neurological Diseases and Blindness.

REFERENCES

ARMBRUSTER, V. B., Early experiences of children attending classes at Central Institute for the Deaf. Master's thesis, Washington Univ. (1966).

DAVIS, H. (Ed.), The young deaf child; identification and management: proceedings of a conference held in Toronto, Canada, on 8-9 October 1964. *Acta Oto-Laryngol,* Supplementum 206, 210-215 (1965).

DAVIS, H., and SILVERMAN, S. R., *Hearing and Deafness* (Revised Edition). New York: Holt, Rinehart (1960).

ELLIOTT, L. L., Descriptive analysis of audiometric and psychometric scores of students at a school for the deaf. *J. Speech Hearing Res.,* 10, 21-40 (1967).

GOLDSTEIN, R., LANDAU, W. M., and KLEFFNER, F. R., Neurologic assessment of some deaf and aphasic children. *Ann. Otol. Rhinol. Laryng.,* 67, 468-480 (1958).

HEBB, D. O., *The Organization of Behavior.* New York: Wiley (1949).

HIRSH, IRA J., The ears of the deaf unstopped. *Volta Rev.,* 68, 623-633 (1966).

McNEILL, D., The capacity for language acquisition. *Volta Rev.,* 68, 17-33 (1966).

WIESEL, T. N., and HUBEL, D. H., Extent of recovery from the effects of visual deprivation in kittens. *J. Neurophysiol.,* 28, 1060-1072 (1965).

³This, of course, is not to suggest that help be withheld from an older child who, regrettably, did not receive education and sound amplification at an early age. While this child may not learn as rapidly or achieve levels of accomplishment which might have been possible with an earlier "start," he deserves every teaching assistance possible and will benefit from it.

⁴While agreeing with the vital need for early education and sound amplification, the second author does not accept the hypothesis that absence of stimulation at an early age may produce effects which are only partly reversible.

BIBLIOGRAPHY

A

Amcoff S: Programmed instruction for Swedish children aged 7-10 years who are deaf or hard of hearing. Amer Ann Deaf 113:318-26, Mar 68

Armelia H: La rehabilitación del ciego y del débil visual. Cir Cir 35:245-9, May-Jun 67 (Spa)

Auxter D: Operant conditioning of motor skills for the emotionally disturbed. Amer Correct Ther J 23:28-31, Jan-Feb 69

B

Bach-y-Rita P, Collins CC, White B, et al: A tactile vision substitution system. Amer J. Optom 46:109-11, Feb 69

Balas R F, Pirkey WP: Hearing aids and "nerve deafness". Rocky Mountain Med J 66:53-7, Feb 69

Baumeister AA, Hawkins WF: Extinction and disinhibition as a function of reinforcement schedule with severely retarded children. J Exp. Child Psychol 3:343-7, Jul 66

Behrens TR, Clack L, Alprin L: Mathematics curriculum supported by computer assisted instruction. Amer Ann Deaf 114:888-92, Nov 69

Bellefleur PA: Critique on current auditory training equipment. Amer Ann Deaf 114:790-5, Sep 69

Bigge JL: Expected learning often comes through unexpected teaching. Exceptional Child 34:47-50, Sept 67

Bloch P: Nuestro enfoque del niño sordo. Acta Otorinolaring Iber Amer 18:350-60, 1967 (Spa)

Blount SJ: Closed-circuit television in a school for the severely deaf. Med Biol Illus 19:246-9, Oct 69

Boydstun JA, Ackerman PT, Stevens DA, et al: Physiologic and motor conditioning and generalization in children with minimal brain dysfunction. Cond Reflex 3:81-104, Apr-Jun 68

Bricker WA, Bricker DD: Four operant procedures for establishing auditory stimulus control with low-functioning children. Amer J Ment Defic 73:981-7, May 69

Brodsky G: The relation between verbal and non-verbal behavior change. Behav Res Ther 5:183-91, Aug 67

Brown RI: Programmed reading for spastics. Spec Educ 55:26-9, Winter 66

C

Christiansen T: Visual imagery as a factor in teaching elaborative language to mentally retarded children. Exceptional Child 35:539-41, Mar 69

Cleland CC, Swartz JD: Work deprivation as motivation to work. Amer J Ment Defic 73:703-12, Mar 69

Cogan DG: So the blind may "see". New Eng J Med 281:215-6, 24 Jul 69

Cogen V: The computers' role in education and use with the exceptional child. Ment Retard 7:36-41, Aug 69

Cohen ML: The ADL sustained phoneme analyzer. Amer Ann Deaf 113:247-52, Mar 68

Cory, P: Symposium on research and utilization of educational media for teaching the deaf. Report on library programs in schools for the deaf. Amer Ann Deaf 112:701-11, Nov 67

Crosson, JE: A technique for programming sheltered workshop environments for training severely retarded workers. Amer J Ment Defic 73:814-8, Mar 69

D

Darling RI: Symposium on research and utilization of educational media for teaching the deaf. Implementing the media program in schools for the deaf. Amer Ann Deaf 112:712-8, Nov 67

Declan M Sister: Loop induction system. Amer Ann Deaf 114:76-8, Mar 69

Delgado G: Symposium on research and utilization of educational media for teaching the deaf. Report on the activities of Media Services and Captioned Films Branch. Amer Ann Deaf 114:822-3, Nov 69

Diamond RM: A rationale for decision: selecting the right tool for the job. Amer Ann Deaf 111:648-56, Nov 66

Doubros SG: Behavior therapy with high level, institutionalized, retarded adolescents. Exceptional Child 33:229-33, Dec 66

Doubros SG, Daniels GJ: An experimental approach to the reduction of overactive behavior. Behav Res Ther 4:251-8, Nov 66

Driscoll J: Educational films and the slow learner. Ment Retard 6:32-4, Feb 68

F

Faris G: Symposium on research and utilization of educational media for teaching the deaf. Quantitative personnel, materials and equipment standards for audiovisual programs. Amer Ann Deaf 112:672-9, Nov 67

Ferguson DG: Teacher assessment of Project Hurdle. Amer Ann Deaf 114:946-61, Nov 69

Fox J: Breaking communication barriers. Spec Educ 58:23-6. Sep 69

Frisina R: The auditory channel in the education of deaf children. Amer Ann Deaf 111:633-47, Nov 66

G

Gardner WI, Briskin AS: Use of punishment procedures in management of behavioral difficulties of the severely retarded. J. Psychiat Nurs 7:5-16, Jan-Feb 69

Gardner WI, Kaufman ME: Verbal conditioning in noninstitutional mildly retarded adolescents as a function of sex of subject and sex of experimenter. Psychol Rep 23:207-12, Aug 68

Gedye JL: Automated instructional techniques in the rehabilitation of patients with head injury. Proc Roy Soc Med 61:858-60, Sep 68

Gisbert Alós J: El problema del niño sordo actualizado. Acta Otorinolaring Iber Amer 18:361-72, 1967 (Spa)

Goodlaw EI: Homework for low vision patients. Amer J Optom 45:532-8, Aug 68

Goodwin MS, Goodwin TC: In a dark mirror. Ment Hyg 53:550-63, Oct 69

Gough JA: Educational media and the handicapped child. Exceptional Child 35:561-4, Mar 68

Gough JA: Report from captioned films for the deaf. Amer Ann Deaf 113:1117-22, Nov 68

Guess D, Rutherford G: Experimental attempts to reduce stereotyping among blind retardates. Amer J Ment Defic 71:984-6, May 67

H

Hamilton J, Allen P: Ward programming for severely retarded institutionalized residents. Ment Retard 5:22-4, Dec 67

Hamilton J, Standahl J: Suppression of stereotyped screaming behavior in a profoundly retarded institutionalized female. J Exp Child Psychol 7:114-21, Feb 69

Happ FW: Teaching aids for the mentally retarded child, Ment Retard 5:33-5, Aug 67

Haring NG, Hauck MA: Improved learning conditions in the establishment of reading skills with disabled readers. Exceptional Child 35:341-52, Jan 69

Henrikson K, Doughty R: Decelerating undesired mealtime behavior in a group of profoundly retarded boys. Amer J Ment Defic 72:40 -4, Jul 67

Heren TG: Deafness in children—fallacies and facts. S Afr Med J 42:848-9, 17 Aug 68

Herrick MR: Aid for the deaf. New Zeal Med J 68:197, Sep 68

Hester MS: Symposium on research and utilization of educational media for teaching the deaf. In-service education program for teachers of the deaf. Amer Ann Deaf 112:724-7, Nov 67

Hester MS: Symposium on research and utilization of educational media for teaching the deaf. Southwest Regional Media Center for the Deaf. Amer Ann Deaf 114:845-6, Nov 69

Hirsh IJ: Use of amplification in educating deaf children. Amer Ann Deaf 113:1046-55, Nov 68

Hollis JH: A liquid reinforcement dish for profoundly retarded children. Percept Motor Skills 24:156, Feb 67

Hollis JH: Development of perceptual motor skills in a profoundly retarded child. I. Prosthesis. Amer J Ment Defic 71:941-52, May 67

Hollis JH: Development of perceptual motor skills in a profoundly retarded child. II. Consequence change and transfer. Amer J Ment Defic 71:953-63, May 67

Holm C, Gospodnetic J: Bedeutung körperlich-vibratorischer Apprzeption für die Diagnostik und Therapie hochgradig hörgeschädigter Kleinkinder. Z Laryng Rhinol Otol 46:848-57, Nov 67 (Ger)

Hurley OL: Applications of videotape procedures to training and research in the area of the emotionally disturbed. Exceptional Child 34:755-6, Summer 68

J

Jackson WD: Symposium on research and utilization of educational media for teaching the deaf. Media production facilities in schools for the deaf. Amer Ann Deaf 112:680-7, Nov 67

212

Jackson WD: Symposium on research and utilization of education media for teaching the deaf. Southern Regional Media Center for the Deaf. Amer Ann Deaf 114:841-4, Nov 69

Jerger J, Speaks C: Annual review of JSHR research, 1966. J Speech Hearing Dis 32:107-11, May 67

Johnson GF: Programed instruction and the exceptional learner. Exceptional Child 34:543-7, Feb 68

K

Keehn JD: Experimental studies of "the unconscious": operant conditioning of unconscious eyeblinking. Behav Res Ther 5:95-102, May 67

Kennedy WA, Sloop EW: Methedrine as an adjunct to conditioning treatment of nocturnal enuresis in normal and institutionalized retarded subjects. Psychol Rep 22:997-1000, June 68

Kent AA: Synthesizing language arts skills with the overhead projector. Amer Ann Deaf 111:617-21, Nov 66

Kimbrell DL, Kidwell F, Hallum G: Institutional environment developed for training severely and profoundly retarded. Ment Retard 5:34-7, Feb 67

Klein G: Practical applications for perceptual training. Exceptional Child 34:50-5, Sep 67

Krasner L: Assessment of token economy programmes in psychiatric hospitals. Int Psychiat Clin 6:155-85, 1969

L

Leib JW, Cusack J, Hughes D, et al: Teaching machines and programmed instruction: areas of application. Psychol Bull 67:12-26, Jan 67 (85 ref.)

Lennan RK: Use of programmed instruction with emotionally disturbed deaf boys. Amer Ann Deaf 114:906-11, Nov 69

L'Heureux RA: IMC dedicated to serving the needs of exceptional children. J NY Sch Nurse Teach Ass 1:19-21, Fall 69

Liberman R: A view of behavior modification projects in California. Behav Res Ther 6:333-41, Aug 68

Ling D, Doehring DG: Learning limits of deaf children for coded speech. J Speech Hearing Res 12:83-94, Mar 69

Lobb H: Trace GSR conditioning with benzedrine in mentally defective and normal adults. Amer J Ment Defic 73:239-46, Sep 68

Lobb H, Moffitt A, Gamlin P.: Frustration and adaptation in relation to discrimination learning ability of mentally defective children. Amer J Ment Defic 71:256-65, Sept 66

Locke BJ: Verbal conditioning with the retarded: reinforcer, sex of subject, and stimulus pacing. Amer J Ment Defic 73:616-20, Jan 69

Lombardi TP, Poole RG: Utilization of videosonic equipment with mentally retarded. Ment Retard 6:7-9, Oct 68

Lu EG: Early conditioning of perceptual preference. Child Develop 38:415-24, Jun 67

Luckey RE, Watson CM, Musick JK: Aversive conditioning as a means of inhibiting vomiting and rumination. Amer J Ment Defic 73:139-42, Jul 68

M

Macdonald D: Aids for the partially sighted. Int Ophthal Clin 7:217-30, Spring 67

McClure RF: Reinforcement of verbal social behavior in moderately retarded children. Psychol Rep 23:371-6, Oct 68

McFarland JN, Peacock LJ, Watson JA: Mental retardation and activity level in rats and children. Amer J Ment Defic 71:376-80, Nov 66

McMahan M: Symposium on research and utilization of educational media for teaching the deaf. Educational Media Center–the Library's new look. Amer Ann Deaf 112:655-69, Nov 67

McManis DL: Marble-sorting, persistence in mixed verbal-incentive and performance-level pairings. Amer J Ment Defic 71:811-7, Mar 67

Marks M, Greene LB: Rehabilitation. Progr Neurol Psychiat 23:590-604, 1968 (243 ref.)

Mazik K, MacNamara R: Operant conditioning at the training school. Train Sch Bull (Vineland) 63:153-8, Feb 67

Meierhenry WC: Symposium on research and utilization of educational media for teaching the deaf. The purpose of educational media in the learning process. Amer Ann Deaf 112:728-33, Nov 67

Meisegeier RW, Stevens RP: Symposium on research and utilization of educational media for teaching the deaf. The history of America–a multi-media approach. Amer Ann Deaf 113:1015-9, Nov 68

Minge MR, Ball TS: Teaching of self-help skills to profoundly retarded patients. Amer J Ment Defic 71:864-8, Mar 67

Mulhern T, Baumeister AA: An experimental attempt to reduce stereotypy by reinforcement procedures. Amer J Ment Defic 74:69-74, Jul 69

N

Nelson RO, Evans IM: The combination of learning principles and speech therapy techniques in the treatment of non-communicating children. J Child Psychol Psychiat 9:111-24, Nov 68

Nisbet G: The deaf child. Public Health 83:63-7, Jan 69

Norwood MJ: Symposium on research and utilization of education media for teaching the deaf. The second decade. Amer Ann Deaf 114:824-8, Nov 69

O

Ohlrich ES, Ross LE: Acquisition and differential conditioning of the eyelid response in normal and retarded children. J Exp Child Psychol 6:181-93, Jun 68

Olshin GM: Special education instructional materials center program. Exceptional Child 34:515-9, Mar 68

Owrid HL: Language and the deaf child. Spec Educ 57:9-14, Sep 68

P

Paschke RE, Simon S, Bell RW: Vicarious discrimination learning in retardates. J Abnorm Psychol 72:536-42, Dec 67

Penney RK, Peters RD, Willows DM: The mediational deficiency of mentally retarded children. II. Learning set's effect on mediational deficiency. Amer J Ment Defic 73:262-6, Sep 68

Perrin DG: The role of media in individualized instruction for teaching the deaf. Amer Ann Deaf 114:912-9, Nov 69

Peterson LW: Operant approach to observation and recording. Nurs Outlook 14:28-32, Mar 67

Pfau GS: Symposium on research and utilization of educational media for teaching the deaf. Project LIFE PI analysis. Amer Ann Deaf 114:829-37, Nov 69

Pialoux P, Valtat M: Nécessité d'une éducation précoce de l'enfant sourd. Ann Otolaryng (Paris) 85:344-8 (Fre)

Piper TJ, MacKinnon RC: Operant conditioning of a profoundly retarded individual reinforced via a stomach fistula. Amer J Ment Defic 73:627-30, Jan 69

Plowman PD: Programing for the gifted child. Exceptional Child 35:547-51, Mar 69

Postlethwait SN: A multi-faceted approach to teaching. Amer Ann Deaf 111:657-60, Nov 66

Propp G: Symposium on research and utilization of educational media for teaching the deaf. Symposium discussion summary. Amer Ann Deaf 112:734-43, Nov 67

Propp G: Symposium on research and utilization of educational media for teaching the deaf. Introduction. Amer Ann Deaf 114:817-20 Nov 69

Propp G: Symposium on research and utilization of educational media for teaching the deaf. Discussion summary. Amer Ann Deaf 114:920-30, Nov 69

R

Rainey DS, Kelly FJ: An evaluation of a programed textbook with educable mentally retarded children. Exceptional Child 34:169-74, Nov 67

Rathe GH Jr: Computer-assisted instruction and its potential for teaching deaf students. Amer Ann Deaf 114:880-3, Nov 69

Rathe GH Jr: Computer-assisted instruction: exciting new tool for teaching the deaf. Amer Ann Deaf 114:884-8, Nov 69

Redd WH, Birnbrauer JS: Adults as discriminative stimuli for different reinforcement contingencies with retarded children. J Exp Child Psychol 7:440-7, June 69

Reid WR: Action verb materials developed for deaf chidlren. Exceptional Child 34:203-5, Nov 67

Reinsch M: Hortraining Z Aerztl Fortbild (Jena) 61:953-5, 1 Oct 67 (Ger)

Relke W: Praktische Hinweise für die Hörprüfung schwachsinniger Kinder. Z Laryng Rhinol Otol 47:168-74, Mar 68 (Ger)

Rentfrow RK, Rentfrow DK: Studies related to toilet training of the mentally retarded. Amer J Occup Ther 23:425-30, Sep-Oct 69 (10 ref.)

Rice HK, McDaniel MW, Denney SL: Operant conditioning techniques for use in the physical rehabilitation of the multiply-handicapped retarded patient. Phys Ther 48:342-6, Apr 68

Roos P, Oliver M: Evaluation of operant conditioning with institutionalized retarded children. Amer J Ment Defic 74:325-30, Nov 69

Ross LE, Headrick MW, MacKay PB: Classical eyelid conditioning of young mongoloid children. Amer J Ment Defic 72:21-9, Jul 67

Rush ML: Use of visual memory in teaching written language skills to deaf children. J Speech Hearing Dis 31:219-26, Aug 66

Rutter M: Concepts of autism: a review of research. J Child Psychol Psychiat 9:1-25, Oct 68 (115 ref.)

S

Scheibe KE, Gray AL, Keim CS: Hypnotically induced deafness and delayed auditory feedback: a comparison of real and simulating subjects. Int J Clin Exp Hypn 16:158-64, Jul 68.

Schlorhaufer W: Die Ergebnisse pädaudiologischer Praxis. Mschr Ohrenhelik 103:241-59, 1969 (Ger)

Schmitt RJ: A multi-media approach in the classroom for the deaf. Amer Ann Deaf 111:661-7, Nov 66

Schowe BM Jr: Symposium on research and utilization of educational media for teaching the deaf. The small school Instructional Materials Center; its diffusion of innovations for learning. Amer Ann Deaf 112:693-7, Nov 67

Seitz S: Pacing effects on performance of an automated task. Psychol Rep 25:204-6, Aug 69

Seitz S, Morris D: Effects of retention interval on recall by mentally retarded subjects. Psychol Rep 25:108-10, Aug 69

Sidman M, Stoddard LT: The effectiveness of fading in programming a simultaneous form discrimination for retarded children. J Exp Anal Behav 10:3-15, Jan 67

Simmons JQ 3d: Emotional problems in mental retardation. Utilization of psychiatric services. Pediat Clin N Amer 15:957-67, Nov 68 (16 ref.)

Simon S, Lotsof EJ, Bransky M: Verbal conditioning of common-word and uncommon-word associations in retardates and normals. J Genet Psychol 108:279-90, Jun 66

Smith C: The tape recorder in the EMR classroom. Ment Retard 4:33-5, Dec 66

Smith CM: Overhead and opaque projectors in the EMR classroom. Ment Retard 5:32-4, Oct 67

Smith DE, Brethower D, Cabot R: Increasing task behavior in a language arts program by providing reinforcement. J Exp Child Psychol 8:45-62, Aug 69

Snelbecker GE, Downes RC: Note concerning individual differences and behavior on programmed materials. Psychol Rep 21:333-5, Aug 67

Sovák M: Význam reflexní theorie ve speciální pedagogice. Acta Univ Carol [Med](Praha) 12:567-78, 1966 (Cze)

Spradlin JE, Girardeau FL, Hom GL: Stimulus properties of reinforcement during extinction of a free operant response. J Exp Child Psychol 4:369-80, Dec 66

Stark RE, Cullen JK, Chase RA: Preliminary work with the new Bell Telephone visible speech translator. Amer Ann Deaf 113:205-14, Mar 68

Stepp RE: Symposium on research and utilization of educational media for teaching the deaf. Midwest Regional Media Center for the Deaf. Amer Ann Deaf 114:847-52, Nov 69

Stepp RE: Symposium on research and utilization of educational media for teaching the deaf. Foreword. Amer Ann Deaf 114:814-6, Nov 69

Sterling TD: A new direction in rehabilitation through advanced instrumentation and computation. JAMA 200:625-9, 15 May 67

Stuckless ER: Planning for individualized instruction of deaf students at the National Technical Institute for the Deaf. Amer Ann Deaf 114:868-73, Nov 69

Sullivan P: Symposium on research and utilization of educational media for teaching the deaf. The idea of the school library and communication. Amer Ann Deaf 112:688-92, Nov 67

T

Thvedt I: Complicated communications challenge the church and chaplains. Amer Ann Deaf 113:959-66, Sep 68

Tissot R, Bovet J: Modifications de l'habituation de la réaction d'arrêt du rythme alpha chez l'homme sous l'effet de la chlorpromazine et du halopéridol. Psychopharmacologia (Berlin) 10:298-307, 1967 (Fre)

Toister RP, Birnbrauer SJ: Facilitation

of repeated free operant discrimination reversals. J Exp Child Psychol 7:492-513, Jun 69

Toki A: [Hearing training in the education of the deaf] Otolaryngology (Tokyo) 38:1404-14, Dec 66 (Jap)

Touchette PE: The effects of graduated stimulus change on the acquisition of a simple discrimination in severely retarded boys. J Exp Anal Behav 11:39-48, Jan 68

Tsunoda T, Hayakawa Y: [Concentrated listening training by a tape recorder and preservation of hearing in children with hearing disorders] Otolaryngology (Tokyo) 38:1391-402, Dec 66 (Jap)

V

Van Wagenen RK, Meyerson L, Kerr NJ, et al: Field trials of a new procedure for toilet training. J Exp Child Psychol 8:147-59, Aug 69

Vouters C, Ernst J, Perdu ML, et al: Les principaux obstacles rencontrés dan l'éducation desdéficients auditifs. J. Sci Med Lille 84:351-62, Jun-Aug 66 (Fre)

W

Wagner H: Gemeinschaftshörhilfe für Horerzehung, Schwerhorigenunterricht und Hortraining. I. Audiologische Grundlagen HNO 14:252-4 Aug 66 (Ger)

Ward T: Development of new instructional materials in the IMC network. Exceptional Child 35:299-301, Dec 68

Watson LS Jr: Application of operant conditioning techniques to institutionalized severely and profoundly retarded children. Ment Retard Abstr 4:1-18, Jan-Mar 67

Watson LS Jr: Applications of behaviorshaping devices to training severely and profoundly mentally retarded children in an institutional setting. Ment Retard 6:21-3, Dec 68

Watson LS JR: Reinforcement preferences of severely mentally retarded

children in a generalized reinforcement context. Amer J Ment Defic 72:748-56, Mar 68

Weinstock FJ: Talking books for the blind. JAMA 211:124, 5 Jan 70

Whalen CK, Henker BA: Creating therapeutic pyramids using mentally retarded patients. Amer J Ment Defic 74:331-7, Nov 69

White JC Jr, Taylor DJ: Noxious conditioning as a treatment for rumination. Ment Retard 5:30-3, Feb 67

Whitenack CI: Symposium on research and utilization of educational media for teaching the deaf. The Instructional Materials Center: a changing concept. Amer Ann Deaf 112:650-3. Nov 67

Wiesen AE, Hartley G, Richardson C, et al: The retarded child as a reinforcing agent. J Exp Child Psychol 5:109-13, Mar 67

Winsberg BG: Programed learning, teaching machines, and dyslexia. Amer J Orthopsychiat 39:418-27 Apr 69 (40 ref.)

Withrow FB: Symposium on research and utilization of educational media for teaching the deaf. Media personnel in a school for the deaf. Amer Ann Deaf 112:698-700, Nov 67

Wyman R: Symposium on research and utilization of educational media for teaching the deaf. Progress report on the visual response system. Amer Ann Deaf 114:838-40, Nov 69

Z

Zeller, MD, Jervey SS: Development of behavior: self-feeding. J Consult Clin Psychol 32:164-8, Apr 68

ANONYMOUS

Amer Ann Deaf: Symposium on research and utilization of educational media for teaching the deaf. Report from captioned films for the deaf. Amer Ann Deaf 112:642-9, Nov 67

Rehab Rec: Mobility goes to high school. Rehab Rec 7:20-1, Jul-Aug 66

INDEX

Armbruster, Virgina B., 195
Attention Span, 103

Behavior Deficits, 160
Behavior Modification, 36, 67
Behavior Therapy, 7, 23
Bijou, Sidney W., 36
Blackman, Leonard S., 138
Brain Damage, 35, 55
Bransky, Malcolm L., 7 0
Buell, Joan, 160

Conditioned Learning, 35

Deafness, 167, 168, 174, 195
Discipline, 146
Discrimination Learning, 70
Doehring, Donald G., 174

Elementary Schools, 188
Elliott, Lois L., 195
Exceptional Learner, 86
Extinction, 109, 131
Eyman, Richard K., 96

Fixsen, Dean L., 131
Freeman, Roger D., 8
Frustrative Nonreward Theory, 116

Gaeth, John H., 188
Gelfand, Donna M., 23
Girarbeau, Frederic L., 131

Hall, R. Vance, 55
Harmatz, Morton G., 67
Hartmann, Donald P., 23
Head Banging, 67
Heal, Laird W., 70
Hearing Aids, 195
Hearing Standards, 168
House, Howard P., 168

Inappropriate Behavior, 160
Instrumental Conditioning, 74

Johnson, Bette M., 74
Johnson, Gordon F., 86

Karen, Robert L., 91

Lask, Emanual, 96
Lohmann, Werner, 96
Lounsbury, Evan, 188

Management, 146, 160
Martin, Garry L., 103
Maxwell, Sandra J., 91
Matching-to-Sample, 70
Methods, 137
Mentally Retarded, 36, 70, 74, 91, 109,
    146, 160
Morris, John P., 109

Normal Children, 74

Parent Education, 160
Picture-Sound Association, 174
Powell, Marcene, 146
Powers, Richard B., 193
Programmed Instruction, 86
Psychiatry, 8

Rasmussen, Warren A., 67
Reinforcement, 55, 131
Reinstatement, 131
Research Methodology, 23
Response, 109, 131
Reward Schedules, 74
Ryan, Thomas J., 116

Self-Help, 91
Speech, 55
Spradlin, Joseph E., 131

Terdal, Leif, 160
Toilet Training, 96
Treatment of Delay, 195

Watson, Peter, 116